NUCLEAR FUEL ELEMENTS

EDITED BY
HENRY H. HAUSNER
Adjunct Professor
Polytechnic Institute of Brooklyn
and
Consultant to Sylvania-Corning Nuclear Corporation

AND

JAMES F. SCHUMAR
Associate Director, Metallurgy Division
Argonne National Laboratory

REINHOLD PUBLISHING CORPORATION
NEW YORK
CHAPMAN & HALL, LTD., LONDON

Library of Congress Catalog Card Number: 59-15714

Printed in the United States of America

FOREWORD

It was particularly fitting that the First International Symposium on Nuclear Fuel Elements, the proceedings of which are compiled in this volume, should have been held at Columbia University in January, 1959, for there, almost exactly 20 years before, and within a few hundred yards of where the delegates sat, the first nuclear fission experiments in America were successfully carried out. Those of us who watched the oscilloscope screen in the basement of Pupin Laboratories on January 25, 1939, and saw the green streaks that demonstrated the enormous energy release from neutron bombardment of uranium knew, of course, that here was the greatest potential source of usable energy man had ever tapped. Yet, although we started drawing sketches of atomic power plants in January, 1939, we could scarcely have foreseen that within two decades it would have become so enormous an industrial reality—so central to the planetary economy of our species—that a conference planned for a few men would attract several hundred distinguished participants from all over the world.

To the casual or uninitiated eye, the subject of this book—reactor fuel elements—might perhaps seem to be only a narrow segment of the whole exciting field of nuclear physics and technology. But the reactor fuel cycle is, in fact, the strategic crux of the whole future atomic power economy. It is plain that uranium, even with the many design problems that still challenge us, is essentially the cheapest fuel available to us—if we can solve the problems of the fuel cycle, and the problem of fuel fabrication.

This was the special importance of the Symposium, and is the significance of this volume. It brings to bear both theoretical mastery and practical engineering production skill upon the questions we must above all answer if we are to bring our vast resources of fissionable material into rapid economic utilization in the world.

DR. JOHN R. DUNNING
Dean, School of Engineering
Columbia University, New York

iii

PREFACE

The nuclear fuel cycle is recognized as one of the significant areas in the economics of electric power generation from the atom. A great deal of attention has been given to nuclear fuel costs in the past, and it is obvious that much more work needs to be done. This interest in costs has grown sharply in the last year as a result of operating experience on first generation power reactors, and it will continue to provide a challenge to the laboratories and to industry.

At a time when research workers are hastily searching for more data, better materials and improved concepts, industrial groups are close behind in reactor construction. This accelerated pace from laboratory to industry to full-scale power reactors has strained the normal communications flow and has forced us to seek an idea exchange. The First International Symposium on Nuclear Fuel Elements was just such an exchange. It served as an international meeting place where the most recent developments were revealed, discussed and fitted into their proper places. Both the formal papers and the informal discussions played a part in the exchange, and each contributed significantly to the over-all picture.

The guiding forces behind the Symposium represented the combined efforts of Columbia University and Sylvania-Corning Nuclear Corporation to foster such an exchange at an international level. The interest in nuclear fuels and the research in nuclear materials are truly international in scope. The significance of nuclear power is not limited by the borders of any one nation, and advancing of the date when nuclear power will become an economic reality is of great significance on the international scene.

Industrial participation in nuclear work is a strong part of the U.S. platform for the development of nuclear power. Sylcor's sponsorship of the First International Symposium on Nuclear Fuel Elements was consistent with the U.S. program, and, we felt, was also in the best interests of the international effort. Prompt exchange of information is necessary for the advance of this most complex field. Through the media of meetings, symposia and published data such as the present book we avoid duplication of development effort and hasten the day of economic nuclear power. It is our hope that this volume compiled from the Symposium reports will provide a basis for future work dedicated to the advancement of the peaceful uses of nuclear energy.

DR. LEE L. DAVENPORT
President, Sylvania-Corning Nuclear Corp.

CONTENTS

EDITORS' INTRODUCTION

During the last few years several meetings were held in this and other countries dealing in part with the problems of nuclear fuels, fuel materials, and fuel elements. The fast development in nuclear fuel element design and fabrication during the period 1956-58, however, made it desirable to arrange a meeting devoted exclusively to fuel elements, and to bring together the fuel element designers and fabricators for a discussion of their problems. This was the purpose of the First International Symposium on Nuclear Fuel Elements, held at Columbia University, New York, January 28 and 29, 1959, cosponsored by Columbia University and the Sylvania-Corning Nuclear Corporation. It permitted a free exchange of ideas with respect to the materials, design and fabrication of nuclear fuel elements. The response to this symposium was considerably greater than anticipated; more than 450 participants representing 22 countries on four continents attended.

The papers delivered at the Symposium covered a great variety of fuel elements and fabrication problems, and indicated also that any fuel element design actually represents a compromise between the requirements of the physicist, the availability of the special form of fuel desired, and the known processes of fabrication. The papers presented at this Symposium represent the main part of this book.

From the above, it is evident that this book is not intended to be a definitive treatise; there are some omissions, and to a certain extent some overlapping of information. The twenty chapters contain less than would be expected from a textbook, but in many cases much more; they contain firsthand information from scientists in this and foreign countries who have worked on the development and fabrication of fuel elements and describe their own experience. Though it could be used as a text, it is mainly intended to serve the materials and fabrication engineer, and to help him to become familiar with the various types of nuclear fuel elements, their respective fabrication problems, and the behavior of these elements in the reactor.

The first chapter, by W. Kenneth Davis, was originally an after-dinner talk, in which the author indicated the path for development of the fuel elements for reactors of the future, based on his long experience as Director of the Reactor Division of the U.S. Atomic Energy Commission. A general review of the basic types of fuel elements is given in the chapter by Stanley B. Roboff, who emphasizes that it is not too early to start standardizing certain types of elements. The third chapter deals with a cost analysis of fuel elements for low-cost fabrication and reprocessing; Robert B. Gordon discloses data on the gross fuel-cycle cost for various types of reactors, the fabrication cost of cast and wrought uranium and various types of other fuel and cladding materials. In the following chapter, James F. Schumar discusses fabrication techniques for various types of fuel elements. Chapters 5 to 8 are devoted to metallic fuel elements made from uranium, thorium and plutonium. Frank Foote describes and discusses the uranium and uranium alloy elements; Ulrich Merten and co-workers disclose their experience on uranium-zirconium hydride elements, which are so successfully used in the TRIGA reactor; Charles C. Woolsey, a pioneer in thorium-type elements, describes the role of thorium for use in the thermal and epithermal region of nuclear reactors; and R. E. Tate reviews the application of plutonium fuel elements based on his experience at the Los Alamos Scientific Laboratory.

The two following chapters deal with dispersion-type fuel elements in which the fissionable material is a compound dispersed in a metallic matrix. William Weinberger discusses the development of fabrication techniques for the Army Power Package Reactor fuel plates, and William Maxwell describes the entirely different fabrication methods for dispersion-type tubular elements. During the Symposium discussion of the dispersion-type elements, a fuel element recently developed at the Argonne International School for Nuclear Science and Engineering was mentioned, and this aroused a great deal of interest. The Editors, therefore, have asked J. Baird, instructor at the Argonne International School, to describe the principles and fabrication technique for this fuel element, which is done in collaboration with his colleagues in Chapter 11.

Chapters 12 to 16 are devoted to high-temperature fuel elements. In the introductory chapter to this section, Chapter 12, Alfred Strasser has given a review of the requirements for high-temperature elements and materials, their properties, and the development of this type of element. The pioneering work on uranium dioxide, performed at the Atomic Energy of Canada, Ltd., and recent development in Canada on this type of fuel, is described by O. J. C. Runnalls in Chapter 13. The aspect of uranium dioxide and uranium carbide fuel elements in France is the content of Chapter 14, by A. Accary and R. Caillat, based on the experience of these investigators at the Centre d'Études Nucleaires at Saclay. There follow two chapters which deal mostly with uranium carbide fuels: A. Boettcher discloses the German ideas for elements to be used for gas-cooled high-temperature reactors, and L. Green discusses the high-temperature creep properties of uranium-loaded graphites.

Some further European development in nuclear fuel elements is described in Chapters 17 and 18. H. K. Hardy discusses fuel element fabrication and fuel element problems for nuclear power reactors in the United Kingdom, based on the experience at the U.K. Atomic Energy Authority, and B. de Lasteyrie gives a complete review of the manufacture of fuel elements for the EL-3 experimental reactor at Saclay, as experienced by a French industrial fuel element manufacturer.

The last two chapters deal with the behavior of fuel elements under reactor operating conditions. J. E. Draley describes the various corrosion problems of fuel elements in water, and L. W. Kates reviews the complex problems of fuel element behavior under irradiation.

During their many years of experience in nuclear engineering, and especially in fuel element development, the Editors have frequently been asked for specifications for fuel elements. Specifications of this type actually vary not only from one type of element to another, but also for elements of the same type, due to the individualistic touch of most of the fuel element designers. It has been thought, however, that an existing specification for any kind of fuel element which is already in operation might be of interest, to be used as a guide for other specifications; the Appendix of this book therefore, contains "Specifications for the APPR-1 Fuel and Control Rod Components," and will probably be useful for many readers as an example in setting up specifications for other fuel elements.

The Appendix contains, further, a sizable bibliography on nuclear fuel elements with 494 references, compiled by Helen C. Friedemann—the first book bibliography of this type—which will be helpful for the reader who wishes to study the fuel element literature.

The Editors wish to express their thanks to their authors for their prompt delivery of the manuscripts; to the members of the committee who have arranged the First International Symposium on Nuclear Fuel Elements, the transactions of which are represented by this book; especially to Professors M. Gensamer and G. Kehl of Columbia University, and to the management of Sylvania-Corning Nuclear Corporation for their invaluable help.

HENRY H. HAUSNER
Adjunct Professor, Polytechnic Institute of Brooklyn
Consultant to Sylvania-Corning Nuclear Corporation
JAMES F. SCHUMAR
Metallurgy Division, Argonne National Laboratory

November, 1959

1. FUELS FOR REACTORS OF THE FUTURE*

W. KENNETH DAVIS

Vice President, Bechtel Corporation, San Francisco, Calif.

The First International Symposium on Nuclear Fuel Elements should be of special significance in the rapidly developing nuclear fuel field, particularly because of its international aspects. It appears that the joint U. S./ Euratom program offers an immediate basis for extensive cooperation in the development of fuel element technology. The opportunity to prove out substantial quantities of fuel elements in additional reactors, both test reactors and power reactors, and the benefit of the work of the scientists and engineers from the Euratom countries should be of very great significance and value in the development of power reactors now under way on a large scale in the United States.

Although it is evident that there is very great confidence in the types of reactor fuel being developed in the United States—even in the present absence of large-scale and long-term tests—this confidence will be enhanced and made convincing by the types of tests and programs which are now envisaged both in the expanded Atomic Energy Commission program for the United States and in the joint U. S./Euratom program.

In referring to "reactors of the future" we mean those reactors which we hope will prove to be economically competitive with conventionally fueled power plants within the next 10 years or so in relatively high fuel-cost areas of the United States, and substantially before that abroad. The problem is to surmount the economic hurdle. It is perfectly all right to speculate about reactors and their fuels beyond that point; and there is interest in these from the technical point of view. However, the immediate and important problem is how to reach the break-even point.

Within this general framework a few general remarks should be made about the development of power reactors to this point, with particular emphasis on the nuclear fuel cycle problems involved.

Status of Power Reactor Development

When capital costs are reduced to about $225 to $250 per kilowatt of capacity and when nuclear fuel cycle costs are reduced to 2 to $2\frac{1}{2}$ mills

* After-dinner speech delivered January 28, 1959.

1

per kilowatt hour, there seems to be general agreement that nuclear power reactors can be considered to be economically competitive with conventional power plants when the latter are in areas of relatively high fuel costs but with large and expanding power requirements.

Costs which could be guaranteed today for units of the size practicable at this time are about 50 per cent higher than these figures for both capital and fuel. While this represents very considerable progress during the 4 or 5 years which have been available for power reactor developments on any scale, it seems likely that the final one-third reduction that is still to be made may be by far the hardest portion of the task. However, there does not seem to be very much doubt but that the goal of economical power can actually be achieved within a relatively short time if a sufficiently aggressive and intelligent program is carried on.

It is not clear which part of the task is going to be the harder: reducing the capital cost or the fuel cycle costs. Opinions vary, but the two appear about equal in difficulty. It is clear that both must be accomplished successfully, neither being sufficient by itself.

There is one significant difference. Once a plant is built, it can still realize a substantial part of the improvements in fuel cycle cost that occur over its useful life. However, once the investment is made in the plant, the capital cost is not reduced by improvements made from that time on, except in very minor ways. Thus confidence in ultimate low fuel-cycle costs may be useful, whereas the capital costs will actually have to be reduced to an acceptable level before what might be called commercial plants can be started.

What types of reactors will be economical? This becomes a much more difficult question if one tries to say which will be most economical, or most economical at any given time. However, it seems likely that, of the types in prominence now, one can say with some assurance that the boiling water, organic-cooled, and high-temperature gas reactors will probably be economical. It would appear that they might achieve this point in about the order mentioned because of the present stage of their development, which is the same.

Other types of reactors may also be able to become economically competitive either generally or under restricted circumstances; and in time one or more of the three listed above may drop out because they are not as cheap as others, even though they may be competitive with conventional power plants. No one type of reactor appears likely to be best under all circumstances or for all time. A variety of types are necessary to meet the various requirements and to balance and utilize the various nuclear fuels.

It is highly desirable to arrive at an orderly and positive program for the development of at least the three types mentioned (boiling, organic- and gas-cooled), to the point where they are on a sound economic base. Such a program should be adaptable to the developments as they occur and to the requirements of the manufacturers and customers. It need not interfere with the development of more advanced types of reactors; but the development of the latter should be kept from interfering with that of the three shorter-range types considered here.

Fuel Element Costs

Fuel element fabrication and processing costs for the first core or two of the power reactors now under construction or contract are overly high. The situation has improved somewhat since Walter Zinn commented that reactor cores were built like Swiss watches and since the cost of the Shippingport Pressurized Water Reactor core was estimated within 10 per cent by assuming it was constructed entirely of the same volume of Swiss watches. However, we still have definitely high costs, which should be susceptible to very considerable reduction.

What might be called current minimum costs for zirconium-clad uranium dioxide fuel rods of about $\frac{1}{2}$ in. diameter are about $140 per kg of uranium content, with some estimated costs running substantially higher. Such fuel will have about 0.5 sq ft of surface per kg, or a cost for the heat-transfer surface of about $300 per sq ft. This is very expensive, particularly since its life is only 2 to 4 years, which means that on a capitalized basis it is costing $550 to $1100 per sq ft.

While considerable improvement is now visualized in these figures, it seems clear that there is considerable room for further improvement almost by an order of magnitude. How will such improvements be brought about?

A substantial improvement will surely be made as the result of further research and development and the testing of fuels in test reactors and in operating power reactors. However, it looks as if the key to reaching the lowest costs lies in the volume of fuel element manufacturing operations.

It is difficult to define what might be called an adequate volume of manufacture of fuel elements of one type to secure the bulk of the advantages of volume. However, it seems clear that a volume of 35 to 50 kg per day of fuel required for a single 150,000 ekw* nuclear power plant can hardly be considered an adequate load for even a part-time pilot plant. The same is true for chemical reprocessing plants, except that these have somewhat more flexibility and demand somewhat less standardization than fuel element manufacturing facilities to reap the advantages of volume operation.

It is fairly obvious that one needs perhaps 10 or 20 large reactors utilizing similar (not necessarily identical or "standardized") fuel in order to ob-

* Electrical kilowatt.

tain fuel fabrication and processing costs which are near those attainable with large-volume operations.

If it is necessary to have the fuel cycle costs resulting from large-volume operation in order to reduce the costs of nuclear power enough so that a sufficient number of utilities are interested in building enough nuclear power plants to reduce the fuel cycle costs, then we have a real "chicken and egg" proposition.

It does not appear that we are so far from this situation. When capital costs have been reduced by improvements and other costs have been reduced as much as possible, it seems likely that the fabrication and processing costs will be critical in the economic comparison of nuclear power with conventional power, even in the higher fuel-cost areas of the United States.

This problem will be alleviated by as much concentration on similar types of fuel as possible; by convincing the utilities that nuclear fuel costs will come down, and that they can project a reasonable average cost over the life of their plant despite somewhat higher costs during the first few years; and by some projection of costs by the manufacturers in pricing their fuel elements, spreading the extra costs of initial low volume production over anticipated larger volume and lower cost production. This obviously requires considerable fortitude on the part of the manufacturer.

Reactor Core Design

While the fuel cycle costs are of great importance in the economics of power reactors, it should also be kept in mind that the return on the investment in a reactor and all its associated equipment, as well as the economics of the over-all reactor system, is also dependent on the heat output of the reactor core. In the case of power reactors, the economics is largely dependent on the *anticipated* output of a given reactor core, since the balance of the system will usually be designed for this heat output. Later alterations and additions to the plant to exploit extra capacity found to be available are generally difficult and expensive in power reactors. In fact, experimental operations even to demonstrate substantially higher capacity for a reactor core are difficult in most power reactor systems. It is true that some provisions for adding capacity at a later date can usually be made at some added expense for the initial plant, but such provisions often turn out to be marginal.

The limitations on higher power operation, or on alterations to permit it, are much less severe in production reactors, test reactors, and many reactor experiments. The spectacular success in increasing the output of heat from many such reactors has led the uninformed to expect similar increases in the electrical output from *power* reactor plants, once they are built and put into operation; but such increases are not to be expected, even though they might be feasible from the point of view of the capacity of the core, if there were no other limitations.

It is thus a matter of concern to those interested in seeing the economics of power reactors improved that many reactor cores appear to be designed with rather extravagant capacity safety factors. This is not to imply that one should adopt unjustified optimism or even that all reactor cores will actually produce more heat than that at which they are being rated. However, it does appear that the subject of proper design ratings for use in over-all reactor power plant design deserves more careful study than it seems to have been given in many cases.

At this point it is recognized that considerable thought is being given to problems of this sort by several design groups and that considerable progress is being made. However, much more can and should be done along these lines.

It must always be kept in mind that the economics of a power plant depends on its performance and output over its useful life, not just on the performance during the initial period of operation. This useful life must be 20 or 25 years or more. This has a bearing not only on the proper evaluation of fuel cycle costs, but also on the selection of the proper design rating of the core when matching it to the design of the balance of the plant.

In the present state of development and operation of power reactors there is an understandable difference between the core power-level ratings for purposes of making guarantees or other assurances and those which can be regarded as having a reasonably high but less than 100 per cent probability. True economic prudence as well as developmental advances almost always indicate that the balance of a power plant should be designed for substantially more core output than can be considered a 100 per cent probability, or close enough to it to serve as a basis for a guaranteed output. Unfortunately, this philosophy does not seem to be adopted in the majority of cases. When it is adopted, it is often viewed as some sort of economic trick rather than as a considered and realistic judgment. Such an attitude indicates a failure to understand the facts about the status of reactor development as they exist today.

The development of design procedures for reactor cores has led to a firmly established ritual of "hot channel factors" and peak-to-average ratios. These have proved to be useful design tools in an exceedingly complex technical problem. However, while these procedures have been helpful, it is believed that they are now often misused and misunderstood and that their use now often leads to excessively conservative core designs.

Many of the factors and ratios in use are fairly definite and are real design quantities resulting from known physical characteristics of a reactor; but many others are essentially statistical factors providing for an indeterminate factor or for manufacturing or operating deviations from the design or design performance. These factors and ratios are generally used by combining or multiplying them as though they were all definite and known ratios; thus the statistical nature of a large fraction of them is ignored. This mathematical looseness in application of what are basically statistical quantities, combined with the generally high degree of conservatism in selecting the factors, can lead to a core design which is highly conservative and considerably overdesigned.

It should also be considered that the design factors for unknowns are basically of two types. The first type represents an unknown which will turn out to have some actual value, but which is not subject to correction or change, either in the core being designed or in subsequent cores. The second is one which turns out to have some definite value, but which is subject to change once its magnitude and effect is actually ascertained, either in the original core itself or in later cores of the same general design. Proper evaluation of factors of this type in terms of possible improvements seems essential to rational plant design. In some cases a major change in the design of the core may be indicated to obtain the results found to be attainable by the initial operation.

Although considerable allowance for improved performance appears justified and appropriate for most power reactor cores, the actual utilization of such design margins and the improved design of future cores depends on an adequate knowledge of the performance of the core as actually installed. While a significant improvement can probably be made in the design procedures for reactor cores now in use, the really substantial improvements will come through verification and analysis of the performance of cores as compared with these procedures.

This implies not only a high degree of instrumentation of reactor cores as installed, but also a continuing interest in obtaining and analyzing the data obtained in terms of the design procedures used. The necessary instrumentation is expensive and poses many mechanical difficulties in installation and operation. The collection and analysis of data are also expensive and time-consuming, and extremely able people are essential for a proper interpretation. Unfortunately, with a few exceptions, reactor cores are not being furnished with instrumentation which is either sufficient or proper to determine the capabilities of a core and to provide adequate data for verification or analysis of the original design. Even those reactors which have operated with highly instrumental cores do not seem to have been subjected to critical analysis in terms of the design procedures originally utilized.

While this is a difficult and expensive area of development, its proper accomplishment seems essential to future advances in the improvement of power reactors, and should be accorded a great deal more attention than has been the case so far. Without it the present conservative approach may go unchecked far longer than is necessary or healthy for the development which we all seek.

Utilization of Natural Uranium

Lately considerable emphasis has been placed on breeding (creation of at least one new fuel atom for each one fissioned) to achieve efficient utilization of natural uranium and thorium resources, and there has also been the suggestion that the use of natural uranium as compared with enriched uranium would improve the over-all utilization of these basic resources.

If we consider a reactor utilizing natural uranium and operating to a fuel life of 3,000 Mwd/ton as characterized by the United Kingdom's gas-cooled reactors, we find that the plutonium production is something like 2.1 or 2.2 g per kg.

If we compare this with a low-enrichment UO_2-fuel at 10,000 Mwd/ton, we would find, at the standard conditions envisaged in the Atomic Energy Commission Price List for enriched uranium, that about 2.2 kg of natural uranium would be needed to re-enrich the used enriched fuel. The equivalent utilization of natural uranium is then about 4,600 Mwd/ton or about 50 per cent more than for the natural uranium fuel. We would also find that the enriched fuel would produce about 7.7 g of plutonium per kg or about 3.5 g per kg of natural uranium required for the cycle.

In other words, to be equivalent to enriched fuel at 10,000 Mwd/ton in terms of use of fuel resources, natural uranium fuel must be capable of achieving irradiations of the order of 4,500 Mwd/ton. In general, it appears that natural uranium fuel must achieve irradiation lifetimes of the order of 4000 to about 6000 Mwd/ton to be comparable with enriched uranium in terms of utilization of natural uranium resources. This may be feasible in some types of reactors, but appears to be limited by both metallurgical problems and reactivity in other types of reactors.

Heavy Water Moderation

Can reactors utilizing heavy water as a moderator lead to substantial economic advantages over other types of reactors under present economic circumstances? This is a question frequently posed these days against a framework of relatively small past interest by the Atomic Energy Commission (AEC) in such power reactor types.

There are possibly two answers to this question, depending on whether one leases the heavy water from the AEC or whether one purchases it. In the first case the annual fixed charges, including losses, are perhaps about 7 per cent per year, while in the second case they would be about 15 per cent.

Reactor designs lead to a heavy water requirement for heavy-water moderated reactors of 2 to 3 lb of heavy water per ekw of power-producing capacity. Such designs are usually under-moderated and would require somewhat more heavy water to attain maximum neutron efficiency. If we take an optimistic figure of 2 lb/ekw and the present price of $28/lb, then the annual costs for heavy water are about 0.6 mill/kwh for the rental case and 1.1 mills/kwh for the purchase case based on 7000 hr of operation per year.

The reactor plant will surely not be significantly cheaper for heavy water moderation than for competitive designs. In fact, the plants are generally larger and more complex and have a somewhat lower efficiency than plants utilizing other moderators. The operating costs will surely be about the same as for other plants. Thus the only possible compensating saving to offset the heavy water costs is in the fuel cycle cost. Is this likely?

The improved neutron economy of heavy water moderation can be used in two ways: lower enrichment of the fuel or greater burn-up of enriched fuel. If one examines the economic advantages to be gained in either way, it does not appear that they can exceed 0.3 or 0.4 mill/kwh with 0.5 mill/ kwh as an outside figure, assuming comparable development of the fuel cycles for the other types of reactors. Thus, there are no apparent advantages to the use of heavy water at present prices even if the reactor portion of the plant is not increased in cost, although the costs may be very nearly equal for the case where the heavy water is rented. If one assumes that sometime in the future it will become necessary to purchase enriched uranium rather than to rent it from the government at 4 per cent per year, then the fuel cycle costs for the competitive reactors will increase. However, it is only logical to consider, then, that the heavy water would necessarily be purchased too, and it will be found that the use of heavy water still would not make up for the difference.

There probably is a heavy water price, perhaps one-half of the present price or something less than that, at which its use as a moderator would appear attractive in competition with other types of reactors. However, it does not appear realistic to expect such a price reduction at the present time.

If a further restriction is placed on the heavy-water moderated systems, namely, that they must utilize natural uranium, then the cost penalty is further increased. Although heavy-water moderated systems are likely to give optimum operation with natural uranium feed plus plutonium recycle, they appear to require some enrichment for minimum cost without plutonium recycle.

This is not to imply that we should drop the development of heavy water-moderated reactors, since they may have some special areas of usefulness and since there may be some substantial improvements. However, it would be unwise to shift a great deal of emphasis to them under the present circumstances.

Need for Breeders

In recent months, in official and semiofficial AEC announcements, there has been a much increased emphasis on the need for breeder reactors to insure complete utilization of the supplies of uranium and thorium. In fact, in some cases it has been implied that scarcely any other type of reactor merits further serious support.

It could be a serious mistake, practically and realistically, to take too seriously this point of view. One would not like to be accused of a lack of foresight or of recommending the waste of our natural resources; but it is possible that such a conclusion could seriously delay our arriving at economically useful nuclear power. Indeed, this delay itself could still further retard the attainment of breeder reactors, since their development seems unlikely to be supported over a very long period without some economically practical and useful results coming from the over-all reactor development program.

The present uranium production in this country could support our present electric power-production industry if it were all nuclear, without recourse even to plutonium recycle, much less breeding. Since a nuclear electric power industry equal to the current total electric power production capacity is not expected before another 20 to 30 years (depending on one's optimism), there scarcely appears to be great urgency for the development of breeders and still less economic incentive for their use unless they turn out to be cheaper than other types of nuclear power plants at current uranium prices. The use of plutonium recycle could probably keep the nuclear power industry going for another 10 years or more without increasing the annual uranium requirements above the present production rate. Thus, there might develop around 1990 or 2000 A.D. a need for breeders, if the uranium production rate could not be increased or could be improved only at a large increase in costs.

It would certainly be undesirable to utilize any appreciable fraction of the world's uranium resources without switching to breeding, since this might decrease the total recoverable energy. However, if breeders are achieved, as they surely will be in time, the fact that some small fraction of the total U^{235} available was utilized without breeding would not appreciably affect the total energy picture, even though it might increase the over-all costs slightly. It seems unlikely that any very appreciable fraction of the world's uranium will be utilized before the year 2000 A.D.

While full support of the continued development of both thermal and fast breeders seems advisable, their development should not be permitted to interfere in any way with the development of economically useful power reactors at the earliest practicable time.

When nuclear power reactors have arrived at a sound economic point, there will be a necessary supply of money invested in their further development and improvement. Improved utilization of the fuel will surely be a key item of such a development and will become of increasing importance as the cost of nuclear raw materials increases relative to the other costs. The cost of the developments will come largely from the income derived from the nuclear power industry, in the same way that other improvements in the power industry have been brought about during the past 50 years or more.

An unwarranted insistence on breeders today will only delay the development of economic nuclear power, and this in turn will prevent the establishment of an industrial base for the further development of power reactors, including breeders.

It may be observed that a drastic reduction in fuel fabrication and processing costs will improve uranium utilization since it will lead to a lower optimum irradiation time with substantially less loss of neutrons to control rods and fission products.

Nuclear Superheat

Direct nuclear superheat, particularly for water-cooled reactors, has also been emphasized lately. There is no question but that it is an area which deserves intensive study and experimentation, and that it will help improve the economics of power reactors if it can be successfully accomplished.

What seems to be forgotten, however, is that what one is really considering is a gas-cooled reactor of a fairly difficult type from the point of view of the materials involved and some of the safety problems. It is not clear that the incremental capital and fuel costs for direct nuclear superheating (and possibly reheating) of steam from boiling or pressurized water reactors will be offset by the increased power production. There is enough optimism to believe that a substantial development program will find ways of doing this with an over-all improvement in the economics.

However, it is not expected that the improvements will be very large and, in particular, there is little justification for the implied conclusion that nuclear superheat is likely to make the difference between a boiling water reactor (for example) being economical and not being economical; it might happen, but one should not count on it. We should try to make reactors economical without it, but continue work on nuclear superheat, and count ourselves fortunate if it should prove to give us still somewhat cheaper power.

In particular it would not be encouraging to see a misplaced enthusiasm for direct nuclear superheat slowing down the necessary development of the basic reactor concepts or delaying their demonstration. There is some danger of this happening if we are not careful.

Conclusion

In brief, we are within sight of the development of sufficiently cheap reactors and sufficiently cheap fuel for them so that we can expect to achieve economically useful power reactors within a fairly short time, if we follow a path of straightforward and aggressive development along lines already laid out. There are several good possibilities already substantially along in development as far as types of reactors go, and the same is true of fuel elements for them. Here again the problems are ones of straightforward development and of volume.

There are many intriguing possibilities for the future, and many ways of improving on what we now visualize as being the minimum required for economics. These deserve substantial support. Diversions to follow too many of these possibilities will only weaken the program and delay the time of arriving at the first goal which is itself a prerequisite to the later improvements.

2. SOLID FUEL ELEMENTS—PRESENT AND FUTURE

STANLEY B. ROBOFF

Director of Marketing, Sylvania-Corning Nuclear Corporation
Bayside, Long Island, N. Y.

It is now more than 13 years since the Smyth report first explained to the world that a controlled nuclear chain reaction could be accomplished, and that a whole new era of energy production was about to unfold. For years following the publication of the Smyth report, boundless numbers of predictions issued from every corner of the globe as to the untold benefits of the low-cost energy which would soon be available in unlimited amounts. In view of these predictions, it appears today that the enthusiasm displayed during this period has, for the most part, mellowed as a series of unforeseen problems presented themselves to the nuclear industry. In spite of these difficulties, the benefits of atomic energy first described in 1946 still appear to be the long-sought goals of government and industry throughout the world.

There is no doubt that we have come a long way in the development of nuclear energy in the past 10 years. We have learned much about the design and construction of reactors which points the way to further economies in the future. Nevertheless, there still remain many major obstacles which must be surmounted before nuclear energy will truly become a low-cost research tool and an economical source of power.

To explain the present high costs of nuclear energy, a number of reasons are usually given. Among those most frequently mentioned are: (1) the high cost of engineering and designing nuclear reactors; (2) the high capital charges still inherent in reactor construction; (3) the fact that little or no standardization exists in reactor design; and (4) the high cost of the nuclear fuel cycle. Much has been said and much is being done to help alleviate the first three items. However, it is only recently that full recognition has been given to the significant cost contributions of the complete nuclear fuel cycle, and concerted efforts have been undertaken to find means of reducing these costs.

In recognition of the importance of reducing fuel cycle costs as one of the few means available for providing lower-cost nuclear energy, a number of programs are being undertaken both in the United States and overseas to develop new techniques which will provide lower-cost fuel elements, longer life for these fuels in reactors, and lower-cost techniques for spent-fuel reprocessing. The recently announced decision of the U. S. Atomic Energy Commission to support a number of programs specifically aimed at lowering the cost of the nuclear fuel cycle undoubtedly will result, over the next few years, in major cost savings to be achieved in the fuel cycle. It is also interesting to note that an important segment of the development activity to be sponsored under the joint United States-Euratom Agreement will be concerned with finding means of improving the technology of the nuclear fuel cycle and in finding ways of lowering the costs of the fuel cycle. In addition to these government-sponsored programs, there are a number of privately sponsored programs within the nuclear industry which have the same objective.

Although technological changes in any part of the fuel cycle unquestionably affect the technology in other parts, it seems that the key item in the entire fuel cycle is the basic design of the nuclear fuel element. The composition of the fuel core, the type of cladding used, the nature of the bonding materials, the type of closures and end fittings which are employed, the degree of enrichment used, the fuel shape and method of fuel assembly—all have an important bearing on each of the steps in the nuclear fuel cycle. The criteria used in the design of the nuclear fuel element will govern, to a great extent, the cost of the basic raw material procurement and conversion, the cost of the fuel fabrication, and the degree of burn-up and corrosion resistance achievable in a reactor. Finally, the fuel design and its material composition are the key factors which govern the degree of expense for chemical reprocessing of the fuel.

Because so much is dependent upon the nature of the fuel element itself, a summary is given of the present types of fuels most commonly used in reactors, and what progress is currently being made on each of these to provide better performance at lower costs. Finally, a forecast of what lies beyond the immediate future will be given and an explanation of what will be the direction of nuclear fuel development which will lead, ultimately, to an economical fuel cycle.

It is convenient to classify the reactors in use today into four major categories: (1) plutonium production reactors; (2) research and test reactors; (3) package power reactors; and (4) stationary power reactors. There is, of course, a specific area of naval reactors, but for reasons of security it will be best to omit this category. Each of these four categories uses a type of fuel which is peculiar to the reactor group. Of course there is overlapping of fuel types within the reactor types; however, for the most part each reactor classification connotes specific fuel types.

Thus, in the area of plutonium production reactors, the basic fuel employed both in the United States and overseas comprises a natural uranium metal rod or slug, clad in aluminum or magnesium. This type of element has provided excellent service for the use to which it has been put; nevertheless, its basically simple shape limits the specific power level of the production reactors and, hence, plutonium generation. Increasing the surface-to-volume ratio of the fuel slugs or rods would provide for greater heat transfer, and thereby enable these reactors to operate at higher specific power levels without increasing the maximum central temperature of the fuel. This is basically the reason for the trend toward hollow slugs or tubular fuel elements which permit coolant flow both inside and outside of the fuel. The desire to achieve high specific power levels in these reactors also explains the increasing interest in the use of zirconium cladding as replacement for the lower-temperature aluminum and magnesium cladding.

Until quite recently, fuels for research and test reactors have followed a fairly definite pattern; that is, these reactor types have employed fuels the design of which is essentially that of the Materials Testing Reactor (MTR) fuel type with variations in the number of plates used and in the design of the end boxes. For the most part, research and test reactor fuels have comprised uranium-aluminum alloy flat-plate cores, clad in aluminum, and brazed into a boxlike assembly. The number of plates in each box assembly varies from 10 to 18, depending on the amount of uranium used and the purpose of the reactor. Until recently, fuel elements assembled by brazing techniques have proved entirely satisfactory for the relatively low power levels and low water-flow rates used in the research and test reactors.

However, for a growing number of higher-powered test reactors, a brazed assembly of box-type fuel elements has proved unsatisfactory. Among the problems encountered with brazed assemblies has been their inability to withstand fast water-flow rates. This arises from the fact that, during the brazing operation, the aluminum is annealed and becomes soft, with virtually no ability to retain its shape when large water-flow stresses are applied. Brazed elements also suffer because of residual lithium left over from the braze flux, and the ever-existing possibility of braze corrosion when these elements are left in reactors for an extended period of time.

To overcome the problems of brazing, a number of mechanically assembled MTR fuel types have recently been developed and introduced for use, usually at prices lower than brazed elements. These assemblies, which have the fuel plates mechanically fastened instead of brazed to the side plates, have considerably more strength and rigidity. This is because assembly of the fuel element is performed at room temperature, and therefore the resultant fuel element maintains the stiffness and rigidity of the cold-rolled aluminum plates. This additional rigidity has permitted mechanically assembled fuels to be in operation for sustained periods at water-flow rates well above 40 ft per sec without distortion of the element.

The lack of brazing in mechanically assembled elements also precludes the possibility of lithium contamination of the element—a factor which has proved to be of considerable importance in heavy-water moderated reactors.

For a number of reasons there is also a growing trend toward the use of tubular types of fuels for test reactors, such as those currently employed in the CP-5 (Chicago Pile) reactor at Argonne, the Westinghouse Test Reactor, and the Nuclear Development Corporation's Materials and Test Reactor currently under construction in Mol, Belgium. Tubular fuels, of course, possess an inherent strength normally associated with curved surfaces. In addition, this type of fuel element provides a means of obtaining an unusually uniform and high flux within the central portion of the fuel element itself. Furthermore, because they are usually mechanically assembled, tubular elements also possess the rigidity advantages already described for mechanically assembled fuels. Because of their basic advantages, tubular fuel elements for research and test reactors are gaining in popularity, and within the next few years it is likely that an increasing proportion of test reactors in this country and abroad will employ tubular elements.

The wide experience which has been gained in the manufacture and use of research and test reactor fuels has enabled a standardization of certain types of research and test reactor fuels to be accomplished. Such standardization, as recently announced by Sylvania-Corning Nuclear Corporation, is providing another important avenue for lowering the costs of research and test reactor fuels. Standard fuels mean standardized tooling, dies, fixtures, tolerances, and basic designs. Thus, from the fuel manufacturer's viewpoint, standard fuels reduce or eliminate many costs which are presently involved with each new and different research reactor fuel order. Standardized fuels can be one of the major factors leading to a lower-cost fuel cycle.

In the area of package power reactors, and particularly package reactors of the Army Package Power Reactor (APPR) type, the basic MTR plate and box design has been carried over; but stronger, more corrosion-resistant, and higher-temperature materials have been employed. The material of this basic fuel plate, instead of being a uranium-aluminum alloy, consists of uranium dioxide dispersed in a matrix of stainless steel. This core plate is completely clad in stainless steel. Eighteen such plates are brazed into side plates, and when end boxes are attached the resultant fuel element resembles somewhat the MTR element. Reactor performance of this type of fuel has been most encouraging, and the UO_2-stainless steel matrix composition has shown itself capable of providing high specific power outputs with fairly high uranium burn-up. Because of the initial success of this type of element there has been no marked incentive to change its design or material composition. There are studies under way, however, to find lower cost means of assembly for this element.

In the gas-cooled type of package reactor, the basic APPR fuel design may prove acceptable as a starting point; however, the efficiency of gas-cooled reactors increases materially as temperature levels increase, and it is quite probable that materials other than stainless steel will ultimately be considered for use. Furthermore, there is some question as to whether the plate and box design is the most efficient type for gas-cooled systems; hence, we may find that more complex geometric configurations will be considered so that optimum heat transfer and pressure drop conditions can be achieved in gas-cooled reactors.

Finally, in stationary power reactors, uranium oxide fuel cores, clad with either stainless steel, Zircaloy or aluminum, hold the stage at the moment. Elements of this type have offered considerable promise in providing the kind of fuel which is necessary to the economics of large-scale nuclear power generation. Offhand, it would appear that the manufacture of UO_2 fuels clad in metal tubes would be relatively inexpensive, although experience to date indicates that there are more problems than were originally thought. Burn-up performance has been most encouraging, and there seems to be a growing confidence that UO_2 fuels will ultimately provide considerably more than 10,000 megawatt days (Mwd) per ton of burn-up. Nevertheless, as matters stand today, far more knowledge of UO_2 fuel in-pile behavior is required.

Uranium oxide fuels offer an additional major advantage in the fuel cycle. This advantage accrues from the fact that uranium oxide fuels will probably be reprocessed at relatively low cost. Thus, with uranium oxide fuels, we may have all the ingredients of a low-cost fuel cycle, namely low-cost fuel fabrication, high burn-up and long life in reactor use, and relatively low-cost fuel reprocessing. It is in the area of oxide fuels of this type that a considerable saving in nuclear power costs can be achieved within the near future.

Solid uranium oxide fuels, however, are not turning out to be the panacea for all types of power reactors. Uranium oxide does have some disadvantages, among which is its poor thermal conductivity. This property makes its use questionable in power reactors which are designed for high specific rates of heat output, such as package power reactors, liquid metal-cooled reactors, and gas-cooled reactors. As a result, it appears that liquid metal-cooled reactors and gas-cooled reactors will require other ceramic materials which yield the advantages of uranium oxide regarding cost and burn-up, but which are not faced with its heat conductivity problem. Uranium carbide and uranium dispersions in graphite are currently being investigated in a number of quarters and already appear to offer considerable advantage for use in liquid metal- and gas-cooled power reactor systems. Furthermore, in addition to the carbide and graphite fuels for gas-cooled and liquid metal-cooled reactors, cermet systems, again based on the APPR fuel element type, are receiving increasing interest and will continue to be of interest as newer high-strength, high-temperature and corrosion-resistant metals and alloys are developed.

Having just discussed the present trends of fuel designs, a projection beyond the immediate future will now be given and a brief list of thoughts as to the direction of future growth and development of nuclear fuels. These predictions, however, are made in the light of trends which it is believed have already started, and in the light of certain economic truths which must be accepted if atomic energy is to be a useful tool 10 or more years hence.

(1) *The present technical arguments on "solid vs. liquid" nuclear fuels will be settled in favor of solid fuels.* By this it is not meant that liquid-fueled reactors will not be used for a number of purposes, but that the vast majority of reactors built in the future will be solid-fueled. This prediction is made because of a conviction that solid fuels are more likely to meet the stringent reactor operating conditions of the future and lend themselves better to an economical fuel cycle than liquid fuels. Liquid fuels have already shown themselves to be difficult problems from a corrosion point of view, and, as reactor temperature requirements increase, this corrosion problem will undoubtedly become more severe. Liquid fuels also, for the most part, require a recirculation system of some sort, and this in turn means additional shielding outside of the reactor to provide for safe operation around the entire liquid fuel circuit. Again, because a large proportion of the liquid fuel is circulating outside the core of the reactor, higher initial fuel investments are required.

On the other hand, solid fuels—notably ceramics and metal-ceramic combinations—have shown particularly good promise for ultrahigh-temperature operations. It also appears that solid fuel-coolant systems can be found which will be relatively noncorrosive at the higher temperatures at which reactors will be operating in the future. Furthermore, a solid fuel element provides a handy package for containment of the fission products, so that shielding problems can be restricted to the reactor alone and need not extend to the entire coolant cycle.

(2) *Ceramic fuels will become one of the most important types of fuel for nuclear reactors.* The reasons for this prediction are based on the fact that future temperature levels will be required whereby the use of metals, except in certain special cases, becomes unattractive technically and impractical economically. Ceramic fuels, of course, offer many distinct dis-

advantages, but we will find ways of living with these disadvantages because of the overriding ability of ceramic fuels to provide long burn-ups at high temperatures.

(3) *In spite of the increasing use of ceramic fuels, metal fuels and metal-ceramic combinations will continue to be used, even as a series of new high-temperature and, in some cases, highly oxidation-resistant alloys come into use.* There will be some reactor types where large outputs of heat in small volumes will not permit the use of low heat conductivity ceramic elements. For these types of reactors the continued use of metals will be important, and metals and alloys will be developed which will permit high-temperature, long burn-up operation under what we normally consider to be extremely corrosive conditions.

(4) *There will be a series of fuel systems developed which employ unclad fuel elements, with provisions being made for fission products escaping from such fuels to be removed from the coolant stream by scavenging agents.* At the moment there are some studies being made which indicate that economies are to be gained in the fabrication and chemical reprocessing phases of the fuel cycle when unclad fuels are considered. These economies accrue because it is not necessary first to apply fuel claddings, with their subsequent dissolution and separation and handling in a chemical plant. These savings could be of such a magnitude as to cover easily the additional expense of an efficient scavenging system in a coolant stream. The unclad fuel plus scavenger system could well first come into use in the closed cycle gas-cooled reactor concepts.

(5) *Major cost reductions in the fuel cycle will come about through standardization of fuel elements of various basic types.* Such standardization not only will lower the cost of the fuel fabrication part of the fuel cycle but also will produce concurrent cost reductions in all the other phases of the nuclear fuel cycle. We need not dwell here on the surprising effects of standardization in lowering costs. A great many studies have been made by management and industrial engineering groups which bear out that standardizing almost any product will cut costs by one third to one half or more. Standardizing fuel designs is bound to result in similar savings in fuel costs.

(6) *Should a breakthrough occur in thermoelectric development, fuel elements will become the key components of reactors which will then be developed and designed for direct conversion of nuclear heat into electric energy.* At the moment, this seems a long way off; nevertheless should an efficient thermoelectric system be devised, nuclear fuel with its built-in thermal gradients and multimaterial structure offers many of the features which probably will be required for a good thermoelectric generator.

In conclusion, it becomes evident that the establishment of an economical fuel cycle offers one of the major means we presently have available of achieving low-cost nuclear energy, and that a concerted effort to reduce the cost of the fuel cycle through improvements in the basic design of the fuel element may provide *the* economic breakthrough which is so necessary for the ultimate success of nuclear power.

3. ENGINEERING OF FUEL ELEMENTS FOR LOW COST FABRICATION AND REPROCESSING

R. B. GORDON

Deputy Director, Fuels and Materials
Atomics International Division of North American Aviation, Inc.,
Canoga Park, Calif.

Concern over the present high cost of power reactor fuel elements is widespread. Nuclear fuel costs must be lower than those of fossil fuel to compensate for the higher capital costs of nuclear plants. Fuel cycle costs must be lowered by as much as a factor of 2 before this goal can be realized. Two important elements of the over-all fuel cycle—fabrication and reprocessing—will be discussed in this chapter. The economics of materials, mechanical design, and fabrication of solid fuel elements for land-based power reactors will be considered. Nuclear and heat transfer aspects and fuel elements for plutonium-producing, mobile, and research reactors will not be covered.

Low-cost fabrication and reprocessing implies more than low initial cost per unit of fuel. The contribution of these two operations to the cost of electrical power expressed in mills/kwh is the important consideration. The fuel cost, so expressed, is strongly influenced by the important factor of fuel element lifetime, or burn-up. Although a considerable amount of irradiation data is at hand on the burn-up capabilities of small samples of several fuel materials, there are no significant data on performance of full scale power reactor fuel elements. It is not known whether the fuel element designs now being produced are capable of achieving the reactor lifetimes predicted from the materials tests. Only actual performance data on a number of full core loadings, which will not be available for several years, will permit us to evaluate the relative integrity of various over-all fuel element designs. Further complicating the matter of fuel element integrity is the difficulty in locating and removing a defective fuel element and the consequences of a major failure in an operating power plant. These factors

20

have produced an intense desire for conservatism in design, leading to high fuel costs in first generation reactors.

A quantitative treatment of the subject of power reactor fuel element costs is made difficult by the fact that very little reliable cost information is available. Only one full core loading, that of the Shippingport Pressurized Water Reactor (PWR), has been completed. The cost of this admittedly uneconomical core provides a very poor basis for extrapolation to other designs. Fortunately, however, for at least one type of fuel element, namely, UO_2 rods, some cost estimates based on fixed price vendor quotations are at hand. These provide a measure of where we stand today and indicate what further gains must be made before the goal of economical nuclear power is achieved.

IMPORTANCE OF FUEL FABRICATION AND REPROCESSING COSTS

To provide a background for a discussion of fuel element costs it is desirable to look at the proportion of the final electrical power costs attributable to fuel. Figure 3-1 gives the relative contribution of fuel and other costs for various reactor types now under active development. As shown, fuel costs range from 20 to 50 per cent of total power cost. This variation results from differences in specific power and enrichment as well

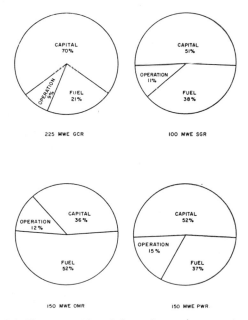

Figure 3-1. Power cost breakdown for various reactor types.

NUCLEAR FUEL ELEMENTS

TABLE 3-1. GROSS FUEL-CYCLE COSTS FOR VARIOUS REACTORS

Reactor Data:	(1)	(2)	(3)	(4)	(5)	(6)	(7)
Reference	GCR*	BWR	PWR	SGR	SGR	SGR	F. Br.†
Reactor type	UO_2	UO_2	UO_2	UO_2	UO_2	U-10 Mo	U-10 Mo
Fuel	S.S.	Zircaloy	S.S.	S.S.	S.S.	S.S.	Zirconium
Clad	2.0	—	2.6	3.6	3.1	3.5	27
% U^{235}							
Avg. burn-up, Mwd/ton	7,400	10,000	10,000	11,000	13,700	5,000	10,000
Fuel Cycle Cost (mills/ekwh):							
In-core inventory	0.8	0.4	0.6	0.8	0.7	1.0	1.4
UF$_6$ conversion	⎫	⎫	⎫	0.4	⎫	0.8	⎫
Fabrication	⎬ 0.5	⎬ 2.4	⎬ 1.5	0.8	⎬ 1.3	0.3	⎬ 2.4
Ex-core inventory	0.1	⎭	⎭	0.3	⎭	0.7	⎭
Uranium recovery	0.3	0.4	0.4	0.5	0.6	0.8	1.6
Fuel burn-up	1.9	1.4	2.3	2.2	2.0	2.4	2.1
Shipping	—	0.3	0.3	0.2	—	0.4	—
Total	3.6	4.9	5.1	5.2	4.6	6.4	7.5

* Gas-cooled reactor
† Fast breeder reactor

as fuel element type. Estimated net fuel cycle cost for various reactors ranges from about 2.5 to 5 mills/kwh of electricity produced. Only in areas where conventional fossil fuel power costs are very high can nuclear power, with its present fuel costs, compete. The need to reduce nuclear fuel costs by 50 per cent presents a very real challenge to all engineers involved in the design and processing of fuel elements.

Over-all fuel cycle costs are made up of three major items: (1) interest charges and burn-up of the fissionable material, (2) fabrication cost of finished fuel elements, including cost of cladding and other materials, and (3) cost of reprocessing of the spent fuel elements and recovery of the fissionable material. Table 3-1 gives the fuel cycle cost figures for two important fuel materials when applied in various types of reactors. The totals shown are gross costs from which a plutonium credit is deducted in determining net fuel costs. These costs apply only to the quite high average fuel burn-ups assumed. Lower burn-ups will result in sharply increased costs as shown in Figure 3-2.[6] Although the data shown are for UO_2, the same general relationship between burn-up and fuel cost holds for all fuels. In the range of interest, over-all fuel costs vary roughly inversely as the square root of the burn-up. Of the total fuel cost, averaging about 5 mills for most of the examples, only about 1.5 mills, or 30 per cent, are involved in fabricating finished fuel elements from UF_6, including out-of-core inventory charges. Even when uranium recovery costs of 0.5 mills are added, only 40 per cent of the gross fuel cycle costs are directly associated with fabrication and reprocessing. This represents less than 20 per cent of the total power cost. The very important costs for in-core inventory and fuel burn-up are beyond the control of the reactor materials and fuel element processor. They are determined by the enrichment and size of the core loading which involve nuclear and other nonmaterials considerations. Furthermore, the burn-up and inventory charges are based on prices set by the Atomic Energy Commission. Hence only the fabrication and reprocessing portions of the total cost are amenable to cost reduction (in the usual sense) by industry at this time.

The principal elements of the fuel fabrication costs are: (1) cost of converting UF_6 to the desired fuel material, (2) cost of alloying elements for the fuel, (3) cost of material used for cladding, (4) cost of the process of cladding the fuel material, (5) cost of fabricating fuel material to required shape, (6) cost of assembling fuel elements, (7) interest charges on fuel during fabrication, (8) miscellaneous hardware costs, and (9) packing and shipping costs. Costs in each of the above categories are borne by all reactor fuels utilizing enriched uranium. Their relative magnitude and im-

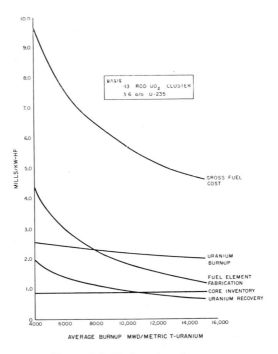

Figure 3-2. Fuel cost *vs.* burn-up.

portance are a strong function of the materials, shape, and fabrication process used. These subjects are discussed in the following sections.

FUEL ELEMENT MATERIALS

Fuel

Many factors must be considered in selecting the fuel material for a power reactor. A principal objective is to use a fuel with high uranium density to produce a good conversion ratio and hold the enrichment level as low as possible. This keeps the uranium burn-up charges low and the plutonium credit high. The economic disadvantage of using high enrichments is clearly shown in Figure 3-3 where the AEC price of uranium hexafluoride (UF_6) per kg of contained uranium is plotted *vs.* weight per cent U^{235}.[8] This consideration eliminates fully enriched fuels of both the alloy and dispersed particle types which are widely used for research and military reactors.

Another very important consideration is dimensional stability of the fuel under reactor operating conditions. This involves resistance to thermal cycling, thermal stresses, and changes induced by the fission process. Dimensional stability under irradiation is a necessity if fuels are to achieve the high burn-up required for low fuel cycle costs. It is desirable but not essential that the fuel material have good thermal conductivity. In many reactors compatibility of the fuel with the coolant is important in order to reduce the consequences of a cladding break. This last consideration has led to the almost universal adoption of uranium dioxide (UO_2) as the fuel

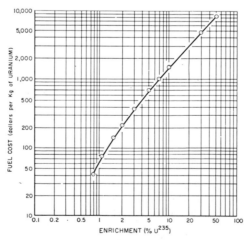

Figure 3-3. AEC price of UF_6 *vs.* enrichment.

material for water-cooled reactors, despite its low uranium density and poor thermal conductivity. For sodium-cooled reactors, uranium alloys such as the gamma-phase 10 % molybdenum-uranium alloy have been chosen. For organic-cooled reactors operating at lower temperatures, an alloy of the 3 % molybdenum-uranium type may be appropriate.

At the present time total fabrication costs for UO_2 fuel elements are estimated to range from \$80 to \$180/kg of uranium depending on cladding material and geometry, whereas uranium-molybdenum alloy elements of similar low enrichment are estimated at \$30 to \$70/kg. However, since the peak burn-up capability of UO_2 as a material is thought to be over 20,000 Mwd/ton, estimated fuel cycle costs for this material are lower than those of the uranium alloy with a burn-up capability of about 10,000 Mwd/ton. If metallic fuel developments now underway are successful in extending the burn-up limitations, then fuel cycle costs for metals will become attractive relative to UO_2.

Another fuel material of great interest at the present time is uranium carbide which offers the possibility of high burn-up at high temperatures, as in the case of UO_2 combined with higher uranium density and good thermal conductivity. Unfortunately, since uranium carbide (UC) is quite reactive with water, it can be considered only for sodium and gas-cooled reactors. Fabrication costs of UC are not known but will probably fall between those of uranium and UO_2.

Cladding

Initial screening of potential cladding materials is based primarily on compatibility with the fuel and coolant. This involves consideration of corrosion resistance, and the possibility of solid phase reactions and eutectic formation. Zircaloy-2 and stainless steel can be used with UO_2 fuel with both water and sodium coolants. Stainless steel can be used in addition with organic and gas coolants. Aluminum-base materials, handicapped by low melting points and poor mechanical properties at elevated temperature, have been considered only for relatively low temperature operation with organic- and water-cooled reactors. Beryllium and niobium offer some promise for use in high-temperature gas-cooled fuel elements. Both of these are high priced, and, in addition, beryllium has limited fabricability and is probably subject to volume change at elevated temperature due to the formation of helium when this material is neutron-bombarded.

When more than one cladding material can be used in a given application, the final choice is based on economic considerations. This must take into account not only the cost of the cladding in the finished fuel element but also the relative effects of the neutron absorption on the fuel enrichment

TABLE 3-2. BREAK-EVEN PRICE FOR ZIRCALOY-2 CLADDING
IN SEVERAL REACTORS[9]

Reactor	% U^{235}	Cost of Zr-2/lb
Nuclear Power Demonstration	0.7	$104
Sodium Graphite Reactor..................	1.8	57
Yankee....................................	2.6	51
Merchant Ship Reactor.	3.6	44
Vallecitos Boiling Water Reactor...........	93.0	10

and consequently on the interest and burn-up charges. The price at which Zircaloy, for example, becomes economical in competition with stainless steel will vary from one type of reactor to another. An interesting study[9] along these lines has been made with the results shown in Table 3-2. The Zircaloy prices given in this table are those at which the lower cost of the uranium inventory and burn-up is just balanced by the difference in cost between Zircaloy and stainless steel priced at $5/lb. A somewhat different approach has been taken to determine the economic feasibility of substituting aluminum for Zircaloy in a boiling-water reactor.[10] Here it was assumed that the reactor operating temperatures would have to be reduced when using aluminum, thus producing reduced thermal efficiency and higher power costs. It was concluded that savings of $27/kg of uranium were attainable with aluminum cladding. This saving would be balanced by the loss of 2.8 per cent net thermal efficiency resulting from a 50°F reduction in the temperature of the steam produced. It was concluded that higher strength aluminum alloys would have to be developed to compete successfully with zirconium.

FUEL ELEMENT DESIGN

Shape

Fuel element shape is determined largely by mechanical and heat transfer considerations, and to a lesser extent by nuclear, materials, and fabrication considerations. In several reactor types such as those cooled by gas or organic liquids, the poor heat transfer coefficients demand use of shapes with high surface-to-volume ratios such as flat plates or rods with extended finned surfaces. On the other hand, reactors cooled with liquid metal permit considerably greater latitude in choice of fuel element shape since maximum surface area is not essential. Although in principle fuel elements can have a wide variety of shapes, in actual practice simple shapes such as rods, tubes, and plates are almost universally used. Typical fuel elements employing these common shapes are shown in Figures 3-4 through 3-6.

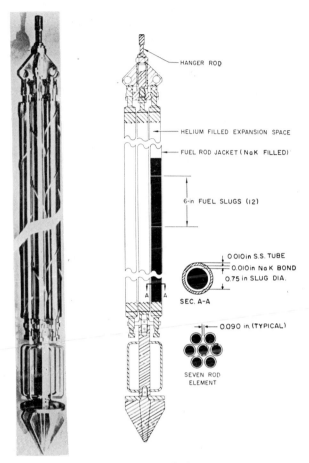

Figure 3-4. SRE fuel element.

Rod-type fuel elements have the advantage of being able to resist external, or contain internal, pressures with a minimum of cladding. The cladding need not be bonded to the fuel for structural reasons. In the case of plates, the cladding usually has very little rigidity and must of necessity be bonded either to the fuel or to the opposite cladding surface by spacers in the fuel. This results in higher fabrication cost. Despite this disadvantage, however, plate-type elements may be selected in order to reduce the fuel thickness and lower central temperatures. Such an element with UO_2 fuel is under active development for the second blanket of the Shippingport PWR. Tubular fuel elements have many of the advantages of both plates and rods, and have intermediate structural rigidity.

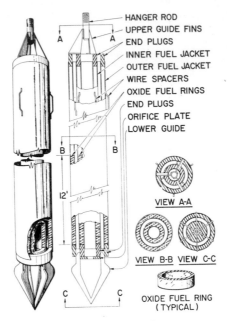

HANGER ROD
UPPER GUIDE FINS
END PLUGS
INNER FUEL JACKET
OUTER FUEL JACKET
WIRE SPACERS
OXIDE FUEL RINGS
END PLUGS
ORIFICE PLATE
LOWER GUIDE

VIEW A-A

VIEW B-B   VIEW C-C

OXIDE FUEL RING
(TYPICAL)

Figure 3-5. Tubular oxide fuel element.

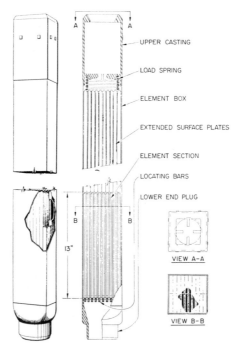

UPPER CASTING

LOAD SPRING

ELEMENT BOX

EXTENDED SURFACE PLATES

ELEMENT SECTION

LOCATING BARS

LOWER END PLUG

VIEW A-A

VIEW B-B

Figure 3-6. Extended surface metal plate element.

Thickness

Once the basic shape of the fuel element has been fixed, the section thickness is selected. This depends upon several factors. Many fuel element sections are determined by the limiting central temperature of the fuel. In the case of uranium metal, this was formerly placed at approximately 1200°F, the temperature of the α- to β-phase transformation. Uranium is subject to gross dimensional and volume changes if thermally cycled through the transformation temperature. However, recent fuel-swelling data indicate that lower central temperatures may be necessary to achieve high burn-up with acceptable volume change. In the case of UO_2 fuel, 5000°F, the melting point of UO_2, is usually the extreme upper limit, with most designs using 4000°F for a margin of safety. At or near the melting point of the fuel, fission gas release and possible fuel redistribution by volatilization are matters of considerable concern. Where heat transfer from the fuel element to the coolant is the limiting factor, the need for high surface area usually eliminates the central temperature problem but introduces another. If, for heat-transfer reasons, it is necessary to use finely divided fuel, then the ratio of cladding to fuel tends to become quite high. This causes very high fuel fabrication costs where cladding materials such as zirconium are used.

The primary functions of cladding are to protect the fuel from the coolant and to prevent passage of fission products from the fuel to the coolant. If the cladding is perfectly leak-tight, an extremely thin layer will suffice to keep fission recoils out of the coolant. Normally, a considerably thicker cladding is required to assure integrity both initially and through the expected lifetime of the fuel element. There are few experimental data for determining optimum cladding thickness for the various types of fuel elements. In those cases where a given thickness is required for mechanical strength reasons, such as to contain fission gas pressure from UO_2, the thickness so determined is usually quite adequate to insure integrity from the standpoint of metallurgical soundness, corrosion resistance, etc. Occasionally, with metallurgically bonded elements produced by co-working of the metal and cladding, appreciable local variations in the cladding thickness may be encountered. In this case, the average cladding may have to be increased to provide minimum thickness.

Bond

Fuel elements with diverse shapes and materials can be categorized according to the type of bond between the fuel and the cladding. The principal types are: (1) mechanical bond, (2) metallurgical bond, and (3) liquid or gas bond. The type of bond chosen for a given application depends upon the materials and thermal conditions involved.

A metallurgical bond is often desired for heat-transfer reasons and to reduce the consequences of a pinhole cladding failure in those cases where the fuel is subject to corrosion by the coolant. Some material combinations cannot be bonded—for example, UO_2 fuel in a metal cladding—while with others, formation of brittle transition zones or differences in thermal expansion may destroy the bond during reactor operation. In some cases metallurgical bonding, although possible, is too expensive to be considered.

Fuel elements which do not require a metallurgical bond can use a wide range of fuel and cladding materials. The necessary heat transfer may be effected by simple mechanical contact of fuel and cladding or by use of a conducting gas or liquid to fill the gap. UO_2 fuel elements usually employ helium gas as the bond to take advantage of its good thermal conductivity, but its effect is partially lost during irradiation due to the decrease in conductivity from the fission gases. In those cases where applicable, use of a liquid metal bond is most effective in minimizing the temperature drop between fuel and cladding. It has the advantage of permitting the use of large clearances in assembly of the element. This may permit the use of unmachined fuel slugs, which reduces cost. Space can also be provided for possible fuel swelling. It has the minor disadvantage that special care in assembly is required to promote wetting of the fuel and cladding surface by the liquid metal.

Assembly

Most fuel elements are more or less rigidly assembled into various arrays whose specific geometry depends upon the modular arrangement of the reactor core. The examples illustrated in Figures 3-4 to 3-6 have the fuel elements arranged for parallel coolant flow which is normally preferred for hydraulic reasons and because it minimizes the number of individual fuel elements. Although fuel element assemblies with cross flow of coolant are often proposed because of the heat-transfer advantage, the additional pressure drop involved and the large increase in number of individual fuel elements usually combine to discourage their acceptance. Another type of fuel having many attractive features but as yet unused in an operating reactor is nonrigid or bulk fuel with the elements used in a packed or random bed arrangement. Bulk fuel elements consisting of uranium carbide fuel contained in a central cavity in graphite spheres of 5 to 6 cm in diameter are proposed for a gas-cooled reactor.[11] The use of bulk fuel offers many potential advantages in both fabrication and reprocessing because of the fact that the fuel element assembly costs are completely eliminated.

From the fabrication standpoint, fuel element assemblies have almost infinite variety but can be subdivided into two main classes: (1) mechanically joined assemblies, and (2) welded or brazed assemblies. A relatively simple and low cost type of mechanical assembly is illustrated in

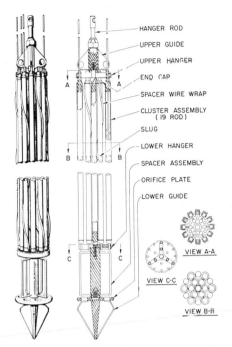

HANGER ROD
UPPER GUIDE
UPPER HANGER
END CAP
SPACER WIRE WRAP
CLUSTER ASSEMBLY
(19 ROD)
SLUG
LOWER HANGER
SPACER ASSEMBLY
ORIFICE PLATE
LOWER GUIDE

VIEW A-A
VIEW C-C
VIEW B-B

Figure 3-7. Mechanical fuel rod assembly.

Figure 3-7. This type, which uses wrapped wire spacers, is only semirigid with considerable flexibility in the individual fuel rods. It can be applied only where fretting corrosion at contact surfaces does not occur with the coolant and cladding concerned. More rigid types of mechanical assemblies use mechanical fasteners to lock the fuel elements into the array. A successful adaptation of this concept to plate geometry was made in the case of the stainless steel-UO_2 element for the Organic Moderator Reactor Experiment (OMRE).[12]

Brazed or welded subassemblies have the potential advantage of greater freedom from fretting and crevice corrosion. Whether or not this is realized in practice depends on both design details and quality of workmanship. They also may have higher strength and rigidity for a given material cross section. It is difficult to generalize on the relative cost of different assembly types but it is fair to state that the cost usually increases from mechanical to brazed to welded designs. Spot-welded assemblies are probably an exception to this statement. An attractive spot-welded assembly design employing Zircaloy-2 was developed for the first Experimental Boiling Water Reactor (EBWR) core.[13] Attaining optimum fuel assembly designs leading to minimum fuel cycle costs is difficult at this time due to the great dearth

TABLE 3-3. COSTS FOR STAINLESS STEEL-CLAD UO₂ FUEL ROD CLUSTERS[15]

Cluster size	19-rod	37-rod	61-rod
UO₂ diameter (in.)	0.50	0.43	0.36
No. of clusters in core	243	135	84
Enrichment (% U²³⁵)	3.5	3.5	3.5
Average burn-up (Mwd/ton of UO₂)	11,100	10,200	9,600
UO₂ loading (lb)	56,000	40,000	26,000
Cluster fabrication cost*	$10,900	$14,000	$17,300
Initial loading cost	$2,650,000	$1,920,000	$1,450,000
Annual inventory cost	$410,000	$290,000	$190,000
Annual fuel fabrication cost	630,000	680,000	830,000
Total fuel-cycle cost (mills/ekwh)	4.97	4.92	5.12

* Includes UF₆-UO₂ conversion, material and labor, scrap recovery and shipping.

of reactor experience on full-size fuel assemblies. It is to be hoped, however, that in the next few years this experience will become available for several important assembly types.

Compartmentation

One of the urgent problems that confronts the fuel element designer is that of compartmentation or subdivision of the fuel. This is intimately tied up with an estimate of the probability of a cladding failure and with the consequences of release of fission products or fuel to the coolant. Fabrication cost of fuel elements is a strong function of the amount of compartmentation. With UO₂ fuel elements of the Shippingport PWR design, the cost of end closures and rod assembly is inversely proportional to the length of the individual rods. Hence there is a strong economic incentive to use long rods with intermediate supports between the ends. Although commercial reactor designs following PWR are utilizing somewhat longer fuel rods, a desire for compartmentation to reduce the possibilities of fuel ratcheting is still present. In the case of the Yankee* power reactor, a design employing brazed stainless steel spacers at intervals within the fuel tube is being considered.[14] Subdivision of fuel is also attained by decreasing rod diameter, thus reducing the volume of fuel that can be involved in a single cladding failure.

Table 3-3 shows the fabrication and fuel cycle costs for a series of stainless steel-clad UO₂ rod clusters for a 75 Mwe sodium graphite reactor.[15] It is noted that as the UO₂ rod diameter decreases, more rods are required per cluster, resulting in an appreciable increase in the cluster fabrication cost. Due to the smaller number of clusters required, however, the total fabrication cost for the initial core loading decreases with rod number.

* Yankee Atomic Elec. Co., Rome, Mass.

Using these data alone, one would conclude that it would be advantageous to use even more finely divided fuel. This is not the case, however, since the smaller cores require more frequent refueling. The annual refueling cost is a minimum for the 19-rod cluster. When the costs of the complete fuel cycle are obtained, a shallow minimum occurs at 37 rods. This is due to the combined effects of fabrication plus the lower inventory charges associated with a smaller core. This example serves to illustrate how difficult it is to generalize on the subject of fuel element costs. It should be stressed, however, that this study did not take into account the possible variation in fuel element integrity with changes in design such as rod diameter. It was assumed that all three fuel clusters were capable of achieving the average burn-ups listed. Only when statistical data on actual fuel element life, in-pile, are available will it be possible to evaluate alternates quantitatively and decide on the minimum cost design.

Inspection

Inspection costs for power reactor fuel elements are an important part of the fabrication cost. It behooves the designer, therefore, to consider seriously the inspectability of the product during the conceptual design stage. The several basic fuel element assembly types differ appreciably in inspectability. There may be little possibility for improvement where a given assembly design is required. Fortunately, however, great progress has been made in nondestructive techniques applicable to inspecting various fuel elements. It has become possible, for example, to measure characteristics such as bond integrity, fuel and cladding thickness, etc., with considerable reliability. This places on the fuel element designer the burden of setting realistic quality standards so that a minimum number of useful elements will be rejected and no really defective elements will be passed.

Fuel assembly designs vary widely in regard to inspectability of such items as coolant channel dimensions and joint integrity. They also vary in their need for inspection, depending upon the type of operations performed in assembling the elements. Thus, for example, a simple mechanical assembly of fully inspected fuel elements can provide a high degree of assurance that coolant channel tolerances are met even in those cases where inspection of the finished assembly is difficult or impossible. The assembly operation is subject only to mechanical damage from human errors. In the case of the brazed or welded assembly, however, serious distortions and dimensional changes can occur during the assembly operation. Overheating or burn-through can cause serious damage to fuel elements or can jeopardize their integrity. Inspection of these types is mandatory after the final manufacturing operation. Cost of this inspection may be quite high unless the design permits use of relatively simple equipment and techniques. Perhaps

most important of all is the fact that salvage and repair of defective assemblies of the brazed and welded types is usually difficult, if not impossible.
Cost of scrap losses, then, is apt to be an important element in the over-all
cost of such assemblies.

FUEL ELEMENT FABRICATION

Fuel Components and Cladding

Fuel element fabrication costs include all of the cladding and structural
materials and the conversion cost and use charge associated with govern-
ment-owned fissionable material. The cost of the cladding and fuel components is a major part of the total fuel element fabrication cost. These
items offer much promise for future cost reduction as fuel element production volume increases. Lower costs should also follow from adoption of more
reasonable quality standards where these are shown to be possible by
operating experience. An example of this is the substitution of welded for
seamless tubing in fuel element cladding. The desire for conservatism and
utmost reliability in fuel for first generation nuclear power plants has led
to wide adoption of seamless cladding in both stainless steel and Zircaloy.
This may well prove to be an unnecessary expense. Welded tubing is less
expensive and can be made with more uniform dimensions. Experience to
date in using 3000 ft of $\frac{3}{4}$-in. diameter $\times$ 0.010-in. thick welded 304 stainless steel tubing in the Sodium Reactor Experiment (SRE) has been highly
satisfactory. No fuel element cladding failures have been experienced in
the first year of operation.

Conversion of slightly enriched UF_6 to either uranium metal or UO_2 in
commercial plants is in its infancy. Present low volumes and attendant
high amortization costs have resulted in fuel conversion costs which are
running as high as 1 mill/ekwh. Reduction in fuel conversion costs will
occur with larger quantities and lower enrichment levels. Figure 3-8 gives
average estimated costs of several producers to convert UF_6 to UO_2 versus
U^{235} content. The lot size is 50,000 pounds.

Metallic fuel slugs of uranium or a uranium alloy can be produced by
casting, by rolling or extruding, and by powder metallurgy. A recent study
of cost to produce 0.6-in. diameter by 6-in. long uranium alloy slugs gives
the figures shown in Table 3-4.[16] Wrought slugs cost more than cast slugs
principally due to the additional ingot stage, fabrication of the ingot, and
the appreciably higher cost of scrap recovery. Unfortunately, there are no
directly comparable costs of slugs produced by powder metallurgy. These
are undoubtedly higher than the figures for wrought slugs shown. No data
are available to indicate the relative burn-up capabilities of the same material produced by the three routes. In a program which is being started at

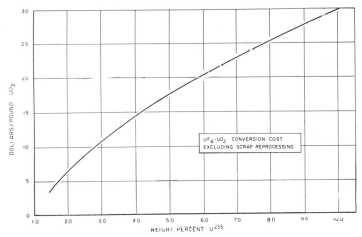

Figure 3-8. UF$_6$-UO$_2$ conversion cost *vs.* enrichment.

TABLE 3-4. FABRICATION COST OF CAST AND WROUGHT URANIUM
(2.5% U^{235}) SLUGS[16]

Operation	Cost ($/lb)	
	Cast	Wrought
UF$_6$—derby................................	2.34	—
UF$_6$—ingot................................	—	4.31
Derby—slug................................	7.54	—
Ingot—slug................................	—	10.75
Scrap recovery.............................	2.54	4.85
Shipping...................................	.66	.86
Interest charge (4%).....................	6.50	7.50
Total.....................................	$19.58	$28.27

Atomics International, the in-pile behavior of cast and wrought slugs of a uranium-10% molybdenum alloy will be evaluated.

Ceramic fuels have assumed a position of major importance in the power reactor field as a result of the pioneering AEC-sponsored work on UO$_2$ for the Shippingport PWR. Due to the limited time available for development of compacting and sintering processes for optimum dimensional control, Westinghouse adopted the practice of centerless-grinding the cylindrical surface and face-grinding the ends of the pellets. The first was done to assure more uniform heat-transfer conditions in the fuel rod and the second to achieve maximum fuel loading. A considerable amount of fabrication development work on UO$_2$ has been completed since that time but dimensional control of as-sintered pellets remains a problem. Economical yields (pelletizing cost of $5 to $10/lb for slightly enriched UO_2) required tolerances of at least ±0.002 in. on a 0.4-in. diameter pellet. The additional cost to centerless grind to ±0.0005 in. is approximately $1/lb including the cost of recovery of the grinding losses. This cost is of the same order of magnitude as that required for 100 per cent inspection of as-sintered pellets. Hence, for the Pressurized Water Reactor (PWR) type of helium-bonded element, it may still be economical to grind the periphery and use a sampling inspection plan. The use of liberal length tolerances and relaxed requirements for parallelism permit elimination of the face-grinding operation and consequent cost savings.

Metallurgically Bonded Elements

Fabrication costs of metallurgically bonded elements will vary widely depending upon the materials, shape, and process used. The picture frame process normally employed in producing fuel plates is inherently expensive due to the large amount of hand labor involved in operations which are difficult, if not impossible, to do automatically. The process also tends to be wasteful in generation of scrap. Unrecoverable scrap is several times greater than in the production of gas-bonded elements. Monetary value of this scrap may be low in the case of aluminum cladding but will be very high for zirconium. With zirconium it has been found that high surface quality is required on the cladding components to assure good bonding. This requires expensive machining of hot-rolled shapes, or, almost as expensive, intermediate conditioning in the preparation of cold-finished shapes of adequate quality. Another disadvantage of roll-clad plate-type fuel elements stems from difficulty in controlling the thickness, width, and length dimensions of the fuel. Since the fuel is buried between one or two layers of other metals varying in plasticity, fuel plate rolling has and always will be an art requiring good equipment and skilled operators. Abnormal dimensional effects usually occur at the ends of the fuel and use of expensive premachined shapes is often necessary to prevent this trouble.

Some interesting work on fabrication of metallurgically bonded fuel elements by coextrusion has been described[17] in which several fuel rods with integral end closures can be extruded from a common billet. An illustration of the billet design used is shown in Figure 3-9. Although ingenious work of this kind will tend to minimize the cost of fabricating this fuel element, nevertheless this type as a whole is at an economic disadvantage due to the relatively high cost of making the necessary components. The coextrusion process is most economically applied to long fuel elements involving a minimum number of end closures. Shorter elements may be produced relatively economically if fully bonded end closures are not required. Thus,

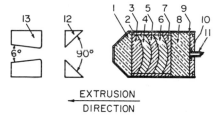

EXTRUSION
DIRECTION

Figure 3-9. Section of die and billet for extruding clad fuel rods with integral end closures.

in the case of the fuel elements for the Enrico Fermi reactor, a relatively simple mechanically bonded end closure is produced by swaging a cap on the ends of the coextruded zirconium-clad U-10% Mo fuel rod.[18]

A much less expensive approach to the production of clad fuel plates is that of pressure bonding. This involves practically no deformation so that dimensional control is reduced merely to achieving normal machining tolerances on the components used. Satisfactory pressure bonding of both zirconium and aluminum clad fuel elements has been achieved. In the Organic Moderator Reactor prototype fuel element shown in Figure 3-10, uranium alloy fuel is electroplated with nickel and clad with aluminum by heating in a helium atmosphere at 8000 psi at 1000°F for 10 minutes. A high quality metallurgical bond results. Preliminary irradiation results on

Figure 3-10. Pressure bonded OMR type fuel element.

this type of element employing a U-3.5% Mo fuel material are quite encouraging.

Liquid Metal-Bonded Elements

Where liquid metal-bonded elements can be used, they offer several important advantages. One of these obviously is good heat transfer between the fuel and cladding. Another is the ability to provide room for dimensional and volume changes in the fuel as a result of irradiation. Fuel elements of this type containing uranium metal slugs bonded to a stainless steel tube with sodium-potassium alloy (NaK) have been operating quite successfully in the Sodium Reactor Experiment. This element, shown in Figure 3-4, has an attractively low fabrication cost. Some specialized equipment is required for filling the fuel tube with NaK but the results of manufacturing approximately 100 elements of this type for two core loadings have indicated that the necessary operations can be performed economically and reliably. These elements have been fabricated with a variety of fuels including unalloyed uranium, thorium-uranium, uranium-molybdenum, and uranium-zirconium. Experimental elements containing uranium carbide are planned for the near future.

The use of bond metals which are liquid at fuel-element operating temperatures is restricted to those reactor systems in which chemical compatibility of the bond metal and the coolant can be obtained. To date, this type of element has been restricted to sodium-cooled systems such as the Experimental Breeder Reactor and the Sodium Reactor Experiment. For water-cooled reactors, a somewhat different approach has been used in the Borax-IV fuel elements which employ a solid lead bond between ThO_2-UO_2 fuel and aluminum cladding.[19] Although this particular combination of materials is suitable only for relatively low-temperature operation, fuel elements of this type employing a higher temperature cladding and a higher melting bond metal may prove useful. Serious problems of compatibility of the cladding, fuel, and bond materials must be solved, however, before the fuel element can be used with confidence.

Gas-Bonded Elements

Extensive use of gas-bonded UO_2 fuel rods is being made in pressurized and boiling water reactors. Production processes for this type of element lend themselves to automation and considerable use of labor-saving devices has already been achieved. However, UO_2 fuel elements still cost more to fabricate per kilogram of uranium than metal elements due to the lower fuel density and the greater degree of subdivision involved. Although assembly of fuel into the cladding of a gas-bonded element is a simple mechanical operation, the need to minimize the temperature drop across the gas gap makes mandatory the use of a close fit and tight dimensional tolerances. One reactor project has attempted to overcome this difficulty by using a stretching operation after assembly to reduce the diameter of stainless steel cladding and provide a closer fit to the UO_2 fuel pellets.[14] Another potential disadvantage of this type of element is the possibility of cladding distortion by thermal ratcheting. This problem, which is more serious with friable materials such as UO_2, results from cyclic stresses produced by differential expansion of fuel and cladding. A further disadvantage with the gas-bonded element is that once a cladding failure occurs all of the fuel in an element or compartment is exposed to the coolant and considerable release of fission products and fuel to the coolant system can occur. Despite all these problems, continued widespread use of this type of fuel is anticipated and ultimate realization of relatively high burn-ups by fuel elements of this type should be possible.

An interesting development has been the production of high-density UO_2 fuel rods by swaging rather than by compacting and sintering.[20] By use of high-density UO_2 powders of proper size distribution, it is possible to tamp-pack directly into an oversize cladding tube to a density of about 8 g/cc. This tube is then hot- or cold-swaged to the final diameter and with reductions of 33 per cent, final densities of at least 10 g/cc can be obtained.[21] If irradiation studies now under way indicate that rods so produced have adequate in-pile behavior, a substantial saving in the fabrication cost will be realized.

Although UO_2 has been employed principally in round and tubular shapes, its use in the form of Zircaloy-clad compartmented plates is contemplated for the Shippingport PWR blanket No. 2. In this element, pressed and sintered UO_2 platelets are inserted in recesses in the cladding components which are then pressure-bonded together.[22] Although pressure-bonding of long fuel plates involves substantial development and equipment costs, it is capable of achieving fairly low unit-fabrication costs once it is perfected. The Zircaloy-clad version of this element uses a large quantity of expensive zirconium; hence, very high burn-ups are required if low fuel-cycle costs are to be achieved. The use of this same type of fuel element but with aluminum cladding would seem to have considerable promise in organic-cooled reactors.

Gas-bonded elements have not been used to date in power reactors with fuels other than UO_2. It is expected, however, that this type of element may be utilized with other compounds such as uranium carbide. Where the characteristics of the fuel are such that compartmentation is desirable, this type of element is much more economically fabricated than the metallurgically bonded type.

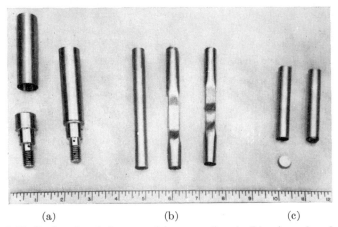

Figure 3-11. Fuel rod end closures: (a) conventional; (b) crimped and resistance welded; (c) heliarc spot welded.

End Closures

Production of completely reliable end closures is an urgent problem for all types of fuel elements except those in which all cladding components are bonded in a single operation. With rod geometry the usual practice is to machine an end cap and join it to the cladding by a circumferential weld. Although successfully used on many thousands of fuel elements, this type of closure, shown in Figure 3-11(a) is relatively expensive to produce. Attempts to reduce the cost of this type of end closure followed two approaches.[23] The first of these, the crimped and resistance-welded type shown in Figure 3-11(b), proved to be deficient in bursting strength and somewhat unreliable with respect to leak tightness. The second approach, shown in Figure 3-11(c), which involves the use of a heliarc spot weld produced by a stationary tungsten electrode positioned over the center of the end cap, has produced very successful welds with stainless steel cladding thicknesses of 0.007 and 0.010 inches. This process is simple and inexpensive and appears to have considerable promise for those designs where it can be used.

Structural Components

Complete fuel element assemblies include not only the cladding and fuel of the elements themselves but also a considerable quantity of structural and hardware items. These range from a structural enclosure or tube around the full length of the element to end supports and spacers. Conventionally, these items are fabricated from stainless steel or Zircaloy. Their cost may be a substantial fraction of the total fabrication cost of the fuel element.

This results from the complex configuration and close dimensional tolerances and, in the case of Zircaloy, the high material cost. With most of the items, small quantities are involved and extensive production tooling costs cannot be justified. Standardization of design will ultimately make this possible and cost savings will result. Use of the investment-casting or shell-molding process is feasible for some stainless steel hardware items, producing parts requiring a minimum of machining. Until recently, this method of reducing fuel element costs has not been possible with Zircaloy since no suitable casting process was available. Considerable progress has been made, however, in production of Zircaloy castings by skull arc melting and pouring into an expendable graphite mold.

A typical example of a Zircaloy end support produced by the vacuum casting process is shown in Figure 3-12. Estimated costs of producing this part by machining from solid stock, forging and casting are given in Table 3-5 [24] Mechanical properties of cast Zircaloy-2, as shown in Table 3-6,[25] compare very favorably with those of wrought material at both room and elevated temperature. The ductility and impact strength of the cast ma-

(Courtesy Oregon Metallurgical Co.)
Figure 3-12. Cast Zircaloy end support.

TABLE 3-5. COST OF CAST *vs.* WROUGHT ZIRCALOY END SUPPORT[24]

	Sold Stock	Forging	Casting
Material	$222	$152	$ 57
Forging or casting	—	45	95
Machining	146	132	54
	$368	$329	$206
Relative cost	1.8	1.6	1.0
Material recovery	23%	34%	90%

TABLE 3-6. COMPARISON OF TENSILE AND IMPACT PROPERTIES OF
CAST AND WROUGHT ZIRCALOY-2[25]

	Test Temp. (°C)	Tensile Properties					Impact Properties	
		No. of Specimens and Direction	0.2 Yield Strength (psi)	Tensile Strength (psi)	% Elong. in 2 in.	R.A. (%)	No. of Specimens and Direction	ft/lb
Cast	R.T.	15	55,500	74,500	21.6*	29.3	16	6.6
"	260	13	30,100	42,100	25.5*	45.2	16	24.2
Wrought	R.T.	Long.	35,000	60,000	14.0	23.0	3, Long.	5.2
"	R.T.	Trans.	51,000	57,000	15.0	31.0	3, Trans.	2.0
"	260	3, Long.	20,700	34,800	36.0	64.0	3, Long.	22.8
"	260	3, Trans.	25,500	34,100	32.5	49.5		

* Elongation, % in ¾ in.

terial are surprisingly high; furthermore, the material is free of the pronounced directional effects of the wrought material. Greater use of cast
Zircaloy in the future is certainly indicated.

REPROCESSING

Reprocessing of spent fuel elements is required for recovery of the un-
burned U^{235} and the plutonium produced by conversion of U^{238}. Since only
a small fraction of the original U^{235} is burned in a single reactor cycle, fuel
will normally be recycled many times in any practical nuclear reactor
power system. At the present time all fuel element reprocessing is done in
AEC facilities using an aqueous chemical solvent extraction process. Costs
of this work are based on a government price schedule and a process which
produces uranium of high purity essentially free of fission products and
radioactivity.

In this process the spent fuel is first allowed to "cool" for several months.
It then goes through a series of mechanical operations in which the maximum amount of non-fuel-bearing material is removed. The remainder is
then chemically dissolved and processed to uranium nitrate. The uranium
nitrate is converted to UF_6 which is the basic raw material for the start of
the fuel cycle. Shipping charges for the "hot" fuel and inventory charges
during the entire series of recovery operations are important parts of the
reprocessing costs. When incorporating uranium fuel recovered by the
aqueous process into finished elements, normal "cold" fabrication procedures are used. Costs of aqueous reprocessing are high, with the result
that there is a strong incentive to achieve high fuel burn-ups. This is clearly
shown in Figure 3-2 for UO_2 fuel, where uranium recovery costs are cut in
half when fuel life is doubled.

Fuel element materials and design can have important effects on chemical reprocessing costs. The type of bond between the fuel and cladding will greatly affect the ease with which mechanical separation can be achieved. With gas-bonded UO_2 fuel elements, for instance, it should be possible to completely remove the cladding and structural materials before dissolution of the fuel. The type of cladding material also has an effect in dictating the type of equipment and chemicals needed. For example, aluminum is much more readily dissolved than zirconium and has a lower level of radioactivity which would tend to reduce recovery costs. A combination of materials such as zirconium and stainless steel on the same fuel element is undesirable.

Although the reprocessing part of the over-all fuel cycle has not been given the attention it deserves, nevertheless significant development work has been under way on nonaqueous reprocessing and remote refabrication of fuel elements.[26-28] In the fuel cycle proposed for the EBR II (Experimental Breeder Reactor) a pyrometallurgical reprocessing plant and hot fuel element fabrication facility is being designed as an integral part of the reactor plant.[29] Spent fuel elements consisting of uranium alloys sodium-bonded to stainless steel cladding will be mechanically disassembled in a hot facility after which the uranium will be freed of all gaseous and some metallic fission product activity in an oxide drossing operation. In this operation the fuel is sufficiently freed of poisons to permit re-enrichment and reuse. It is only partially decontaminated and hence requires remote handling through all subsequent fuel element fabrication steps. This work is appreciably more expensive than normal fabrication of cold material with direct personnel contact. Nevertheless, for those fuel elements whose design is simple enough to lend itself to remote fabrication, cost studies have shown that an appreciable saving can be achieved by this route as compared to the aqueous-direct fabrication route.

The two elements presently being used in power reactors which are suited for pyroprocessing are uranium metal, or alloy slugs bonded with liquid metal, and gas-bonded UO_2 pellets. A preliminary comparison of fuel cycle costs on these two fuels reprocessed by the aqueous-direct route and the pyro-remote route is given in Tables 3-7 and 8.[30] These figures must be considered as tentative due to the considerable cost uncertainties in several important steps in the process for both fuels. They indicate that the potential saving in fuel-cycle cost with pyro-reprocessing is greatest for low burn-up fuels. Thus, uranium metal fuel with an average exposure of 3000 Mwd/ton shows an approximate 2 mill saving, while the UO_2 fuel with 10,000 Mwd/ton average exposure shows a saving of only 0.7 mill. These savings result from a number of factors such as the reduction in out-of-pile inventory charges due to the use of short-cooled fuel, lower shipping charges, a considerable reduction in the cost of decontaminating the spent fuel, and

TABLE 3-7. FUEL CYCLE COSTS FOR 2.5 PER CENT ENRICHED URANIUM METAL WITH AN AVERAGE BURN-UP OF 3000 MWD/TON REPROCESSED BY TWO ROUTES

	Mills/kwh	
	Aqueous-Direct	Pyro-Remote
In-core inventory............................	.58	.58
Ex-core inventory...........................	.67	.54
Uranium burn-up............................	2.81	—
Re-enrich and make-up......................	—	1.40
Pyro-process and cast.......................	—	.49
Solvent extract.............................	1.12	—
UF_6-U slug...............................	.87	—
Fabrication.................................	.44	.55
Scrap recovery.............................	.25	.13
Shipping...................................	.60	.50
	7.34	
Net plutonium credit....................	1.11	
Total......................................	6.23	4.19

TABLE 3-8. FUEL CYCLE COSTS FOR 3.5 PER CENT ENRICHED UO_2 WITH AN AVERAGE BURN-UP OF 10,000 MWD/TON REPROCESSED BY TWO ROUTES

	Mills/kwh	
	Aqueous-Direct	Pyro-Remote
In-core inventory............................	.75	.75
Ex-core inventory...........................	.31	.25
Uranium burn-up............................	2.38	—
Re-enrich and make-up......................	—	1.35
Pyro-process and granulate..................	—	.29
Solvent extract.............................	.49	—
UF_6-UO_2 pellet........................	.49	—
UO_2-pellet...............................	.21	.27
Fabrication.................................	.25	.31
Scrap recovery.............................	.03	.12
Shipping...................................	.18	.15
	5.09	
Net plutonium credit....................	.88	
Total......................................	4.21	3.49

recycling of the plutonium content without chemical separation. In addition to the work on uranium and UO_2, development work is now under way or planned at Atomics International on pyro-reprocessing of thorium-uranium alloys and UC fuel. Preliminary studies have shown feasible methods that are capable of achieving important cost savings on these fuels.

SUMMARY

Although fuel fabrication and reprocessing costs amount to only 40 per cent of total fuel-cycle costs and less than 20 per cent of total nuclear power costs, nevertheless they represent two areas in which significant cost reductions are possible. Low fuel-cycle costs are favored by use of fuels of high uranium content and low enrichment. Fuel element lifetime or burn-up is of paramount importance and can easily outweigh high initial materials cost for cladding and alloying materials. UO_2 appears to have the highest burn-up capability of available fuels; however, developments on uranium alloys and uranium carbide may change this picture.

Choice between Zircaloy and stainless steel as cladding material for water-cooled reactors is close, with Zircaloy having the advantage of lower fuel costs for extremely high burn-ups. Aluminum is the only other base material economically useful at present for power reactor cladding.

Design of fuel elements for low fuel-cycle cost is complicated by many factors and is severely handicapped by lack of statistical data on in-pile performance of full scale fuel elements. Basic fuel element shape is largely set by mechanical and heat-transfer considerations, with the cross section dimension usually being limited by materials properties such as transformation and melting temperatures, irradiation swelling, etc.

Cladding thickness is usually determined by mechanical rather than by corrosion or metal soundness factors. Use of a liquid or gas bond between fuel and cladding reduces fuel fabrication cost as compared with the metallurgically bonded type of element. Liquid metal bonds also have the advantage of providing room for irradiation swelling, hence extending useful fuel element life.

Replacement of the conventional parallel-flow type of fuel element assembly by the cross-flow type is not warranted on economic grounds. However, the use of bulk fuel in the form of pellets has potential cost advantages. Fabrication costs for fuel element assemblies are a minimum for the mechanically joined type and a maximum for the full welded type. Cost of brazed and spot-welded assemblies fall between these extremes.

Compartmentation of fuel to minimize consequences of a cladding break leads to higher fabrication costs regardless of how it is accomplished. It can be economically justified only when such design complications produce longer fuel element life. Fuel element inspectability varies widely among the several types with the mechanical assembly again having advantages over the welded or brazed type.

Cost of fabricating fuel and cladding components is expected to drop as processors gain experience and volume of business increases. Cast uranium fuel slugs are less expensive than the equivalent wrought product. The question of whether or not to centerless-grind UO_2 pellets remains open on a purely economic basis.

Production of clad fuel plates to power reactor quality standards by the picture frame process is inherently expensive. Use of a pressure bonding process may lower costs.

UO_2 fuel elements have higher fabrication costs per kilogram of uranium than metal elements due to the lower fuel density and greater degree of subdivision involved. Production of high-density UO_2 by swaging rather than by compacting and sintering may reduce fabrication costs. Use of UO_2 in compartmented plate geometry shows promise of achieving high burn-ups and ultimately low fuel-cycle cost.

Development of a successful heliarc spot-weld process has reduced the cost of end caps on rod type elements. Vacuum melting and casting of Zircaloy-2 in graphite molds is an economical way of producing high-quality structural components for fuel assemblies.

Fuel element materials and design affect ease of mechanical separation of fuel and cladding prior to chemical reprocessing. Type of cladding material affects ease of dissolution and irradiation levels during reprocessing. Development work on nonaqueous pyro-reprocessing and remote refabrication of fuel elements gives promise of reducing costs of the present aqueous-direct fabrication process.

References

1. "The ORNL Gas-Cooled Reactor," ORNL 2500, Pt. IV (April 1, 1958).
2. Zebroski, E. L., "Proceedings of the Reactor Fuel Technical Meeting," Atomic Industrial Forum, May 1958.
3. Appendix H, Euratom Working Papers, Section III, p. 15.
4. Corcoran, W. P., Atomics International Div., unpublished data.
5. Gerber, R. C., Atomics International Div., unpublished data.
6. Aronstein, R. E., Atomics International Div., unpublished data.
7. Ladd, C. M., "Proceedings of the Reactor Fuel Technical Meeting," Atomic Industrial Forum, May 1958.
8. AEC Press Release, November 18, 1956.
9. Transcripts of Symposia on "Economic Comparison of Zirconium and Stainless Steel in Nuclear Power Reactors," sponsored by Columbia-National Corporation, Feb. 13 and March 11, 1958.
10. Albrecht, W. L., "Effect on Power Cost of Substituting Aluminum for Zirconium Fuel Cladding in a Boiling Water Reactor," ORNL CF-58-7-86 (July 24, 1958).

11. Boettcher, A., Schulten, R., and Wirths, G., "Fuel Elements for a High-Temperature Reactor," A/CONF.15/P/15/1005 (June 10, 1958).
12. Armenoff, C. T., and Binstock, M. H., "Fuel Elements for the Organic Moderated Reactor Experiment," NAA-SR-1934 (Dec. 15, 1957).
13. Stone, C. C., Noland, R. A., and McCuaig, F. D., "Welding of the EBWR Fuel Subassemblies," ANL-5646.
14. Coen, I. H., and Garbe, R. W., "Monthly Progress Report for the Period March 1 to 31, 1958," YAEC-66 (April 20, 1958).
15. Flynne, W. A., Atomics International Div., unpublished data.
16. Gradle, B., Atomics International Div., unpublished data.
17. Kaufmann, A. R., Klein, J. L., Loewenstein, P., and Sawyer, H. F., "Zirconium Cladding of Uranium and Uranium Alloys by Coextrustion," NMI-TJ-8 (Oct. 4, 1957).
18. Dietrich, J. R., and Zinn, W. H., "Solid Fuel Reactors," Reading, Mass., Addison-Wesley Publishing Co., 1958.
19. Walker, D. E., Noland, R. A., McCuaig, F. D., and Stone, C.C., "Borax-IV Reactor: Manufacture of Fuel and Blanket Elements," ANL-5721 (March 1958).
20. General Electric Co., Hanford Atomic Products Operation, "Fuels Development Operating Quarterly Progress Report (for) July, August, & September 1957," HW-53488.
21. Webb, B., Atomics International Div., unpublished data.
22. "Pressurized Water Reactor (PWR) Project Technical Progress Report for the Period April 24, 1958 to June 23, 1958," WAPD-MRP-74.
23. Cook, E. F., Atomics International Div., unpublished data.
24. Schwartz, E. G., and Frankhouser, W. L., "Evaluation of Vacuum Cast Transition Pieces for PWR Core I Blanket," WAPD-NCE-4860 (June 5, 1957).
25. Zabielski, C. V., and Rubenstein, L. S., "Properties of Vacuum-Cast Zircaloy 2," WAPD-ZH-10 (Aug. 1958).
26. Sinizer, D. I., "An Engineering Experiment in Low Decontamination of Metallic Uranium Fuels," *Trans. ANS* (Dec. 1958).
27. Dodge, F. W., Murbach, E. W., and Hanson, L. A., "Low Decontamination of Thorium-Uranium Alloys by Induction Drip Melting," *Trans. ANS* (Dec. 1958).
28. Ballif, J. L., "The Oxide-Drossing Furnace for the Processing Refabrication Experiment," *Trans. ANS* (Dec. 1958).
29. Schraidt, J. H., "EBR II Fuel Cycle Plant and Processes," TID-7548 (Oct. 31, 1957).
30. Mattern, K., Atomics International Div., unpublished data.

4. FABRICATION TECHNIQUES FOR VARIOUS TYPES OF FUEL ELEMENTS

JAMES F. SCHUMAR

Associate Director, Metallurgy Division
Argonne National Laboratory, Lemont, Ill.

The process chosen for fabricating a given fuel element is dependent upon many technical compromises as well as economics. Nuclear physics establishes the number of fissionable atoms and their ratio to fertile, moderator or diluent atoms. Heat transfer establishes the geometry and size, and whether it is necessary to bond the jacket to the core. Materials engineering establishes the type of fuel core and cladding needed to meet the requirements of heat transfer, physics, reprocessing and economics. The fabricator is then left with the problem of making a usable fuel element that meets the demands of the mentioned compromises and a fuel element that will function in the specified reactor.

With these compromises in mind he calls upon the art of blacksmithing to produce the "heart of the reactor," the fuel elements. The processes that the fabricator uses are melting, casting, rolling, pressing, forging, welding, machining, pressing, sintering, etc.—in any or all combinations—to produce a usable fuel element. Perhaps the best way to illustrate the problems of the fabricator is to describe some manufacturing techniques of a few specific fuel elements, the problems associated with their manufacture, and how these problems were solved by using one or several metal fabricating processes.

In the case of a metallurgically bonded jacket-to-core fuel element, for example, bonding can be effected during the fabricating by such solid phase bonding processes as (1) roll bonding, if the shape is a plate or a geometry that can be made by rolling; (2) extrusion cladding; or (3) hot pressing powder in a jacket, etc. In bonding with a liquid metal, the components (jacket and core) are independently made and then assembled into a fuel element.

Since the techniques used are dependent upon materials engineering, the physical and mechanical properties of the core material and cladding material and the compatibility of their respective properties become important in the fabrication process.

Solid Diffusion Bonding

Battelle Memorial Institute, in a report on bonding fundamentals, considers solid bonding to occur in two stages: the points of contact between two solids will be the first areas to bond and subsequently the area will increase by application of pressure, temperature and time. To continue, the ultimate aim of the bonding process is to produce a condition where there is an interaction of atomic forces between the atoms of the two solids over the entire bonding area. To obtain an ideal bond there must be complete mating between the two surfaces to be bonded. This is accomplished by causing (mechanically or thermally) the surfaces to approach each other until the distances between surfaces allow atomic interaction. Difficulty arises if the mating surfaces are not clean—that is, free of oxide films or other impurity layers. These contaminating layers can frequently be rendered ineffective by breaking them up mechanically or diffusing the contaminant away from the interface. In practice then, solid phase bonding depends on the interatomic reactions of materials involved and utilization of the effects of pressure, temperature and time.

Dispersion-Type Flat Plate Fuel Elements

The "picture frame" roll-bonding techniques for making Materials Testing Reactor (MTR) dispersion-type fuel elements are well-known. To improve the quality of bond a different approach for similar plate fuel elements was used for the Argonne Low-Power Reactor (ALPR). A description of this novel technique follows.

One of the requirements this fuel had to satisfy was that it must survive a service period of 3 years without failure for any reason. The core material is an aluminum-17.5 w/o* uranium-2 w/o nickel alloy clad on all sides with alluminum-1 w/o nickel alloy (X8001) metallurgically bonded to the core and to itself at all interfaces. Figure 4-1 is a drawing of the ALPR fuel element giving the dimension of the fuel section and the over-all dimensions of the plate. Each plate was required to demonstrate corrosion resistance to high-purity water at 290°C for 2 weeks and exhibit no detectable unbonded areas, as indicated by examination for blisters after a 288°C (550°F) annealing treatment for 1 hr and an ultrasonic transmission inspection.

The plate components shown in Figure 4-2 consist of a picture frame and

* w/o = Weight per cent.

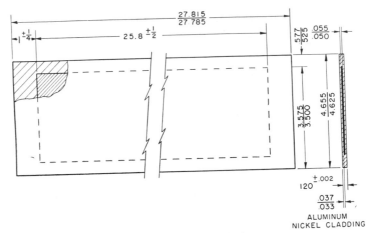

Figure 4-1. ALPR fuel plate.

Figure 4-2. Plate components.

cover plates of the X8001 aluminum alloy and the core alloy. The original thickness of these components is four times their finish thickness. Bonding of the components is not accomplished entirely, if at all, by hot rolling, but is achieved instead by a process known as *silicon bonding*. In this process

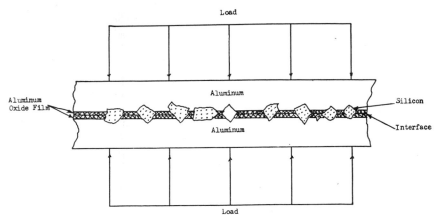

Figure 4-3. Mechanism: aluminum oxide perforation in silicon bonding (idealized).

the articles to be joined are coated at the mating interfaces with elemental silicon powder. The -325 mesh size powder ($<44\mu$) is sprinkled on wet, glycerin-coated surfaces and the glycerin is then baked off. The coated pieces are next brought into intimate contact and placed under pressure in press-mounted dies maintained at a temperature above the formation temperature of the aluminum-silicon eutectic ($577°C$). Pressures in the order of 1000 to 2000 psi are exerted on the assembly until it reaches a temperature of 595 to $600°C$ and held for about 1 minute. The work is cooled to $550°C$ under pressure and is then removed from the die.

Figure 4-3 shows the mechanism underlying this process. The hard, sharp grains of the silicon powder perforate the oxide film on the aluminum and establish an oxide-free aluminum-to-silicon interface. As the joint surfaces are under pressure, no oxygen can reach the exposed perforated surfaces of the aluminum; thus reoxidation is prevented. At a sufficiently high temperature the silicon reacts with the aluminum to form the eutectic, and, on melting, the eutectic undermines the aluminum oxide on both sides of the joint. The pressure applied forces the liquid alloy and oxide out of the joint area permitting a sound joint to be formed. Figure 4-4 is a photomicrograph of a section which was deliberately underheated, and the structure shown tends to support the proposed mechanism. Figure 4-5 is a photomicrograph of a properly bonded section with nearly complete absence of the eutectic in the joint area.

After the hot pressing or bonding operation the compacts are hot-rolled to near-finish thickness and cold-rolled to final thickness. The final operations on the plate consist of blister-annealing, locating the core by radiographic means, shearing to outer dimensions, and some bond inspection.

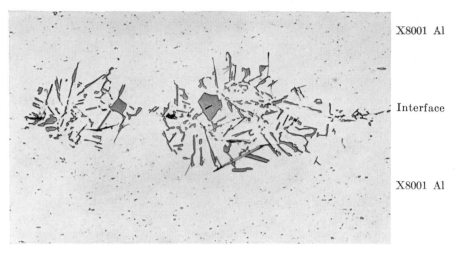

X8001 Al

Interface

X8001 Al

Figure 4-4. Silicon bonding: unreacted silicon particles surrounded by rejected silicon in underheated section. (Micro 21677; Etched; 500×)

X8001 alloy

Interface

Al-U alloy

Figure 4-5. Typical microstructure at core-to-cladding interface. (Micro 23021: Etched, 2% NaOH: 100×)

The decided advantage of bonding by the silicon powder technique over the conventional roll cladding is the "washing out" of the oxide on the mating surfaces and the ease of keeping the mating surfaces clean. In the conventional roll bonding the oxide layer is disrupted or broken up by the stretching of the surfaces during rolling, thus allowing the mating surfaces to be in contact and fairly clean. The use of the silicon, however, is much more positive and bonding is essentially accomplished before the rolling. In this case the rolling has only one function which is to give the desired dimensions to the plate. In the conventional aluminum roll cladding process it is questionable during which hot-roll pass the bond is actually effected, and the reduction in thickness of the composite billet assembly at a given rolling temperature becomes very important. With the silicon bonding technique the dimensions and location of the fuel core with respect to the cladding are much easier to control and maintain. The quality of this type of bond is excellent, and, more important, the areas of nonbonds are completely eliminated.

Roll-Bonded Zircaloy-Clad Uranium Fuel Elements

Another technique worthy of discussion is the roll cladding of a uranium alloy with Zircaloy, as in the case of the fuel plates for the Experimental Boiling Water Reactor (EBWR). For this fuel element it is necessary to produce a fuel plate in which the uranium alloy core is completely and integrally clad with Zircaloy-2. The plates are approximately $\frac{1}{4}$ in. thick $\times 3\frac{5}{8}$ in. wide $\times$ 54 in. long. The cladding thickness is 0.020 in. on each face, 0.155 in. on each side, and 1.5 in. on each end. The most important factors contributing to the fuel plate quality were determined to be (1) the bond between the cladding and the uranium alloy core, (2) the bonding between the Zircaloy-2 and Zircaloy-2 interfaces, (3) the end closure, and (4) the dimensions.

The metals in this fuel element possess several favorable properties and several others which are rather unfavorable to the fuel-plate fabricator. The technique of roll bonding was selected on two basic premises: (1) uranium and zirconium form a complete series of solid solutions above 800°C (1472°F) in the gamma phase; (2) zirconium self-welds easily, due in part to its ability to dissolve its own oxide. Although the uranium-1.5 w/o Nb-5 w/o Zr alloy for the core was chosen for other reasons, its hot-working properties fortunately closely matched those of Zircaloy-2.

The somewhat unfavorable properties of the cladding and core material are their chemical reactivities. Uranium reacts with air to form a film that would inhibit bonding at the mating surfaces. Zircaloy-2 is very sensitive to any cleaning procedure which in turn is reflected not only in its ability to roll-bond to itself, but also in its corrosion properties to high temperature boiling water. In order to satisfy the conditions contributing to high plate quality, it became apparent that proper composite billet preparation, both in geometry and cleanliness of mating surfaces and retaining the cleanliness during rolling, becomes very important.

The components of the composite billet, shown in Figure 4-6, are the

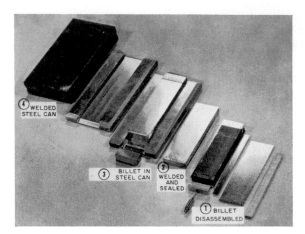

Figure 4-6. Cladding billet at various stages of assembly.

cast uranium-5 w/o Zr-1.5 w/o Nb alloy core, the Zircaloy-2 cladding, and the steel can. The cladding consists of cover plates, side plates, end plugs and seal pin. In order to economize on the use of Zircaloy metal, no picture frame is used. Instead, the Zircaloy plates and end plugs are assembled around the cast uranium alloy core plate and welded into a can. The seams formed by these mating Zircaloy components are sealed by inert gas-shielded (argon) tungsten arc welding. Subsequent to welding of the seams, billets are evacuated and purged several times, and the purge openings are then sealed by a special vacuum arc welding process. The composite billet is then encased in a steel can and formed into plate by hot rolling.

A great deal of development work was necessary to establish the original dimensions and geometry of the composite billet to yield a fuel plate in which the uranium alloy was completely clad and bonded on all mating surfaces, and still maintain within close tolerances the fuel core dimensions and location. The hot-working properties of the core alloy and the cladding at the rolling temperature, the per cent reduction in thickness to effect the bond and yield the dimensions, the shape of the composite billet, and the cleanliness all had to be carefully investigated. Rolling plates from castings and maintaining good dimensional control is in itself an art. Coupled with this, the requirement to roll two dissimilar metals and effectively bond them demanded the integration of many variables into an optimum rolling procedure.

Although the hot-working properties of the uranium-zirconium-niobium core alloy match fairly closely those of the Zircaloy-2 cladding, it was found to be necessary to shape the uranium alloy core with a 90° included angle-taper at each end. This diminished the tendency for the core to build up at

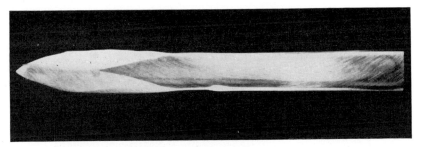

Figure 4-7. Build-up of the uranium alloy core at the ends of EBWR fuel pins.

the ends, resulting in a thinner cladding at these positions. Figure 4-7 illustrates this effect. Tapering the alloy casting did result in a tapering of the uranium alloy core, and maintaining this taper to a minimum was accomplished with the 90° included angle. The other dimensions of the composite billet components were set to give the desired dimensions of the core and cladding thickness, and sufficient reductions to effect good bonding with a total reduction in thickness of 80 per cent from billet to plate.

The preparation of the components that comprised the composite rolling billet was meticulous in every detail. The surfaces of the Zircaloy cover plates and side plates were not machined, but were used in the as-rolled condition, cleaned by vapor blasting with -400 mesh Al_2O_3 powder, followed with pickling in a HNO_3-HF bath, and subsequent rinsing and drying. To employ this procedure the quality of the Zircaloy must be the highest obtainable; and laps, seams, striations, blisters, etc., are not tolerable. The end plugs with the 90° included angle, to accommodate the tapered ends of the uranium core, were machined from rolled Zircaloy plate. It is interesting to note that the orientation of the end plugs within the rolled plate stock from which they were made was chosen to take advantage of the rolling characteristic resulting from texture in this plate. The direction of maximum spread was positioned within the end plugs so that maximum spread was developed in the end plug during roll bonding. This was found necessary to develop the pressure required for bonding between the end plug and the side plate, the interface of which was positioned parallel to the applied rolling pressure.

The uranium alloy core was cast close to size and approximately $\frac{1}{32}$ in. per face was allowed for grinding to width and thickness. These cores were cleaned with wet abrasive blasting, again using -400 mesh Al_2O_3 and a water-blast washing to remove the abrasive. They were rinsed in distilled water, then in absolute alcohol, and were stored in vacuum chambers in 10^{-6} mm Hg range until used.

As stated before, the assembly of the components into a composite billet

Figure 4-8. Press welding machine used for seal-welding Zircaloy-2 components around uranium alloy core.

Figure 4-9. Billet evacuation-seal welding equipment.

was accomplished in such a manner as to preserve the microscopically clean mating surfaces and to provide protection to these surfaces from contamination resulting from entrapped gases evolving from the steel jacket during heating. The cladding components were sealed around the billet core by shielded arc welding after a kind of "auto dry box" had been made by press-cladding the components together hydraulically, and the entrained air had been displaced by argon purging introduced through an opening in one of the end plugs. Figure 4-8 shows the press-welding machine for sealing the seams. The weld zones were restricted through use of water-cooled chills.

Removal of the purging gas and back-diffused air and the sealing of the purge opening in the composite billet were performed in the equipment shown in Figures 4-9 and 4-10. The equipment consists of a vacuum chamber, vacuum pumping system, racks, electrodes, etc., and is capable of producing a vacuum in the order of 10^{-6} mm of Hg. The composite billets were loaded into the chamber and evacuated and back-purged with air several times before final evacuation and sealing. The back-purging was done to insure against argon being sealed in the billet. Small amounts of

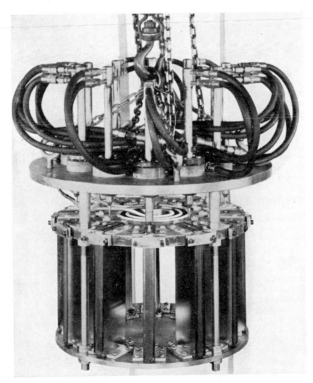

Figure 4-10. Rack for support of billets during evacuation and sealing.

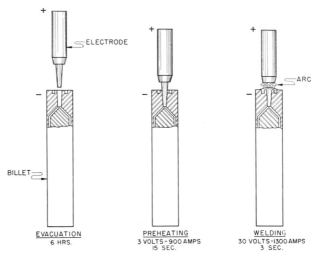

Figure 4-11. Billet evacuation and seal welding.

inert gas in the billet were found to produce blisters on the finished plate. Upon completion of the final evacuation the purge openings were plugged by seal pins which in turn were made leak-tight by a vacuum arc welding process. Figure 4-11 shows schematically the seal welding cycle.

The composite billet was encased in a steel jacket for rolling. The function of the jacket was twofold. First, it provided necessary protection of the Zircaloy cladding against atmospheric contamination during the hot rolling. The sensitivity of surface contamination to the corrosion resistance and the ductility of Zircaloy become more important as the cladding is reduced in thickness. Loss in ductility could initiate a fracture in the cladding during service. Secondly, the restraining influence of the steel jacket upon shifting of the billet components was important in maintaining the proper relationship of core and cladding components during initial stages of hot rolling before bonding occurred. The steel jacket design has a great influence upon the spread during rolling, and the restraint imposed in the rolling direction kept the Zircaloy end plug in its proper location instead of being pushed from the billet. The strength of the steel at the rolling temperature, the cross sectional areas, the spread in the rolling direction and at right angles to the rolling direction, had to be considered.

Liquid Metal-Bonded Fuel Elements

The fuel elements for the Experimental Breeder Reactor (EBR-II) are an excellent example of a liquid metal-bonded system. The fuel element core and jacket are independently fabricated, assembled and then bonded by liquid sodium. This fuel element was selected for its relative ease in fuel

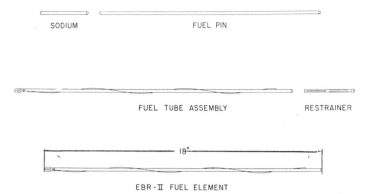

SODIUM   FUEL PIN

FUEL TUBE ASSEMBLY   RESTRAINER

18"

EBR-II FUEL ELEMENT

Figure 4-12. EBR-II fuel element.

reprocessing in a fast breeder type reactor. Remote control methods will be used for reprocessing and refabricating the fuel without decontamination to levels required for conventional fabrication.

This type of fuel element and its parts are shown in Figure 4-12. The fuel is a U^{238}-U^{235} fissium* alloy 0.144 in. in diameter $\times$ 14.22 in. long contained in 304 stainless steel tube with 0.174 in. OD $\times$ 0.009-in. wall thickness. A 0.006-in. annulus between the pin and the tube is sodium-filled to provide the thermal bond between the cladding and core. A spiral wire on the outside of the steel tube serves to space the fuel elements in the sub-assemblies. A restrainer cap is welded to the upper end of the fuel element in the final assembly. It serves as a closure, provides a void space into which the sodium may expand, and also holds the fuel pin below the surface of the sodium.

A simple casting technique was chosen for the fabrication of the fuel pins by remote control and in hot cells. Other fabrication processes were also considered; however, the metallurgical properties of the uranium-fissium alloy strongly favored a casting technique, which is more adaptable to producing long and slender pins of a relatively brittle, highly radioactive and pyrophoric material.

The casting method selected is a simplified process of nonmechanical gas pressure-injection casting. Figure 4-13 shows the principles of the injection casting, and Figure 4-14 is a diagram of the actual machine. The fissium alloy is induction melted under a vacuum in a refractory-coated graphite crucible to a temperature of 1375° to 1425°C. The molds, in the form of precision-bore, high-silica glass tubes coated on the inside with a thin thoria wash and closed at the upper end, are suspended with open end down,

* Fissium is a term used for the equilibrium alloy containing the fission products not removed in the fuel reprocessing cycle.

Number of Castings at Single Operation – 25
Diameter of Casting   – 14.22 Inches
Length of Casting   – 15 to 17 Inches
Length – to – Diameter Ratio   – >100:1

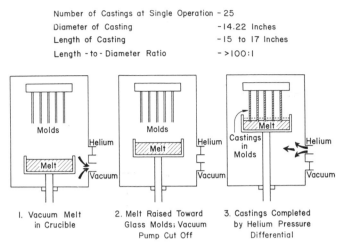

1. Vacuum Melt   2. Melt Raised Toward   3. Castings Completed
   in Crucible   Glass Molds; Vacuum   by Helium Pressure
                         Pump Cut Off   Differential

Figure 4-13. Principle of injection casting of fast-reactor fuel pins.

above the crucible. The assembly of mold tubes is heated by resistance windings within the vacuum chamber. When the molten alloy has reached the selected casting temperature, the vacuum pumping system is isolated and the ram upon which the crucible is mounted is actuated, causing the crucible to rise, submerging the open ends of the tube. The furnace is opened to an inert gas-pressurized accumulator tank, causing a rapid increase in the furnace pressure. The pressure difference between inside and outside of the submerged tubes causes the alloy to rise into the tubes, where it freezes.

The crucible containing the remainder of the molten charge is lowered while the metal in the crucible is still molten, but after solidification of the casting. The glass molds are crushed and pulverized away from the castings by feeding between roughened concave rolls. The castings are then cleaned by wire-brushing and sheared to length.

The stainless steel tubes used for the jacket are closed by welding an anchoring cap on to one end. This cap, a forked plug, locks the fuel tubes into position in the final fuel assembly. A measured amount of sodium is extruded into the tube under inert atmosphere, and the uranium alloy pins are dropped into it. The steel tube containing the uranium and sodium is then heated. This causes the sodium to melt, allowing the uranium to move down into the tube and the level of the sodium to rise above the top of the uranium pin. The end cap is welded on by a miniature arc welding process.

There are many advantages for liquid metal bonding; one in particular stands out for this fuel element application: after the fuel elements have been used in the reactor and are ready for reprocessing, it is a simple opera-

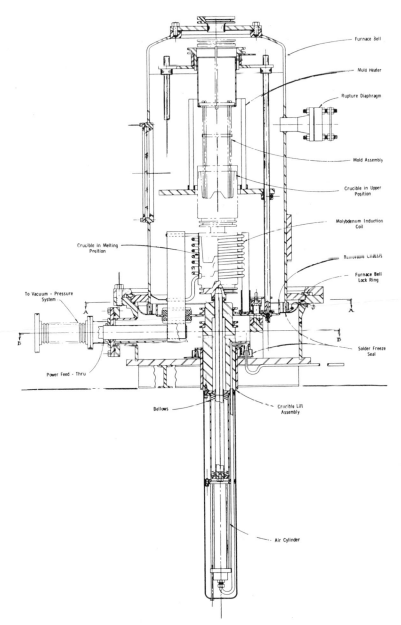

Figure 4-14. Injection casting machine.

tion to remove the uranium alloy from the jacket. Another advantage is that the yield of finished pins made by injection casting is very high. This process is therefore also applicable to uranium-plutonium-fissium alloys, but, for the first loading of the EBR-II, uranium-fissium alloy has been selected.

Extrusion Cladding

Extrustion cladding as a metal working process for the fabrication of fuel elements is a technique that has been much developed and already has had a fair amount of application. Similar to roll cladding, the shaping of the metal and bonding of the cladding to the core is accomplished during the fabrication of the rods, tubes, or flat plates.

As in the case of roll bonding, the extrusion billet must be designed to satisfy a great variety of engineering conditions in order to produce the desired final shape and accomplish the extrusion cladding. These conditions are as follows:

1. The extrusion temperatures must be high enough so that both metals flow at the required reduction in ratio without exceeding the maximum strength of the extrusion tools at the extrusion temperature and pressures.
2. The metal flow must be such that the cladding remains on the surface of the product and is of uniform thickness.
3. The mechanical (hot working) properties of the fuel core and cladding must be approximately the same, otherwise one or the other will not flow uniformly.
4. The cladding material and core material must be metallurgically compatible so that a solid phase bond can form at the selected extrusion temperature and reduction ratios.
5. The flow shape over the cross section of the extrusion must be determined and adjustments made in the billet so that a satisfactory shape is achieved at the ends of the core material in the extruded product.

In the development work on extrusion cladding done by Nuclear Metals, Inc., the conditions stated above have been carefully studied and evaluated.

The shape of the die is extremely important in extrusion cladding. A conical die having an angle between 30 and 60 degrees will allow the surface metal of the billet to flow without shearing and give a more favorable flow pattern. Friction conditions between the billet surface metal, the extrusion container walls and the die also have a marked effect on the uniformity of metal flow.

Matching the stiffness or hot working properties of the metals comprising the coextrusion billet is perhaps the most important condition to be met in extrusion cladding. A substantial difference in cladding and core will

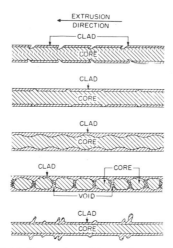

Figure 4-15. Examples of imperfect coextrusions.

result in fluctuations in the relative thickness of each, which in extreme cases result in breaks in the metal. Figure 4-15 shows schematically a variety of typical defects resulting from differences in core and cladding stiffness.

Coextrusion of EBR-I, Mark III Rods

The earlier fuel elements of the EBR-I were uranium alloy rods canned in stainless steel tubes and bonded with 0.010-in. NaK alloy. In this type of element it is possible for the uranium rods to bow or change position inside the jacket, reflecting a change in the physics of the reactor core. It was decided to load the reactor with fuel elements that could be so assembled that a ridged core would result. A solid-phase, bonded jacket-to-core fuel element would give the necessary rigidity. Materials engineering dictated a uranium-2 w/o zirconium alloy core clad with Zircaloy-2. Extrusion cladding was chosen because it could effect a metallurgical bond between the cladding and the alloy core and produce a circular-shaped rod. The finished rod specifications in this case were 0.406-in. outside diameter and 0.362-in. core diameter, with nominal 0.022-in. cladding thickness.

Since the uranium used was fully enriched in the isotope U[235], the design and size of the billet were established to meet the following requirements:

1. The highest yield possible of usable clad rod.
2. Maximum of 5 kg U[235] casting was allowable from a criticality standpoint.
3. Close control of dimensions: outside diameter, cladding thickness and uniformity.
4. Excellent bond strengths.

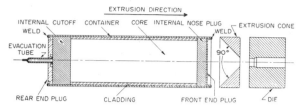

Figure 4-16. Composite billet for coextrusion of EBR-I Mark III blanket rod.

Specifications

Component	Material	Component	Material
Core	U-2 w/o Zr	Front end plug	16 gage Cu sheet punched and cupped
Cladding	Zircaloy-2		
Internal nose plug	Cu-10 w/o Ni	Rear end plug	Deoxidized Cu plate
Internal cut-off	Cu-10 w/o Ni	Evacuation tube	Seamless hard drawn Cu tube
Container	Seamless hard drawn Cu tube	Extrusion cone	Mild steel
		Extrusion die	18-4-1 steel

Figure 4-16 is a drawing of the extrusion billet used and materials that went into the components. The uranium-2 w/o zirconium alloy core was a heat-treated casting, abraded with wet sandpaper (320 grit), degreased in carbon tetrachloride, rinsed in acetone and air-dried. Chemical etching of the uranium alloy was avoided because of the explosion hazard, characteristic to the acid pickling of this alloy.

The Zircaloy cladding components were machined from pre-extruded Zircaloy tube stock, bright-etched in nitric-hydrofluoric acid solution and thoroughly rinsed and dried. The copper nickel components were conventionally fabricated, as were the copper container cans.

After the assembly into the copper can, the entire billet was evacuated to 5×10^{-5} mm of Hg or less, and heated to 800°F in $\frac{1}{2}$ hr and held at this temperature for an additional hour. The billets were then sealed off by pinching the evacuation tube closed.

This billet was hot extruded at 1225°F for a reduction of area of 20 to 1. After removal of the copper jacket by nitric acid pickling the rods were cold swaged 6.2 per cent to the desired size.

It is interesting to compare the core-to-clad interface where the as-cast uranium-2 w/o zirconium alloy was used with the heat-treated alloy core. The heat treatment that produced the more uniform interface consisted of an isothermal quench from 780 to 500°C and subsequent air cooling. Figures 4-17 and 18 show the difference in interface uniformity. The irregular inter-

Figure 4-17. Macrograph of core-to-cladding interface due to microstructure of uranium core.

Figure 4-18. Macrograph of core-to-cladding interface showing the effect of heat treatment on the core material.

face resulted from the larger grain structure of the casting in the as-cast condition.

In this chapter an attempt was made to describe some established fabricating techniques. There are many modifications to the processes discussed above as well as other processes and techniques under investigation. However, the approaches are not basically different, and the basic problems quite similar.

General References

1. Frank, J. W. and Macherey, R. E., "Casting Uranium-5 w/o Zirconium-1.5 w/o Niobium Alloys into Zirconium and Zircaloy-2 Containers," ANL-5442 (1958).
2. Kaufmann, A. R., Klein, J. L., Loewenstein, P., and Sawyer, H. F., "Zirconium Cladding of Uranium and Uranium Alloys by Coextrusion," TID-7546, pp. 157-181, Fuel Elements Conference, Paris, France (1957).
3. Macherey, R. E., Bean, C. H., Carson, N. J., Jr., and Lindgren, J. R., "Manufacture of Fuel Plates for the Experimental Boiling Water Reactor," ANL-5629 (1957).

4. Noland, Robert A., "Manufacture of the Fuel Plates and Fuel Subassemblies for the Argonne Low Power Reactor," presented at the Gatlinburg Conference on Fuel Elements (1958).

5. Ogden, J. R., Reynolds, J. E., Melehan, J. B., and Jaffee, R. I., "Study of Bonding Fundamentals," BMI-1101 (1956).

6. Sawyer, H. F., "Coextrusion of Zircaloy-Clad U-2 w/o Zr Rod for the EBR-I, Mark III Core Loading," NMI-4801 (1958).

7. Schumar, J. F., "Manufacture and Exposure History of Boiling Water Reactor Fuels," presented at the 5th International Electronic and Nuclear Exposition and Congress, Rome, Italy (1958).

8. Shuck, A. B. and Sowa, E. S., "EBR-II Fuel Cycle, Part II. Remote Fuel Element Fabrication and Assembly," presented at Fast Reactor Information Meeting (1957).

9. Shuck, A. B., "Manufacturing Methods for the Experimental Breeder Reactor, Mark I and Mark II Fuel Loadings," presented at Gatlinburg Conference on Fuel Elements (1958).

10. Shuck, A. B., "The Fabrication of Irradiated Reactor Fuel by Remote Control," Atomic Industrial Forum (1956).

5. URANIUM AND URANIUM ALLOY FUEL ELEMENTS*

FRANK G. FOOTE

Director, Metallurgy Division, Argonne National Laboratory
Lemont, Ill.

Introduction

The basic phenomenon on which the nuclear energy business is built was discovered in 1939 and in the past 20 years there has been a vigorous exploitation of this phenomenon of nuclear fission for both military and peaceful purposes. Some years ago there was considerable hope that nuclear fission would give us cheap and abundant power. However, right now nuclear fission can give us abundant expensive power, and the hope is that with diligent and intelligent work for another 10 years costs might be reduced to the point where nuclear energy is economically competitive with another abundant energy source, namely coal. This expectation of eventually breaking even with coal is not actually a strong economic incentive, and one must conclude that the real incentives for the further development of nuclear power are noneconomic.

In the last few years many of us have been so involved in trying to solve the very difficult technical problems associated with nuclear power reactors that we may have lost sight of some of the basic facts of nature and tend to forget what an unusual and unique source of energy we have in the fissionable isotopes. We may have become so concerned with the economics of substituting a few pounds of expensive fissionable material for many tons of cheap coal as fuel for a central station power plant that we forget to ask ourselves whether we should even be attempting such a substitution.

A brief review will be given of the raw material situation and the basic nuclear reactions on which the nuclear energy program operates. The basic raw-materials situation is summarized in Table 5-1, and the major nuclear reactions in Eqs. (1), (2) and (3).

---

* Based on work performed under the auspices of the United States Atomic Energy Commission.

TABLE 5-1. FISSIONABLE MATERIALS AND THEIR MAJOR SOURCE

Natural Isotopes	Fissionable Isotopes
99.3% $U^{238}*$ → Pu^{239}	
0.7% $U^{235}\dagger$ ⇌ U^{235}	
100% $Th^{232}*$ → U^{233}	

* fertile isotope
† fissionable isotope

Eq. 1—Nuclear Chain Reaction

$$\left.\begin{array}{c} [U^{233}] \\ [U^{235}] \\ [Pu^{239}] \end{array}\right\} + n \rightarrow 2 \text{ F.P. (Ga-Dy)} + 2.5^{+} n$$

$$\Delta Q = 4.5 \cdot 10^{9} \text{ kcal/mole}$$
$$= 19.5 \cdot 10^{6} \text{ kcal/g}$$
$$= 22.5 \cdot 10^{3} \text{ kwh/g}$$

Eq. 2—Plutonium Production

$$_{92}U^{238} + {}_{0}n^{1} \rightarrow {}_{92}U^{239} \xrightarrow[\text{min.}]{23.5} {}_{93}Np^{239} + {}_{-1}e^{0}$$
$$\xrightarrow[\text{days}]{2.3} {}_{94}Pu^{239} + {}_{-1}e^{0}$$

Eq. 3—U^{233} Production

$$_{90}Th^{232} + {}_{0}n^{1} \rightarrow {}_{90}Th^{233} \xrightarrow[\text{min.}]{23.5} {}_{91}Pa^{233} + {}_{-1}e^{0}$$
$$\xrightarrow[\text{days}]{22.4} {}_{92}U^{233} + {}_{-1}e^{0}$$

Only the isotopes and nuclear reactions of major concern are shown; there are a number of other fissionable isotopes and quite a number of competing nuclear reactions, but in the first approximation the situation follows the equations given here.

A number of interesting and important conclusions can be drawn from this table and set of equations.

1. There are three major fissionable isotopes (U^{235}, U^{233} and Pu^{239}) which will readily undergo the sort of nuclear reaction shown in Eq. (1).

2. Of these three, only one (U^{235}) occurs in nature and then only as a minor component in natural uranium.

3. The major component (U^{238}) of natural uranium is available as a source of energy only after it has first been converted into Pu^{239} according to Eq. (2).

4. The world's thorium is available as an energy source after it has been converted into U^{233} according to Eq. (3).

5. The fission reaction given in Eq. (1) is autocatalytic, that is, more neutrons are produced by the reaction than are consumed.

6. One of the neutrons produced by the reaction shown in Eq. (1) is required to continue the reaction; some are lost by leakage and to non-productive nuclear reactions; the rest are available for useful purposes.

7. The excess neutrons produced by reaction (1) can be used to carry out the reactions given in Eq. (2) and (3).

8. The neutrons used in reactions (2) and (3) are returned with interest when the products of the reactions (Pu^{239} and U^{233}) are used to carry out reaction (1).

9. We are dealing with a set of interrelated fertile and fissionable materials and nuclear reactions; the one common feature is that neutrons are involved in all of these reactions.

10. The only practical source of neutrons in large quantities and using naturally occurring materials is reaction (1) utilizing U^{235}.

11. U^{235} is more valuable to us as a source of neutrons than as a source of energy and every effort should be made to utilize these neutrons efficiently and effectively.

12. Nuclear fission becomes a truly abundant energy source only if we are able to effectively utilize U^{238}, the abundant isotope of natural uranium, through the use of the Pu^{239} intermediate. Energy resources could be further extended by making use of natural thorium through the U^{233} intermediate.

The above considerations lead to three general categories of reactors in terms of the principal aim or objective of the device.

Special Purpose Reactors take special advantage of the high concentration of energy available in the fissionable materials. In this category would be included such reactors as nuclear explosives; military propulsion devices for submarines, ships, and aircraft; and remote site reactors for use in polar regions, space vehicles, on the moon, etc. In all of these cases, economy of operation is not the major consideration; the primary objective is to achieve effects which are impossible or very difficult to accomplish with any other energy source. We would be justified in including in this group the plutonium production reactors and even such nonreactor operations as isotope separation plants since their main objective is to produce or to concentrate fissionable isotopes. One is justified in using scarce and costly materials in such reactors since cost and material conservation are secondary to performance.

Maximum Utilization Reactors have power as the major objective, but particular attention is paid to high neutron economy, and to high conversion or breeding ratios. A large fraction of the energy released by the device should be obtained from the plentiful fertile isotopes, U^{238} and Th^{232}. While such thermal reactors make use of relatively cheap and plentiful fertile materials, the maintenance of high neutron economy requires the use of materials of low absorption cross section such as coolants, moderators, and claddings. Thus, expensive heavy water may be required as coolant and moderator, and zirconium as cladding and structural material. Unmoderated reactors operating on fast neutrons are not so sensitive to the erratic absorption cross-section variations and one has a wider choice of cladding and structural materials. Water, a moderator, cannot be used as a coolant; liquid metals, such as sodium, can be used, but present a difficult technical problem. In addition, the critical mass of unmoderated reactors is large and the inventory charges high. There is, therefore, some question whether the low cost of the feed materials does not become overwhelmed by these other reactor costs. The most promising appear to be the aqueous homogeneous thermal reactor operating on the Th^{232}-U^{233} cycle and fast reactors operating on the U^{238}-Pu^{239} cycle. The thermal plutonium-recycle reactor type, fueled initially with natural uranium, also belongs in this category.

Competitive Cost Reactors represent a large category of miscellaneous devices of which the primary objective is to produce useful power from nuclear fission at the lowest possible cost. They are, in general, central station power plants competing economically with an already well established fossil-fuel power-generation system. No particular advantage is taken of the highly concentrated energy in nuclear fuels nor is any particular attention paid to maximum utilization of irreplaceable raw materials. It is also an area in which accounting practices and interest rates may override technical considerations. Most of the reactors in the Civilian Power Program fall in this category which includes the boiling-water, pressurized-water, gas-cooled, and sodium-graphite types. Within each type there exists considerable latitude in choice of fuel materials, claddings, moderators, coolants and geometry. Hopefully, somewhere in this complex of possibilities there exists at least one, and preferably several, combinations which can be made economically competitive with fossil fuels. At present, it appears that the boiling-water and the gas-cooled reactor types have the best chance.

Uranium and Uranium Alloy Fuels

In this category are included fuel materials in which uranium is the major component and metallic uranium or a high uranium alloy is the matrix phase. Usually this also means that U^{238} is the major component of the fuel. Enough fissionable isotope is added to the U^{238} to give a chain reaction system of suitable critical mass. This definition excludes from this category fuels in which more or less pure fissionable isotopes are dispersed in or dissolved in inert matrices such as aluminum, stainless steel, or zirconium. We will consider here only fuels of the type:

$$U^{238} + \text{Fissionable Isotope} + \text{Alloying Elements}$$
$$(U^{235}, Pu^{239}, U^{233}) \qquad (Zr, Mo, Nb, etc.)$$

Unalloyed Natural Uranium ($U^{238} + 0.7\% \; U^{235}$). This is by far the simplest and most readily obtainable nuclear fuel since it is a naturally occurring material and can be refined and reduced to metal by what have become more or less conventional chemical and metallurgical processes. It carries fissionable isotope in its cheapest form ($5.62/g as compared to $17.07/g for 90 per cent U^{235} and $12 to $15/g for Pu^{239} and U^{233}). The whole technology of melting, casting, fabricating and heat treating is relatively easy and straightforward and the metal can be handled on a relatively large scale without unusual health or criticality hazards. After use in a reactor, these fuels are easily dissolved and reprocessed. Reactors fueled with natural uranium somewhat automatically have good conversion ratios simply because they contain large amounts of U^{238} which can be converted. Since the fuel is quite dilute, there is no great difficulty in obtaining extended heat transfer surface.

There are, of course, difficulties associated with the use of natural uranium as fuel. Many of these difficulties are inherent in uranium itself and are present to some degree in all uranium-base fuels. These unfavorable properties and behaviors are most prominent and troublesome in natural uranium and will be discussed here. The first difficulty is nuclear: since we are using a fuel quite dilute in fissionable isotope, and the diluent (U^{238}) is an absorber of neutrons, the critical mass is large and a practical power reactor will require 700 to 1000 kg of U^{235} which would be contained in 100 to 150 metric tons of natural uranium. Such reactors are large structures, expensive to build and maintain, and require a large through-put of fuel. Uranium is a chemically active metal and requires coating or jacketing of some sort to protect it against corrosion by coolants, particularly water. The same jacket prevents fission products from entering the coolant and the dual function is served satisfactorily only by coatings or jackets of extremely high integrity.

Uranium metal exists in three solid allotropic forms with transformation temperatures at approximately 660 and 770°C. In unalloyed uranium the high-temperature forms cannot be retained by quenching, and thermal cycling through the transformation temperatures produces gross distortion of uranium fuels. Consequently the maximum operating temperature must be kept below the first transformation temperature and the average temperature will be considerably below this. We must operate with alpha-ura-

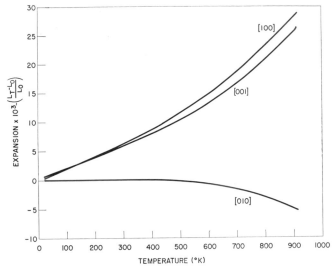

Figure 5-1. Expansion of alpha-uranium; principal directions with temperature as calculated from lattice parameter. (Data of Bridge, Schwartz and Vaughan[1])

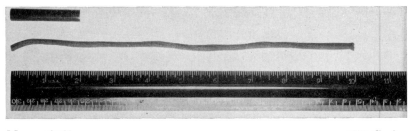

Macro 10,469   2575 Cycles

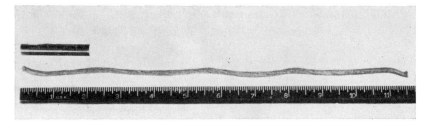

Macro 10.926   3000 Cycles

Figure 5-2. Thermal cycling growth of rolled uranium rod.[2] Rod rolled at 300°C cycled between 50 and 550°C. Initial specimen at top in each case. (Approx. ⅓×)

nium which has an orthorhombic crystal structure and which is highly anisotropic in some of its properties. The best known example of such effects is the thermal expansion characteristics shown in Figure 5-1. This thermal expansion anisotropy when combined with preferred orientation in polycrystalline metal can produce thermal cycling growth, even though the cycling is entirely within the temperature range of stability of the alpha phase. An extreme example of this effect is shown in Figure 5-2. As a result, many of the properties and behaviors of polycrystalline uranium are strongly dependent upon the mechanical and thermal history.

The behavior of uranium under neutron irradiation is particularly discouraging. Single crystals of alpha-uranium undergo considerable distortion

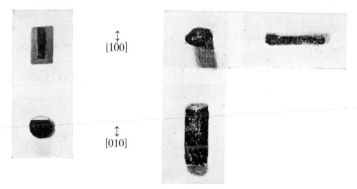

Before irradiation   After irradiation

Figure 5-3. Effect of irradiation on uranium single crystals.[3]
Growth coefficients: 100 direction, −420
010 direction, +450
011 direction,   0

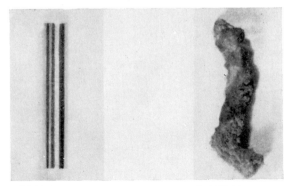

0% Burn-up   0:44% Burn-up

Figure 5-4. Effect of irradiation on coarse grained (cast) uranium.[4]

even at low burn-ups, as shown in Figure 5-3. Coarse grained material such as castings or beta-annealed rods becomes very rough (Figure 5-4). Fabricated rod and plate in which preferred orientation has been developed will grow in a manner related to the kind and degree of preference established by the working conditions (Figures 5-5 and 6). The best dimensional stability is observed in polycrystalline material which consists of fine grains randomly oriented as in beta-quenched (Figure 5-7) or powder metallurgy product. And finally, superimposed on the anisotropic dimensional changes, there is a volume change (swelling) associated with the increase in total number of atoms in any given sample as fissioning occurs (i.e., 2 fission product atoms are produced from each atom fissioned). At temperatures

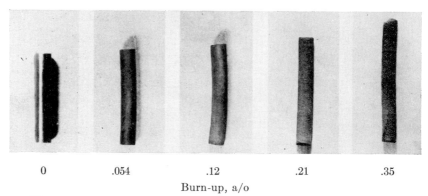

0   .054   .12   .21   .35

Burn-up, a/o

Figure 5-5. Effects of irradiation on uranium rod rolled at 600 C.[5]

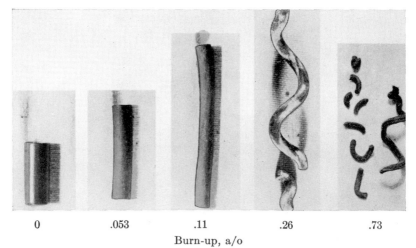

0   .053   .11   .26   .73

Burn-up, a/o

Figure 5-6. Effects of irradiation on uranium rod rolled at 300°C.[5]

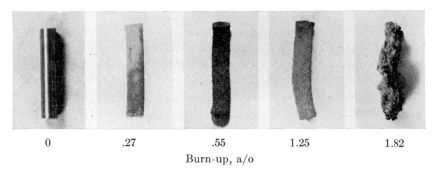

| 0 | .27 | .55 | 1.25 | 1.82 |

Burn-up, a/o

Figure 5-7. Effects of irradiation on uranium rod rolled at 300°C and beta quenched.[5]

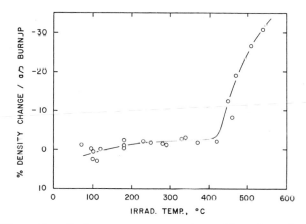

Figure 5-8. Effect of irradiation temperature on the swelling of uranium compacts.[6]

up to about 400°C this volume increase amounts to about 4 to 5 per cent per a/o* burn-up; at higher temperatures it may be several times as large (Figure 5-8).

These rather unfortunate properties of unalloyed uranium make it somewhat unattractive as a power reactor fuel although the United Kingdom is using it in the gas-cooled Calder Hall type of reactor. Its major use is in plutonium producers wherein part of the U^{235} is converted into Pu^{239} and the power dumped.

Unalloyed Enriched Uranium (U^{238} + >0.7% U^{235}). Enriched uranium can be produced by putting natural uranium through some sort of isotope separation process whereby some of the U^{238} is stripped out and discarded. The degree of enrichment may be low, around 1 to 5 per cent; moderate, at around 20 per cent; or high, 90 per cent or better. Enriched

* a/o = atomic per cent

uranium is more expensive than natural uranium since the isotopic separation process is superimposed upon the metallurgical processes for the refining and production of metal. It is less available because only a few of these huge, expensive, and highly specialized isotope separation plants exist. The critical mass of a reactor decreases as the enrichment increases; for low degrees of enrichment the decreased size of the plant and, presumably, the lower capital cost of the reactor, may offset the cost of enrichment. However, it should never be forgotten that a power plant using such fuel is completely dependent upon the continued and uninterrupted operation of isotope separation plants. With highly enriched uranium, the conversion ratio and the specific power (Mw of heat per kg of U^{235}) are adversely affected, the first because not much U^{238} is present, the second because the heat transfer surface per gram of fissionable material is low. However, a special case exists for high enrichment fuels in unmoderated reactors. Here the critical mass for a given power output is high but the conversion ratio can be made large by surrounding the core with a blanket of U^{238}. An example of such a reactor was the Experimental Breeder Reactor (EBR-I) with the Mark-I core. The critical mass was about 50 kg of >90 per cent enriched uranium, the heat output was 1.4 Mw (specific power ~ 0.02 Mw/kg), but the conversion ratio was unity or slightly better. Enrichment has no effect upon the metallurgical properties of uranium and the difficulties associated with natural uranium are present with enriched uranium.

Alloyed Natural Uranium ($U^{238} + 0.7\% \ U^{235} + x\% \ A$). For many years metallurgists have used alloying as a method of improving the properties of metals and it certainly is no surprise that the properties and behavior of uranium can be markedly improved by the addition of small amounts of certain alloying elements. In the case of natural uranium for reactor use we have severe nonmetallurgical restrictions upon the kinds and amounts of alloying elements which can be used. All elements absorb neutrons to a greater or lesser extent and in the thermal neutron region they show wide variations in their absorption cross sections. Alloying elements, therefore, act as poisons in that they absorb neutrons nonproductively and they show wide variations in the poisoning effects. It should be remembered that natural uranium is already a very dilute fuel and that reactors fueled with natural uranium have large critical masses. The addition of alloying elements further increases the size and, unless we show considerable care in selecting the kinds and amounts of alloying element, the critical mass may become infinite. We have therefore a double limitation on our choice of alloying elements: (1) the alloying should do us some good by improving the properties and behavior of uranium, and (2) the nonproductive loss of neutrons must be kept as low as possible by using alloying elements of low absorption cross section in minimal amounts. This double criterion leaves us with very little choice, and zirconium, silicon and aluminum are about the only possibilities. The major effect is that of grain refinement by improving the response to heat treatment.

Alloyed Enriched Uranium ($U^{238} + > 0.7 \% U^{235} + x \% A$). The alloying element still acts as a poison but its adverse effect on reactor size can be overridden by adding more fissionable material. Further, we have a greater latitude in the choice of amounts and kinds of alloying element: we can use larger amounts of the low cross-section elements and modest amounts of elements of moderate cross section such as chromium, molybdenum and niobium. By such measures we can often obtain much improved properties but only at the expense of a further reduction in conversion ratio. Reactors fueled with such alloys can be made to operate even though the neutron economy is relatively poor. With this greater latitude in selection of alloying elements, rather startling improvements in the properties of uranium are possible. As examples, the addition of a few per cent of zirconium, molybdenum, or niobium, singly or in combination, markedly improves the dimensional stability under thermal cycling and under irradiation. Additions of somewhat larger amounts permit the retention of gamma phase by quenching. The aqueous corrosion resistance of uranium can be increased by proper alloying and heat treatment. A recent example of such fuels is the U^{238}-1.44 % U^{235}-5 % Zr-1.5 % Nb alloy used in the Experimental Boiling Water Reactor (EBWR). This alloy is corrosion resistant if quenched from the gamma phase although the alloying content is not sufficiently high to permit the retention of gamma phase. Slowly cooled or isothermally transformed alloys show good stability under irradiation. Unfortunately no heat treatments are known which give both corrosion resistance and dimensional stability simultaneously. The reactor was loaded with alloy, heat treated for dimensional stability rather than corrosion resistance. Larger amounts of alloying elements such as molybdenum and niobium permit the retention of gamma phase which is both corrosion resistant and dimensionally stable.

Again, the special case of the fast reactor should be noted. Here it is possible to achieve good conversion ratios even with moderately or highly enriched fuels and with considerable alloying. An unusual case of such fuels is the reference alloy for EBR-II. This fuel is U^{238}-50 % U^{235}-5 % Fs (fissium), where 5 % Fs = 2.4 % Mo-2.0 % Ru-0.3 % Rh-0.2 % Pd-0.05 % Zr-0.1 % Nb. This rather odd composition derives not from metallurgical considerations but from the fact that these are fission product elements not removed or only partially removed by the pyrometallurgical refining method to be used for recycling the irradiated fuel. The fact that many of these fissium elements are desirable alloying elements for uranium is fortuitous and gratifying.

Alloyed Spiked Uranium (U^{238}-$x \%$ Pu + $y \%$ A). In this type of fuel the U^{235} is replaced by one of the artificial fissionable isotopes. The uranium can be spiked with either plutonium or U^{233}, but preferably with plutonium since this gives a breeder type of reactor in which the new fissionable material being produced is identical with that being destroyed by fission. With U^{233} we would still be dealing with a converter reactor in which U^{233} is being converted into Pu^{239}. U^{233} would probably be best used in thorium-base fuels to again achieve a breeder type reactor. In thermal reactors the U-Pu cycle is certain to operate with a breeding ratio less than unity. The object of the plutonium recycle program is to make this breeding ratio as high as possible and, in effect, to lose fissionable material as slowly as possible. In this type of fuel the uranium carries only a per cent or so of plutonium and a minimum of alloying element. Actually in this type or reactor it would probably be better to segregate the plutonium into separate spiking fuel elements. In this manner the large mass of U^{238} absorber blanket can be manufactured by conventional methods without the need of a plutonium hazard control system. The plutonium would be carried in some inert material such as aluminum or zirconium: we would then be dealing with an aluminum- or zirconium-base fuel alloy but the amount of material which must be handled with plutonium hazard control would be much less.

The best use of plutonium-spiked uranium fuels would be in fast neutron reactors. Here there is no question but that the breeding ratio will exceed unity and that fast power breeders of this type will produce not only power but also more plutonium than they consume. Once started, the reactor requires only a continuing supply of U^{238} and produces a continually increasing inventory of fissionable material. Such a power system not only operates on the major isotope of uranium but also is self-expanding in fissionable isotopes. The Mark-II loading of EBR-II will be a U-20 w/o Pu-10 w/o Fs alloy in which Fs (fissium) has the same general meaning as in the Mark-I loading. The 20 per cent Pu composition was chosen on the basis that this is about the maximum concentration required to fuel a full-size power reactor.

References

1. Bridge, J. R., Schwartz, C. M., and Vaughan, D. A., "X-ray Diffraction Determination of the Coefficients of Expansion of Alpha Uranium," *Trans. AIME*, **206**, 1282 (1956).
2. Chiswik, H. H., and Mayfield, R. M., "Growth Rates and Microstructural Characteristics of 300°C Rolled Uranium Rods on Thermal Cycling," ANL-4956.
3. Paine, S. H., and Kittel, J. H., "Preliminary Analysis of Fission-Induced Dimensional Changes in Single Crystals of Alpha Uranium," ANL-5676.
4. Kittel, J. H., and Paine, S. H., "Effects of High Burnup at Elevated Temperatures on Uranium-0.52 and 1.62 w/o Zirconium Alloys," ANL-5406.
5. Kittel, J. H., and Paine, S. H., "Effect of High Burnup on Natural Uranium," ANL-5539.
6. Kittel, J. H., and Paine, S. H., "Effects of Irradiation on Powder Compacts of Uranium and Some Uranium-Base Alloys." ANL-5664.

6. URANIUM-ZIRCONIUM HYDRIDE FUEL ELEMENTS

ULRICH MERTEN, R. S. STONE, AND W. P. WALLACE

John Jay Hopkins Laboratory for Pure and Applied Science
General Atomic Division of General Dynamics Corporation
San Diego, California

Since the earliest days of reactor technology, safety has always been a prime consideration in reactor design. In many cases, safety requirements have been met by placing the reactor in a remote location or by enclosing it in a specially designed building. In general, only very low power or sub-critical devices have been operated without such precautions. While these measures have served their function of preventing major accidents, they have at the same time interfered with full exploitation of reactors for some purposes. In particular, industries and educational institutions located in populated areas have found it very expensive or impossible to install reactors which operate at significant power levels.

It is apparent that the needs of these organizations can be adequately met only by an inherently safe reactor which can be operated at reasonably high power levels in populated areas, without expensive methods of containment. The fuel elements described in the following paragraphs were developed as a part of a reactor system designed to fill these needs.[1] The most important feature of these fuel elements as originally conceived was that they should contain fuel and moderator in an essentially homogeneous mixture. Hydrogen was chosen as the moderator to minimize critical mass requirements and to avoid the health hazards of beryllium, another potential choice. Zirconium hydride was chosen as the appropriate hydrogenous material for a number of reasons, including the excellent thermal stability of this compound and the low neutron cross section and moderate cost of zirconium.

Since the new fuel-moderator material was essential to the reactor concept, a process for the production of a uranium-zirconium hydride fuel element was worked out as critical experiments on the proposed reactor core were made. By the time a satisfactory process had been developed, the critical experiments had shown that the construction of a prototype reactor was a reasonable next step; the first TRIGA* reactor was the result. In extensive work with this reactor, the properties of the fuel element as a part of the reactor system were studied. At the same time, further experiments on the properties of the fuel-moderator material itself were carried on in the laboratory. At present, three TRIGA reactors have been built and operated, and several more are in various stages of detailed design or construction. As a result of its use in the TRIGA reactor, the uranium-zirconium hydride fuel element is rapidly becoming an established part of reactor technology.

Production of TRIGA Fuel Element

The active part of the TRIGA fuel element is a uranium-zirconium hydride rod, 1.42 in. in diameter by 14 in. long; this rod is a macroscopically homogeneous mixture of 8 w/o uranium, 91 w/o zirconium, and 1 w/o hydrogen, which is equivalent to an atom ratio of $U:Zr:H$ of $0.03:1:1$; the uranium is 20 per cent enriched in U^{235}. Burnable poison is added in the form of two disks which contain samarium oxide mixed in an aluminum matrix. Four-inch lengths of graphite are placed at each end of the fuel material, and the assembly is jacketed with a 0.030-in., 1100-type aluminum can. Figure 6-1 shows the various fuel element components and a finished fuel element.

The fabrication of the fuel rods[2] begins with the preparation of a zirconium-uranium alloy by conventional techniques. Zirconium sponge and uranium metal pieces are arc-melted in a water-cooled copper mold to form an ingot which is machined to clean up the surface and then remelted to insure greater homogeneity. After the second melting, the ingot is machined to 3.8-in. diameter, clad with copper, and extruded at 1450°F to 1.6-in. diameter; the copper cladding is removed by pickling in nitric acid and the long rod is cut into fuel element lengths and machined to the required size. The machined rods are then hydrided. Finally, the hydrided rods are assembled into an aluminum tube, together with the graphite rods and the samarium oxide-aluminum disks; the tubes are sized onto these rods in a drawbench and the end pieces are welded into the tube.

The hydriding of zirconium-uranium alloy shapes[3] is carried out at General Atomic Division in the apparatus shown in Figure 6-2. The piece to be hydrided is placed in a ceramic tube in one of the large tube furnaces and heated under vacuum to the desired temperature, usually in excess of 750°C. Carefully purified hydrogen is let in slowly through an integral-flow meter until the desired hydrogen content has been attained. The tube is then isolated from the hydrogen source and allowed to cool slowly. In the TRIGA fuel elements, the hydriding process is stopped when an $H:Zr$

---

* Training Research Isotope Production Reactor.

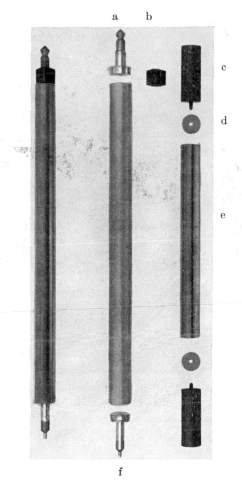

Figure 6-1. TRIGA fuel element. (a) aluminum top end-fixture; (b) spacer; (c) graphite; (d) samarium burnable poison; (e) zirconium hydride, 8 w/o uranium; (f) aluminum bottom end-fixture.

atom ratio of 1:1 has been reached. Although a higher hydrogen content is readily attainable in smaller alloy shapes, cracking and distortion in the large-diameter rods become increasingly serious problems as the hydrogen content is increased. Since these problems have been discussed at some length elsewhere,[3] there is no need to dwell on them here.

The Zirconium-Uranium-Hydrogen System

At the time that development of this fuel-moderator material began, the only reported work on the ternary alloy system was the limited investiga-

Figure 6-2. Hydriding apparatus.

tion of Singleton, Ruka, and Gulbransen.[4] As a result, an investigation of a portion of this system was undertaken, a complete report of which will be published in the near future.[5] Hydrogen dissociation pressure techniques and high-temperature x-ray methods were employed in this work, and a number of results of interest in the application of Zr-U-H alloys to reactors were obtained. Figure 6-3 shows the equilibrium dissociation pressures of alloys with varying Zr:U ratios as a function of hydrogen content at 800°C. It is of interest to note that at high H:Zr ratios, the dissociation pressure is essentially independent of the uranium content; thus, from this standpoint at least, much higher fuel concentrations than those used in TRIGA are permissible.

Figure 6-4 shows a section through the phase diagram at 800°C. Here the observed pressure behavior is seen to exist because the dissociation pressure must be constant over the entire three-phase field in the center of the diagram. It is also noteworthy that at this temperature (which is in the range where hydriding is normally carried out) only very small amounts of uranium are soluble in the zirconium-hydrogen phases with large hydrogen content. As a result, the uranium tends to be rejected from solution as the hydriding proceeds. The composition of the TRIGA alloy at hydriding temperature places it very near the beta-zirconium solid-solution corner of the three-phase field. On cooling, this homogeneous or near-homogeneous structure presumably tends to break down into alpha-zirconium, zirconium hydride, and the epsilon phase of the zirconium-uranium system.

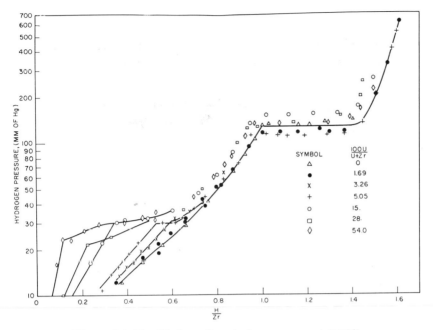

Figure 6-3. Equilibrium dissociation pressure at 800°C.

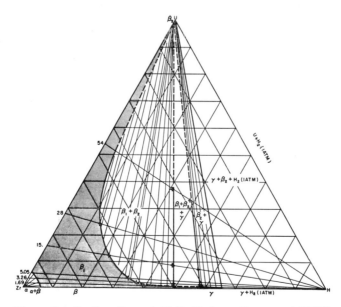

Figure 6-4. Section through U-Zr-H phase diagram at 800°C.

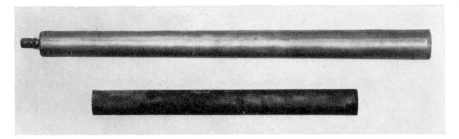

Figure 6-5. Fuel material and can after seventh thermal cycle.

Properties of TRIGA Fuel-Moderator Alloy

Studies of the physical, mechanical, and chemical properties of these alloys have been concentrated on the composition used in TRIGA reactor elements: zirconium, 8 w/o* uranium, 1 w/o hydrogen (3 a/o U, 49 a/o H). Since most of the measurements have already been reported,[2, 3] one need only summarize them here and then discuss several more recent experiments. Mechanically, the alloy fails by brittle fracture at room temperature under a load of about 30,000 psi. The modulus of elasticity is 14×10^6 psi at room temperature. The thermal conductivity is close to that of unalloyed zirconium, ranging from 0.20 to 0.18 watts cm^{-1} °C^{-1} in the range 50 to 400°C. Tests of chemical reactivity, in which the alloy was plunged from a high-temperature furnace directly into water, have failed to show any reaction other than surface discoloration.

Recent work has extended experience with the alloy in thermal shock tests[6] and under irradiation. During a typical reactor transient, the fuel material is heated almost instantaneously and very uniformly to some high temperature and then cooled rapidly by heat transfer across the unbonded fuel material-cladding interface, through the cladding, and into the surrounding water. In an effort to simulate this event, a tapered fuel rod has been cycled 11 times between 900°C and room temperature. The cycle consists of heating the fuel material in an argon atmosphere and then dropping it into a similarly tapered aluminum can which is immersed in water. The fuel material does not touch any other material except the aluminum can. Surface cracking of the material occurred during the seventh cycle but did not noticeably increase in subsequent cycles. The cracking is shown in Figure 6-5. The surface layer of the fuel material is discolored from the reaction of the uranium-zirconium hydride with impurities in the argon. This layer was vapor-blasted off after each cycle to minimize the reduction of heat transfer rate at the fuel material-cladding interface.

* w/o = weight per cent, a/o = atomic per cent

TABLE 6-1. COMPOSITION AND EXPOSURE OF IRRADIATED SAMPLES

Sample	Composition H:Zr	Exposure* (nvt)
1	1.12	6.0×10^{19}
2	1.60	5.9×10^{19}
3	1.58	7.1×10^{19}
4	0.92	7.2×10^{19}

* Flux at surface of 0.25 in. diameter slugs as determined by cobalt monitor activation.

Capsule irradiation tests of alloy samples made with highly enriched uranium in place of the usual 20 per cent enriched material have been carried out at the Materials Testing Reactor (MTR).[7] Visual and microscopic examinations and density measurements show no significant changes in the samples even after the highest exposures used, which correspond to about 4 per cent burn-up of the uranium present in the alloy (the equivalent of 20 per cent burn-up of the U^{235} in the 20 per cent enriched fuel alloy). The hydrogen content of the specimens (all were 7 w/o U) and exposure levels of all samples tested are shown in Table 6-1. The very satisfactory behavior of the samples is partly attributable to the large dilution of the fuel obtained by incorporating it in the moderator. Thus, in this material, 4 per cent uranium consumption means only a 0.12 per cent total atom burn-up.

Tests have been carried out to determine the extent to which fission products might be removed from the surface of a fuel element after shutdown in case of cladding failure.[8] Room-temperature water was circulated at 2 ft/sec past foils of a Zr-U-H alloy (8 w/o natural uranium, 1.1 w/o hydrogen) which had been irradiated for 24 hr in the MTR at a thermal flux of 1.5×10^{14} neutrons/cm²-sec. In Table 6-2, the results obtained by radiochemical analysis of the water are tabulated. The analytical data have been recalculated to indicate the thickness of the alloy layer from which

TABLE 6-2. FISSION PRODUCT RELEASE

Duration of Test (days)	Fission Product Analyzed	Apparent Depth of Erosion (Å)
1	Sr^{89}	11
	Ba^{140}	16
	I^{131}	1600
8	Sr^{89}	16
	Ba^{140}	22
	I^{131}	2600

all of the fission product in question would have to be removed to give the observed activity level. The wide variation suggests that the removal process involves preferential leaching rather than gross erosion. In any case, the fraction of the fission products which would be removed in a few days from a fuel element of reasonable thickness under these test conditions would obviously be quite small. For instance, the 8-day exposure corresponds to a fractional fission product loss of between 10^{-7} and 10^{-5} for a completely unclad TRIGA fuel element.

The neutron-scattering properties of zirconium hydride have recently been studied by Andresen *et al.*[9] Their work shows that the strong hydrogen-zirconium binding in this compound profoundly influences the scattering behavior at low neutron energies. By examining the energy spectrum of scattered neutrons, they determined that the incident particles interacted with at least two distinct optical vibration levels of the lattice—one at 0.13 ev and one at about 0.25 ev.

Performance of Fuel Elements

A fuel element cannot finally be evaluated except as a part of the reactor system which it is to fuel. Thus, the only real test of the merits of zirconium-uranium-hydrogen alloy elements is the performance of the TRIGA reactor for which they were developed.

Figure 6-6 is a cutaway view of the TRIGA reactor. The core contains approximately 60 fuel elements containing a total of about 2.0 kg U^{235}. The core is cooled by light water and reflected with graphite. Although the first TRIGA was designed as a 10 kw reactor, it has been operated for prolonged periods at 100 kw, and some of the models now under construction will operate routinely at this higher power level. Table 6-3 lists the technical data for the TRIGA reactor.

Three distinct types of experiments were performed to study the reactor system.[10] The initial tests were isothermal experiments in which the temperature of the entire reactor system was changed, and the resulting change in system reactivity with temperature was observed. The second group of experiments were quasi-equilibrium experiments in which the reactor was operated at a number of different power levels. Reactivity loss and component temperatures were measured at each power level. These experiments provided a measure of the reactor temperature coefficients and of the heat transfer parameters in the prototype reactor core. This information was then used to calculate the transient behavior of the reactor for the third group of tests, the step reactivity insertions of varying magnitude. The validity of these predictions was established through a series of transient experiments performed on the prototype reactor.

Isothermal Experiments. In the isothermal experiments the reactor

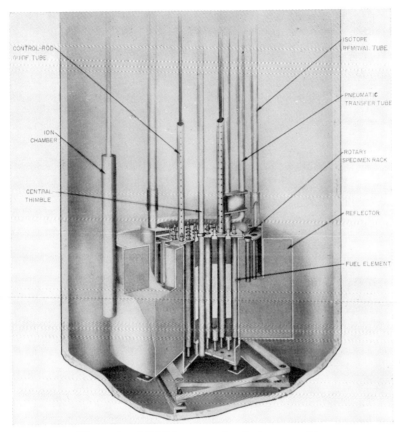

Figure 6-6. TRIGA core and reflector assembly.

control rods were calibrated to establish the relationship between control rod position and system reactivity. The reactor was taken to a low-power level and the critical position of the control rods was determined. By means of thermocouples, the temperature of the reactor system was determined to be uniform. The temperature of the reactor was varied over the range from 10 to 50°C, and the changes in reactivity associated with these changes in system temperature were obtained by observing the position of the calibrated control rods. Within the limits of accuracy of the experiment, no change of reactivity was observed. It therefore follows that the reactivity changes observed in the subsequent quasi-equilibrium experiments can be attributed to differences between the fuel temperature and the average water temperature in the core.

Quasi-equilibrium Experiments. The quasi-equilibrium experiments were performed by operating the reactor at several different power levels.

TABLE 6-3. SUMMARY OF TECHNICAL DATA FOR THE TRIGA REACTOR

Core

Fuel elements:

fuel-moderator material................ 8 w/o uranium, 91 w/o zirconium, 1 w/o hydrogen

uranium enrichment................... 20% U^{235}

fuel-element dimensions................ 1.48 in. diam x 28.4 in. long

cladding............................. 0.030-in.-thick aluminum

Dimensions (active lattice).............. 17 in. diam x 14 in. high

Reflector

Material............................... Graphite

Cladding material...................... Aluminum

Radial thickness....................... 12 in.

Top and bottom thickness............... 4 in.

Nuclear Characteristics

Thermal neutron flux at 10 kw:

average in core....................... $\sim 1.6 \times 10^{11}$ neutrons/cm²-sec

at rotary specimen rack............... $\sim 0.7 \times 10^{11}$ neutrons/cm²-sec

at central thimble.................... $\sim 4 \times 10^{11}$ neutrons/cm²-sec

Core loading........................... ~ 2.0 kg U^{235}

Prompt temperature coefficient of reactivity at 50°C........................... -1.3×10^{-4} $\Delta k/k/°C$

Void coefficient of reactivity in core....... ~ -0.001 $\Delta k/k$ per 1% void

Prompt neutron lifetime................. ~ 80 μsec

Thermal Characteristics

Power.................................. 10 kw/100 kw

Cooling method......................... Natural convection of water

Control

Transient rod.......................... 1

Boron-carbide control rods.............. 3

Structures

Reactor pit, concrete lined.............. 6 ft. 6 in. ID x 21 ft. deep

Shielding

Material............................... 16 ft of water over core

Experimental and Irradiation Facilities

Rotary specimen rack................... 40-position rotary specimen rack located in graphite reflector

Pneumatic transfer tube................ Located near edge of core

Central thimble........................ Located in center of core (region of maximum flux)

Reflector.............................. Region around graphite reflector

The core-inlet water temperature was maintained constant. Component temperatures and reactivity loss were measured. The temperature of the system components as a function of power level is given in Figure 6-7, and the reactivity loss as a function of power level is given in Figure 6-8. If one attributes all of the observed reactivity change to the difference between fuel and water temperature, then Figures 6-7 and 8 provide a parametric relationship for the reactivity loss as a function of fuel temperature rise as

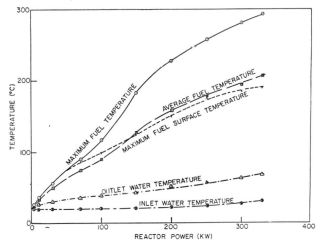

Figure 6-7. Reactor component temperatures vs. power.

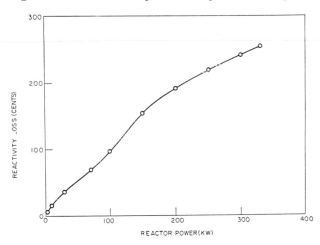

Figure 6-8. Reactivity loss *vs.* power level.

plotted in Figure 6-9. From Figure 6-9 one obtains an average value for the reactor temperature coefficient of -1.6 cents/°C.

Because of the intimate mixing of the hydrogen in the zirconium hydride and the uranium fuel, the moderator temperature follows the fuel temperature with essentially no time delay. One therefore concludes that the observed temperature coefficient must indeed be a prompt coefficient. From the data shown in Figure 6-7, one can also obtain an estimate of the average heat transfer resistance between the fuel material and the cooling water.

The temperature coefficient and the heat transfer resistance obtained

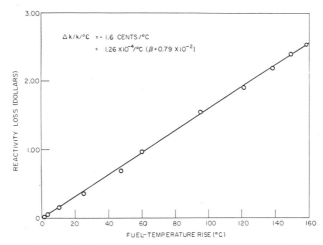

Figure 6-9. Reactivity loss as a function of fuel-temperature rise. Average fuel temperature is measured with respect to average core water temperature.

from these experiments were used as input data for an IBM-704 calculation to predict the transient behavior of the reactor for various step reactivity insertions. The predicted transient behavior is shown in Figure 6-11 and will be discussed below.

Transient Experiments. The preceding experiments established that the temperature coefficient in this reactor was large, prompt, and negative. For the transient experiments, the reactor was equipped with a special control rod mechanism that provided a method of obtaining a step reactivity change of predetermined magnitude in the reactor. A fast-recording galvanometer system was provided to record reactor power level and component temperatures during the transients.

The reactor was pulsed seven times with progressively larger step reactivity insertions, ranging up to 2 "dollars" in magnitude (1.6% $\delta k/k$). The power-level trace for the maximum transient is shown in Figure 6-10, together with a plot of fuel temperature in the hottest fuel element as a function of time. The "2-dollar" reactivity insertion resulted in a 10-millisecond reactor period prior to the time of significant changes in fuel temperature. As time went on, fuel temperature increased, and this change in temperature provided a large reduction in system reactivity. The reactor attained a maximum power level of 250 Mw 100 ms after the reactivity insertion was completed. Immediately following the prompt burst, the power level dropped to approximately 1 Mw and asymptotically approached an equilibrium value of approximately 200 kw.

The energy release in this maximum transient was approximately 20 Mw-sec. During the transient, nearly all energy was stored as thermal energy

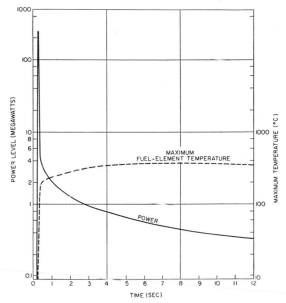

Figure 6-10. Transient power and fuel temperature as functions of time after "2-dollar" reactivity insertion.

in the fuel material. Subsequent to the burst, this heat energy slowly diffused into the coolant water with a characteristic time of approximately 30 sec. During the prompt burst there was no disturbance of the 16-ft column of water above the reactor core. The total radiation dose at the top of this column during the experiment was approximately 20 mrem.

A comparison between the predicted transient behavior of the reactor and the observed behavior is shown in Figure 6-11. The small difference between the predicted and the measured response results from a difference in the prompt neutron lifetime in the reactor and that used for the calculations.

Future Prospects

The experiments just described have demonstrated that the TRIGA reactor has a large, prompt, negative temperature coefficient which, in conjunction with the large heat capacity in the reactor core, provides an extremely high degree of inherent safety in the reactor system. As a result of their performance in the TRIGA reactor, the uranium-zirconium hydride fuel-moderator elements have found a place in research and training reactor technology. Whether they have any further importance is yet to be seen. The next step is likely to be their use in a reactor designed specifically for delivering high-intensity bursts of neutrons. Beyond this,

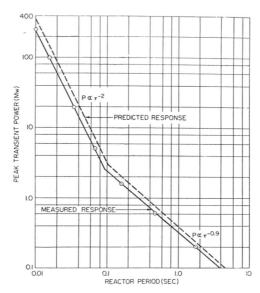

Figure 6-11. TRIGA transient power response as a function of reactor period.

it has recently been proposed[11] that elements of the described type be used in a nuclear superheater for Argonne's Borax-V boiling water reactor. Here, steam would be the coolant, and the incorporation of hydrogen into the fuel elements would be one way to obtain the desired amount of moderation.

In any case, it can be expected that the TRIGA elements will be followed by other fuel-moderator elements for power as well as research reactors, even if their metallurgical composition is quite different. This is likely, not only because of the inherent safety feature, but also because fuel dilution with another useful material—i.e., the moderator—is an attractive way to lengthen fuel element life and increase heat transfer area.

ACKNOWLEDGMENT

Many members of the staff of General Atomic's John Jay Hopkins Laboratory for Pure and Applied Science contributed to the work reviewed in this paper. Their assistance in making recent, unpublished results available is gratefully acknowledged.

References

1. Koutz, S. L., Taylor, T., McReynolds, A. W., Dyson, F. J., Stone, R. S., Sleeper, H. P., Jr., and Duffield, R. B., "Design of a 10-kw Reactor for Isotope Production, Research, and Training Purposes," Second United Nations International Conference on the Peaceful Uses of Atomic Energy, Geneva (1958) P/1017.
2. Wallace, W. P., Simnad, M. T., and Turovlin, B., in *Nuclear Energy*, **5,** American Institute of Mining, Metallurgical, and Petroleum Engineers, New York (1958).

3. Merten, U., Dykstra, L. J., Carpenter, F. D., Hatcher, A. P., and La Grange, L. D., "The Preparation and Properties of Zirconium-uranium-hydrogen Alloys," Second United Nations International Conference on the Peaceful Uses of Atomic Energy, Geneva (1958) P/789.
4. Singleton, J. H., Ruka, R., and Gulbransen, E. A., "The Reaction of Hydrogen with a 50 Weight Percent Alloy of Uranium and Zirconium between 542°C and 798°C," Westinghouse Electric Corporation, Report AECU-3630 (Nov. 16, 1956).
5. La Grange, L. D., Dykstra, L. J., Dixon, J. M., and Merten, U., "A Study of the Zirconium-Hydrogen and Zirconium-Uranium-Hydrogen Systems between 600 and 800°C," to be published in *J. Phys. Chem.*
6. The thermal shock tests have been carried out by B. Turovlin, J. R. Lindgren, and E. Moore of General Atomic Div. of General Dynamic Corp.
7. These experiments have been performed under the direction of L. D. La Grange of General Atomic. The postirradiation examinations were performed by the General Electric Co. at their Vallecitos Atomic Laboratory, under contract with General Atomic Div.
8. These experiments were performed by L. D. La Grange and R. A. Schmitt at General Atomic Div.
9. Andresen, A., McReynolds, A. W., Rosenbluth, M., and Whittemore, W., "Neutron Investigations of Optical Vibration Levels in Zirconium Hydride," *Phys. Rev.*, **108**, 1092 (1957). McReynolds, A. W., Nelkin, M. S., Rosenbluth, M. N., and Whittemore, W. L., to be published in the Proceedings of the Second United Nations International Conference on the Peaceful Uses of Atomic Energy, Geneva (1958) P/1540.
10. These experiments were performed at General Atomic by H. P. Sleeper, Jr., G. West, A. L. Weiman, R. H. Stahl, M. Drake, and one of the authors. Some of the results have been reported in *Nucleonics*, **16**, No. 12, 86 (1958).
11. Schumar, J. F., Argonne National Laboratory, private communication.

7. THORIUM-TYPE FUEL ELEMENTS

C. C. WOOLSEY

Group Leader, Fuel Element Development, Atomics International,
A Division of North American Aviation, Inc.
Canoga Park, Calif.

Several nuclear power plant systems, which are at various stages of planning at the present time, will use thorium as a nuclear "fuel." Although the contribution of fast fission of thorium to reactivity may not be negligible, thorium is primarily a source of nuclear fuel. The three primary nuclear fuel materials are U^{235}, U^{233}, and Pu^{239}. The first of these fissionable fuels occurs naturally, the other two being produced by neutron bombardment of natural materials; such bombardment of thorium and subsequent radioactive decay of intermediate products results in production of the fuel material U^{233}. Similarly Pu^{239} is produced from U^{238}, the major isotope in naturally occurring uranium.

The Th-U^{233} fuel cycle appears attractive for use in thermal- and epithermal-region nuclear reactors as it provides the possibility of breeding. Other advantages for use in high temperature reactors, such as the sodium-cooled, graphite-moderated reactor (SGR) include:

1. Somewhat higher maximum temperatures should be allowable for metallic thorium-base fuel materials than for uranium-base fuels because of the higher temperature at which phase changes occur.

2. The irradiation behavior of metallic thorium-base fuel materials appears to allow reasonable fuel life at the temperatures of interest.

3. Costs for fuel fabrication should be comparable to those for other fuel materials.

Four nuclear power plant concepts, at present, plan to use solid, thorium-type fuel elements; the Sodium Graphite (SGR), the Advanced Epithermal Thorium Reactor (AETR), the Consolidated Edison Thorium Reactor (CETR), and the Elk River Nuclear Reactor.

The SGR study will involve a full loading of the Sodium Reactor Experiment (SRE) with thorium-uranium alloy fuel. This fuel has been fabricated and will be loaded into the SRE within the next few months.

The AETR will be a sodium-cooled reactor designed to operate in the epithermal neutron region. This type reactor is under study by Atomics

International for the Southwest Atomic Energy Associates. It is expected that this type reactor will benefit from the somewhat improved neutron economy in the higher energy spectrum, and hence may have a higher probability of achieving breeding. The present conceptual design calls for the use of a metallic alloy fuel system, probably in a two region arrangement, with the fuel material (thorium-uranium alloy) placed in the core and fertile thorium in a blanket.

The CETR will be a pressurized water reactor, using thoria-urania ceramic fuel material, clad with stainless steel.

The Elk River Nuclear Reactor will be a boiling water reactor, also using thoria-urania ceramic fuel material, clad with stainless steel.

The Borax-IV reactor has operated with fuel elements containing thoria-urania fuel material. Operation of this reactor constitutes the major experience with this ceramic fuel material to date.

The present cost of thorium metal is of the order of \$20/lb or about the same as the price for normal uranium. The Atomic Energy Commission has established a purchase price for U^{233} of \$15/g in the form of uranyl nitrate. This compares favorably with the \$12/g purchase price for metallic plutonium set for material to be used for peaceful purposes only. However, the AEC has also agreed to purchase plutonium for weapons purposes at \$30 to \$45/g, depending upon the Pu^{240} content. This policy exerts a strong influence on the economics of the fuel cycle, the higher prices for plutonium placing a distinct cost disadvantage on the $Th-U^{233}$ fuel cycle. A change in the weapons situation could cause a reversal of this economic picture.

The availability of thorium appears to be sufficient to provide for an extensive power reactor program. One of the major sources of thorium is monazite, found in sands in many parts of the world. Other thorium ores are associated with uranium ores and may yield thorium as a by-product of uranium production. The demands of an extensive reactor program would create the incentive to develop the necessary resources. Several commercial sources for thorium metal or thorium oxide are available in this country, with a combined capacity of about one million pounds of ThO_2 annually. All fabrication of thorium-type fuel elements has been carried out on a relatively small-scale basis. No production-type fabrication facilities exist as there has been only limited demand for production of elements.

Thorium-Uranium^{233} Breeding Cycle

A portion of the chart of the nuclides is given in Figure 7-1, showing the nuclear reactions of primary interest in the $Th-U^{233}$ fuel cycle. That part enclosed by the dotted lines shows the steps in the production of U^{233} from thorium. Starting with Th^{232}, the only naturally occurring isotope, a neu-

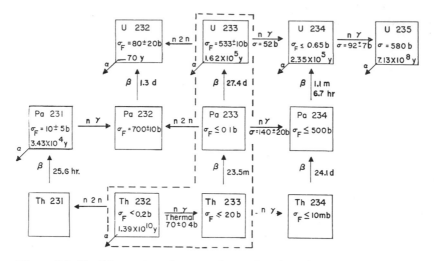

Figure 7-1. Nuclides and nuclear reactions related to the use of thorium in reactors.

tron is absorbed to form the radioactive isotope Th^{233}. This decays with the emission of a beta particle to form protoactinium, which in turn decays with the emission of another beta particle to form U^{233}. The U^{233} is easily fissionable with the slow neutrons which are produced in thermal reactors. With all three fissionable fuels, the result of the capture of a neutron by the fissionable nucleus may be either fission or the production of a heavier nucleus and thus an atom of a different element. The three fissionable materials differ in their characteristics in this regard. U^{233} is the most efficient; for every thermal neutron absorbed by U^{233}, 2.27 neutrons are produced. Of these, one is required to maintain the fission chain-reaction and the other 1.27 are available for absorption by the fertile material, and the various parasitic (non-neutron-producing) absorbing materials in the reactor core. The neutron production ratios (*eta*) for U^{235} and plutonium fuels are about 2.1 and 2.0, respectively.

All nuclear reactors have some parasitic absorbers; fuel cladding, coolant, coolant channel materials, even moderating materials absorb neutrons to a small degree. It is obvious then, that if one could construct a reactor such that these parasitic materials would absorb not more than 0.27 neutron per neutron absorbed by the fuel, the U^{233} system would provide, in addition to the reactor neutron requirements, one neutron for absorption by the fertile thorium to produce a new atom of U^{233}. Thus, new fuel material would be produced at the rate it is being used and breeding would be achieved.

It is equally obvious that in the case of plutonium, breeding can be achieved only if there is no parasitic absorption. However, *eta* changes when so-called fast reactors are considered; these involve neutrons whose energies are millions of times greater than those of the slow neutrons. In these cases, the plutonium fuel cycle may be significantly better than the Th-U^{233} cycle, although both will definitely act as breeders.

Radioactivity of Uranium^{233}

It will be seen in Figure 7-1 that one of the side reactions occurring in a reactor involves the absorption of a neutron by a U^{233} nucleus, the subsequent emission of two neutrons (which is the n, 2n reaction) to produce U^{232}. Also the reaction Pa^{233} (n, 2n) $\rightarrow$ Pa^{232} occurs, with the subsequent beta decay to produce U^{232}. The uranium isotopes cannot be readily separated from one another and thus all U^{233} carries with it a fraction of a per cent of U^{232}. U^{232} in itself is not detrimental, but it does decay by alpha-emission to a series of radioactive products, some of which have high gamma activities. Within a matter of a few weeks after the chemical separation of U^{233} (with its attendant U^{232}) from the irradiated thorium, the gamma levels become sufficiently high that all handling operations must be carefully shielded. This would mean that all fuel fabrication involving U^{233} would have to be done shortly after the chemical separation or that it would have to be done by remote methods in shielded equipment. The latter would have a significant effect on the fuel element cost.

In view of the probability that remote fabrication will be necessary for producing fuel elements containing U^{233}, it would appear that the whole reprocessing cycle would be especially adaptable to new techniques now under study. For a metal fuel, these techniques, which preserve the fuel material in the metallic state, involve melting, contacting with certain scavenging agents, and finally recasting either to fuel slugs or billets for further fabrication into fuel elements. Such techniques remove many of the fission products and reduce the radioactivity somewhat. Since remote fabrication of fuel elements is in any event necessary with U^{233}, the other activities remaining would create no added problem. Similar schemes are also under study for the partial decontamination and remote refabrication of fuel elements containing oxide fuel materials.

It might be mentioned that both U^{233} and plutonium are extremely toxic materials and special handling procedures are required, exclusive of the radiation hazard mentioned above.

Radiation and Thermal Stability

Physical Metallurgy. The basic properties of thorium metal indicate that much better performance would be obtained under irradiation at elevated temperatures than has been the case with uranium. Uranium undergoes a phase transformation at about 660°C from its lower temperature orthorhombic structure to a complex tetragonal structure; and a second transformation at about 770°C to a body-centered cubic structure. Thorium undergoes but one phase transformation, at about 1360°C, from a face-centered cubic to a body-centered cubic structure.

The alpha-beta phase transformation (at 660°C) in uranium is accompanied by a volume increase of about 1.5 per cent. Because of thermal stresses which would be generated in an unalloyed uranium, or low uranium-alloy fuel element, present operating temperatures are limited to just below this level. For thorium fuels, this condition does not exist and much higher operating temperatures may be achieved.

Studies of the thorium-uranium system[1, 2] have indicated the solubility of uranium in thorium to be about 1 per cent at room temperature and about 2 per cent at 1000°C (see Figure 7-2). Since most of the alloys of interest as reactor fuels are in the range of 5 to 10 per cent uranium, they are two-phase alloys. A study of the microstructures indicates that the uranium-rich phase exists as a very fine precipitate dispersed in a thorium-rich matrix in the as-cast samples. On prolonged heating at temperatures of interest for reactor operation (periods of a year at 600 and 800°C), experiments[3] performed out-of-pile demonstrate that this precipitate agglomerates, but in a manner which should not affect the irradiation behavior.

Low Temperature Irradiations of Metallic Fuels. Irradiations were made of thorium-uranium alloys as early as 1953.[4] Three plates of Th-1.2%

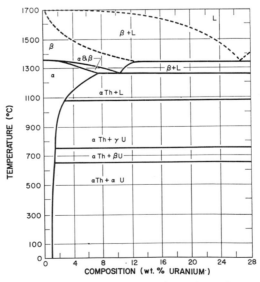

Figure 7-2. Partial thorium-uranium phase diagram.

U^{235} alloy, clad with aluminum, were irradiated in the Materials Testing Reactor (MTR) to a burn-up of approximately 1 per cent of total atoms in the fuel alloy. The plates were about 0.070 in. in thickness by 1 in. wide by 8 in. in length. Fuel irradiation temperatures were relatively low, as cooling was accomplished by direct contact with the MTR process water. Post-irradiation examination indicated excellent dimensional stability and a decrease in density of about 2 per cent. It is of interest to note that the total amount of fissionable material after irradiation was greater than before irradiation. However, this can hardly be considered to be breeding, since this was one small experiment influenced by the reactor in which it was run.

Argonne National Laboratory[5] irradiated a series of thorium-uranium alloys in the MTR at temperatures ranging from 50 to 200°C, with burn-ups up to 4.4 per cent of total atoms in the fuel alloy. Specimens included unalloyed thorium and alloys containing 0.1, 1, and 5 w/o* U^{235}. Dimensional stability was found to be excellent, with volume increases averaging 1 per cent per atomic per cent burn-up.

Elevated Temperature Irradiations of Metallic Fuels. A series of irradiations of thorium-uranium alloys has been conducted by Atomics International[6] at higher temperatures, those of interest to operation of sodium graphite reactors. Fuel samples were $\frac{3}{8}$ in. in diameter by $1\frac{1}{2}$ in. in length and were of an alloy containing 10 w/o U^{235}. By the use of thermal barriers in the capsules containing the specimens, higher fuel central and surface temperatures could be achieved even though the capsule surface was cooled by MTR process water. Design temperatures for the experiments were 1200°F at the center and 1000°F at the surface of the fuel. Central temperatures were measured and surface temperatures calculated. Results of these tests are given in Table 7-1. It will be seen that these alloys can be irradiated to burn-ups of 1 per cent at the temperatures of interest with volume increases of the order of 5 per cent, a volume change which can easily be accommodated by proper fuel element design. Additional tests are under way to investigate effects of higher burn-up and higher temperatures. Central temperatures up to 1500°F will be included in these tests.

Ceramic Fuels. Studies of the thoria-urania (ThO_2-UO_2) systems have been under way for some time as a potential nuclear fuel system. Certain inherent advantages exist with such a ceramic fuel system; (a) corrosion resistance in water, (b) high melting point, and (c) potentially good irradiation behavior, as demonstrated by UO_2 alone. The poor thermal conductivity tends to offset the high melting point advantage and directs fuel element design to short heat paths and large numbers of small fuel bodies.

* w/o = weight per cent

TABLE 7-1. DIMENSIONAL CHANGES IN IRRADIATED TH-10% U SPECIMENS

Burn-up, Total Atom Per Cent[a]	Central Temp. Measured (°F)	Surface Temp. Calculated (°F)	Maximum Increase in Diameter (%)	Increase in Volume[b] (%)
0.3	1059	866	1.6	0.47
0.3	1172	957	0.8	0.78
0.3	1214	991	1.1	0.86
0.3	1219	995	1.5	1.9
0.3	—	—	2.4	1.6
0.55	1071	876	0.7	2.9
0.60	1198	979	1.4	4.7
0.63	1187	970	1.3	4.1
0.66	1252	1022	2.3	5.1
0.68	1130	924	4.4	7.7
0.94	970[c]	800	1.1	3.2
1.00	1030[c]	850	1.5	2.7
1.10	1100[c]	900	1.5	4.4
1.11	1100[c]	900	1.9	4.8
1.14	1100[c]	900	1.7	4.1
1.13	1100[c]	900	1.5	4.9

[a] Based on chemical analyses of some specimens and heat balance on all specimens.

[b] Based on density measurements.

[c] Brief thermocouple life required that these temperatures be calculated.

Irradiations of thoria-urania fuels have been conducted by Argonne National Laboratory.[5, 7] Materials studied included those having UO_2 contents of 2.5, 6.36, and 10 w/o. Specimens were in the form of pellets, approximately 1/4 in. in diameter by 5/8 in. in length, with densities of 85 to 90 per cent of theoretical. Dimensional stability of all samples was excellent. Cracking did occur in the oxide bodies but the fragments were large and, in general, held together by the metal container. The 6.36 and 10 per cent samples were irradiated in tubes of Al-1 % Ni alloy, some with an argon-helium gas mixture in the annulus between pellets and cladding, but most with lead in that annulus. Specimens with the 6.36 per cent UO_2, with lead annulus, cooled directly with 45°C water, were irradiated to burn-ups of several per cent of metal atoms with surface heat fluxes of the order of 500,000 Btu/hr-ft² with no failures or distortion.

Specimens containing 10 per cent UO_2 were irradiated under conditions allowing the cladding to reach temperatures close to the melting point and jacket failures occurred. In one sample there was evidence of melting in the interior of the ceramic fuel body. Comparison was made of lead bonding and gas bonding in two specimens irradiated at somewhat lower temperature (2000°C central and 480°C fuel surface). It was found that the lead tended to hold together the fragments of the ceramic body while the gas did not. A rupture of the cladding occurred in the gas-bonded specimen, apparently caused by the shifting of a ceramic fragment whose sharp edge projected outward from the fuel body.

Description of Thorium-Type Fuel Elements

Most of the thorium "fueled" reactors contemplated at present plan to use U^{235} for the initial fuel loading. As the system operates, U^{233} will be produced and eventually the Th-U^{233} breeding cycle may take over. The improved neutron economy will be achieved slowly as the U^{233} content builds up to the point at which the system is operating almost entirely on the U^{233} cycle. U^{235} will have to be added to the system occasionally to maintain reactivity.

A comparison is given in Table 7-2 of the fuel elements for the several reactors which will use thorium-type fuel elements.

Sodium-Graphite Reactors. The use of thorium-uranium alloy fuel has been given serious consideration for the sodium-cooled, graphite-moderated nuclear power plant system under development by Atomics International. No specific reactor of this type is planned at present, but the Sodium Reactor Experiment (SRE) will be used to study the behavior of Th-U^{235} alloys under reactor conditions of irradiation and temperature. The SRE has been operating to date on a fuel loading of slightly enriched, unalloyed uranium. This will be replaced by a full loading (about 2 tons) of thorium-uranium alloy fuel.

The fuel element for the SRE consists of a cluster of seven rods (see Figure 3-4). Each rod is made up a of thin-walled (0.010 in.) stainless steel tube containing a column of 12 fuel slugs, each 0.750 in. in diameter by 6 in. in length. A 0.010-in. annulus between the cladding tube and the fuel slug is filled with eutectic sodium-potassium alloy (NaK), as is about half the 2-ft space above the fuel column. The balance of the free space is filled with helium at atmospheric pressure. The stainless steel jacket is closed with a stainless steel plug by welding. A 0.092-in. stainless steel wire is wrapped around each of the six outer rods to prevent the rods from touching each other or the coolant tube. The rods are supported by a spider at the upper end, and a similar fixture at the lower end retains them as a bundle. This type of element has been used both for the initial unalloyed uranium loading of SRE, and for the thorium-uranium loading.

The thorium-uranium fuel elements for the second loading of the SRE have been fabricated as a joint effort of Nuclear Metals, Inc., and Atomics International.[8] The alloy used, 7.6 w/o highly enriched uranium in thorium, was selected on the basis of fissionable material requirements to attain criticality in the SRE (with sufficient excess for control and burnout of

TABLE 7-2. FUEL ELEMENT DATA FOR THE THORIUM "FUELED" REACTORS

Reactor	SRE	CETR	Elk River	Borax-IV
Reactor power, thermal Mw	20	585	58	14.4*
Fuel material and composition, (highly enriched U in each case)†	Th-7.6% U Alloy	ThO_2-5.7% UO_2	ThO_2-4.1% UO_2 and ThO_2-9.8% UO_2	ThO_2-6.35% UO_2
Fuel body dimensions (in.)				
Diameter	0.750	0.2625	0.407	0.225
Length	6.0	0.5	0.5	$\frac{5}{16}$-$\frac{5}{8}$
Cladding				
Material†	Type 304-SS	Stainless steel	Type 304 ELC-SS	Al-1% Ni (M-388)
Tube outer diameter (in.)	0.790	0.3125	0.450	0.300
Tube wall thickness (in.)	0.010	0.020	0.020	0.020
Fuel rod assembly				
Annulus, material	NaK	He	He	Pb
Annulus, thickness (in.)	0.010	0.005	0.002	0.012
Fuel column length (in.)	72	95.25	60	24
Number of fuel bodies	12	190	120	~50
Number rods per element	7	206	25	47
Total number of fuel elements	37	120	148	59*
Total number of rods	259	24,720	3,700	2,770
Total number of fuel bodies	3,108	4,700,000	440,000	~120,000

   * Borax-IV was operated under both transient and steady state boiling condition at various power levels, with from 28 to 59 fuel elements. Maximum steady state power achieved was 14.4 Mw with 59 fuel elements, under 300 psi pressure.
   † Material composition given in weight percentages.

fuel). For a full-scale nuclear power plant, lower enrichment would suffice and a lower uranium content could be used. The fabrication process selected for the fuel slugs included alloying and casting of a billet, extrusion to a rod, swaging to final slug diameter, cutting off to slug length, loading into stainless steel tubes, and final assembly into 7-rod fuel elements. The first two of these operations were performed at Nuclear Metals, Inc. and the rods were shipped to Atomics International where the elements were completed. The nature of this alloy required careful consideration of each step from the standpoints of criticality, materials accountability, and radio-activity.

Alloying, melting and casting were performed in 100-lb batches by vacuum induction melting techniques. After the initial ingot was cast, subsequent charges included varying amounts of clean scrap from earlier operations. The melt was held for a short time for solution-preheat at 1750°C and was then poured at 1700°C. The billet was machined lightly (about 0.125 in. removed from the surface) and placed in a copper jacket for extrusion.

The billet was preheated at 870°C for 3 to 4 hr and then extruded through a die preheated to 260°C. The extrusion reduction ratio was 30 to 1. The copper jacket was then removed by pickling, leaving a fuel rod about 0.810 in. in diameter.

The alloy rod was swaged to the required 0.750-in. diameter. This required three passes through the swager (0.790, 0.770, and 0.750 dies). In some cases it was necessary to pass the rod through one die size two or three times to bring it to dimension. After cleaning and repickling, the rod was rough-cut to slug length on a power hack saw. The ends were machined to final length and sharp corners were removed. Some 3800 such slugs were produced.

Yields at the various steps in the process resulted in an over-all yield of acceptable slugs of 60 per cent. However, by recycling the scrap from each of the steps, an over-all yield from raw materials to acceptable slugs of 90 per cent was achieved.

The thorium-uranium alloy fuel slugs were loaded into stainless steel tubes, NaK-bonded, which were sealed to provide the fuel rods described earlier. The rods will be assembled into 7-rod cluster elements at the time they are required for loading into the SRE.

Development work is under way to obtain a lower cost and more efficient method for producing fuel alloy slugs. It is believed that vacuum induction melting and direct casting to slugs can be achieved and that such a process would attain the stated objective. Preliminary experiments have been quite encouraging; it appears probable that thorium-uranium alloy slugs can be cast and used with no further surface finishing required, other than sand blasting or pickling. A group of slugs from these trials is shown in Figure 7-3. Direct casting would be particularly advantageous as a method for remote refabrication of reprocessed, irradiated fuels.

Pressurized Water Reactors. One of the major reactors planned for the use of thorium is that of the Consolidated Edison Company of New York, known as the Consolidated Edison Thorium Reactor (CETR).[9] This reactor is a pressurized water type, cooled by circulating water at about 1500 psi. The reactor alone will produce 163,000 ekw; a conventionally

Figure 7-3. Thorium-7.6 w/o uranium slugs with as-cast surface.

fueled superheater will provide an additional 112,000 ekw. As originally designed, this reactor was to have fuel elements with alternate plates of thorium metal and highly enriched uranium-zirconium alloy, each plate to be clad with Zircaloy-2; thus the U^{233} would be produced in the thorium plates, keeping it separated from the U^{235} in the original fuel plates. About 2 years ago,[10] it was announced that the reactor would be fueled with uranium and thorium oxides rather than the metals, in the interests of improved irradiation stability and corrosion resistance.

The fuel element for the CETR consists of 206 fuel rods arranged in a square lattice, contained in a Zircaloy-2 can (see Figure 7-4). Each rod is a

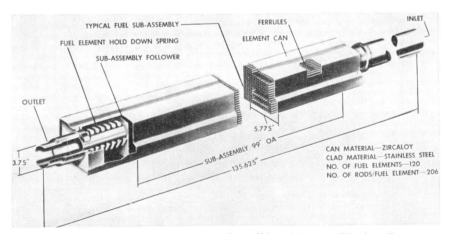

Figure 7-4. Proposed fuel element for Consolidated Edison Thorium Reactor.

stainless steel tube 0.3125-in. OD by 0.020-in. wall loaded with fuel pellets; the active core length is approximately 8 ft. The fuel pellets, each ¼ in. in diameter by ½ in. in length, consist of a homogeneous mixture of ThO_2 and UO_2 of high density. Composition is approximately 5.7 w/o of highly enriched UO_2. Sufficient clearance is provided between the pellets and cladding to allow for assembly and differential expansion. The core will require about 5 million pellets.

Boiling Water Reactors. Another reactor which will use thorium-type fuel elements is that of the Rural Cooperative Power Association of Elk River, Minnesota.[11] The Elk River Nuclear Reactor is a boiling-water, indirect cycle type; that is, the steam generated in the reactor is condensed in the primary side of a heat exchanger to generate steam on the secondary side. This secondary steam is used to drive the turbine. This reactor, supplemented by a separately fired superheater, will produce 22,000 kw of electricity.

The Elk River reactor will use a fuel element consisting of a 5 by 5 array of fuel rods, each rod being a stainless steel tube loaded with thoria-urania pellets. Two compositions will be used to give two levels of enrichment; 148 elements for the initial loading will have pellets with a UO_2 (highly enriched) content of about 4.1 w/o, and 22 spare elements, which are scheduled for insertion as replacement elements after 15 months of operation, will contain 9.8 w/o UO_2, similarly enriched.

The fuel rods will consist of Type 304 ELC stainless steel tubes, 0.450-in. OD by 0.020-in. wall thickness, loaded with 5 ft columns of pellets. The pellets will be 0.407-in. in diameter by ½ in. in length. Helium gas will act as the heat transfer medium between pellets and cladding.

The Borax reactor experiments were designed to study the self-limiting characteristics of water-cooled reactors and the operating characteristics of boiling water reactors. Borax-IV was one of these reactor experiments; one of its purposes was to study a new type fuel element, one which had a relatively long thermal time constant (approximately 0.9 sec as compared to 0.006 sec for earlier Borax experiments). The longer time constant more nearly approached those which would be expected in boiling water power reactors.

The fuel element is constructed rather simply of a group of six aluminum tube plates loaded with thoria-urania pellets.[7] Details of the aluminum tube plate extrusion are shown in Figure 7-5 and the assembly is shown in Figure 7-6. The fuel material is ThO_2 with 6.35 w/o of highly enriched UO_2. The pellets are high-fired, with a 0.225-in. diameter; they vary in length from 5/16 to 5/8 inch. The fuel column in each tube is 24 in. in length.

The tube sheet is an extrusion of an Al-1 w/o Ni alloy (Alcoa M-388) containing 8 tubes which are joined by integral webs, as shown in Figure

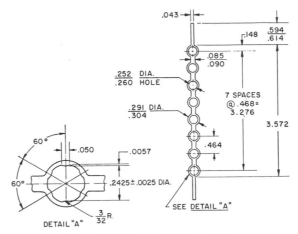

Figure 7-5. Borax-IV tube plate.

Figure 7-6. Borax-IV fuel subassembly.

7-5. Tube diameter tolerances are not particularly tight; relatively large clearance has been allowed between pellet and tube ID. This space is filled with lead to provide suitable heat transfer. Tube closure is accomplished by a high-temperature pressure-brazing technique utilizing elemental silicon in granular form.

The edges of the tube sheets are bent to form flanges, which are spot-welded to M-388 alloy side plates to form the fuel subassembly (see Figure 7-6).

These fuel elements have operated in the Borax-IV reactor in a satisfactory manner for more than a year. The nature of operation of the Borax experiments has limited the burn-up in the fuel elements to rather low levels, perhaps of the order of 0.1 per cent of the total metal atoms in the fuel, or less.

CONCLUSIONS

The number of nuclear reactors in which it is planned to use thorium-type fuel elements is quite limited as compared to the number in which the use of uranium fuel elements is proposed. This can be attributed perhaps to the fact that much of the development efforts in the past have been directed toward the use of uranium. The past few years have seen increased development efforts directed toward the use of thorium; and, from a fuel material standpoint, these have confirmed earlier predictions of excellent behavior. There still remain certain basic nuclear physics questions to be answered and these answers can be obtained only by reactor operating experience. The capability of breeding in the Th-U^{233} fuel cycle in a thermal or epithermal region reactor is perhaps the paramount question.

Even though actual breeding is not achieved, the Th-U^{233} cycle does provide a high conversion ratio and an improved neutron economy. Its use will make available the extensive thorium supplies as potential nuclear fuel, making a significant contribution to the future power producing capacity of the world. The problems involved in handling U^{233} will require attention. New technology is not required, merely the adaptation and improvement of existing technology. Remote fabrication of fuel elements has already been under study in connection with the development of pyrometallurgical reprocessing of irradiated fuels, where only partial decontamination is achieved.

Results of experimental irradiations of thorium-uranium alloys indicate suitable dimensional stability for operation for reasonable fuel life at elevated temperatures. Such alloys give promise of providing an economical fuel cycle for high-temperature reactors such as the sodium-cooled, graphite-moderated reactor type.

It can be expected that the use of thorium in nuclear reactors will increase rather slowly during the next few years as the research and development programs and the few thorium "fueled" reactors yield results which give confidence to its use. After that time, one might expect its use to increase in an exponential manner similar to that which is expected of the nuclear power plant business itself.

References

1. Bentle, G. G., "Study of the Thorium-Uranium Alloy System," Second United Nations International Conference on the Peaceful Uses of Atomic Energy, Geneva (1958) P/706.
2. Wilson, W. B., Austin, A. E., and Schwartz, C. M., "The Solid Solubility of Ura-

nium in Thorium and the Allotropic Transformation of Thorium-Uranium Alloys," BMI-1111 (July 12, 1956).

3. Bentle, G. G., "Annealing Effects in Th-U Alloys," NAA-SR-2969, (June 1, 1959)

4. Carroll, R. M., "The Effects of Reactor Irradiation on Thorium-Uranium Alloy Fuel Plates," ORNL-1938, (Sept. 7, 1955).

5. Kittel, J. H., and Paine, S. H., "Effect of Irradiation on Fuel Materials," Second United Nations International Conference on the Peaceful Uses of Atomic Energy, Geneva (1958) P/1890.

6. Hayward, B. R., Wilkinson, L. E., and Woolsey, C. C., "Radiation Behavior of Fuel Materials for Sodium Graphite Reactors," American Society for Testing Materials Symposium on Radiation Effects on Materials, Volume 3, 1958, pp. 127-134, Special Publication No. 233.

7. Handwerk, J. H., "Ceramic Fuel Elements in the ThO_2-UO_2 and UO_2-PuO_2 Systems," Fuel Elements Conference, Paris, TID-7546, Book 2, pp. 526–548 (Nov. 1957).

8. Hayward, B. R., and Corzine, P., "Thorium-Uranium Fuel Elements for SRE," Second United Nations International Conference on the Peaceful Uses of Atomic Energy, Geneva (1958) P/785.

9. Milne, G. R., Ward, F. R., and Stoller, S. M., "The Consolidated Edison Company of New York Nuclear Electric Generating Station," Second United Nations International Conference on the Peaceful Uses of Atomic Energy, Geneva (1958) P/1885.

10. "New Core Design for Con. Ed.: Higher Power, Higher Price," *Nucleonics*, **15**, No. 3, R1, (March 1957).

11. Kramer, A. W., "Boiling Water Reactors," pp. 507–522, Reading, Mass., Addison-Wesley Publishing Co., Inc., 1958.

General References

1. Bentle, G. G., "A Physical Metallurgical Study of Thorium-Rich, Thorium-Uranium Alloys," NAA-SR-2069 (Jan. 15, 1958).

2. Cuthbert, F. L., "Thorium Production Technology," Reading, Mass., Addison-Wesley Publishing Co., Inc., 1958.

3. Handwerk, J. H., Hoenig, C. L., and Lied, R. C., "Manufacture of the ThO_2-UO_2 Ceramic Fuel Pellets for BORAX-IV," ANL-5678 (Aug. 1957).

4. Hayward, B. R., and Bentle G. G., "Effect of Burnup on Metallic Fuel Elements Operating at Elevated Temperature," Second United Nations International Conference on the Peaceful Uses of Atomic Energy, Geneva (1958) P/617.

5. Howe, J. P., "The Role of Thorium in the Nuclear Field," in "The Metal Thorium;" Proceedings of the Conference on Thorium Held October 11, 1956 at Cleveland, Ohio. American Society for Metals, Cleveland, 1958.

6. Kittel, J. H., and Handwerk, J. H., "Preliminary Irradiations of the Ceramic Fuels UO_2, UO_2-Zr, and ThO_2-UO_2," ANL-5675 (Oct. 1958).

7. Kratzer, M. B., "U. S. Export Policies," *Nucleonics*, **16**, No. 8, 82–85 (Aug. 1958).

8. Manowitz, B., "Thorium," *Nucleonics*, **16**, No. 8, 91–95 (Aug. 1958).

9. Mash, D. R., and Ottenberg, A., "Status and Future Requirements for the Uranium-233 Power Reactor Program," ASAE-S-4 (July 1958).

10. Rough, F. A., and Bauer, A. A., "Constitution of Uranium and Thorium Alloys," BMI-1300 (June 2, 1958).

11. Starr, C., and Dickinson, R. W., "Sodium Graphite Reactors," Reading, Mass., Addison-Wesley Publishing Co., Inc., 1958.

12. Walker, D. E., Noland, R. A., McCuaig, F. D., and Stone, C. C., "BORAX-IV Reactor: Manufacture of Fuel and Blanket Elements," ANL-5721 (March 1958).
13. Woolsey, C. C., "High-Temperature Irradiation of Thorium-Uranium Alloys," Thorium-Uranium-233 Symposium, Sponsored by U.S. AEC at Brookhaven National Laboratory, January 9–10, 1958, BNL-483 (1958) pp. 121–123.
14. Woolsey, C. C., "Role of Thorium in Atomic Energy," Paper given at AIME Regional Reactive Metals Conference, Los Angeles, May 29, 1957.

8. PLUTONIUM FUEL ELEMENTS*

R. E. TATE

Los Alamos Scientific Laboratory, University of California
Los Alamos, New Mexico

Full utilization of that portion of the world's energy resources represented by naturally occurring uranium will be realized only if practical plutonium-fueled breeder reactors are developed. Conversion of U^{238} to plutonium by breeding, and the subsequent utilization of the plutonium for production of power will extend the world's uranium fuel reserves by a factor of more than 100. Only in recent years, however, has serious attention been given to the development of plutonium-fueled reactors and of plutonium-bearing fuel materials. Two principal reasons may be cited for the lag in plutonium fuel technology. First, plutonium is a man-made element that has been available in relatively large amounts only for military uses. Second, the extremely toxic nature of plutonium and plutonium-bearing materials greatly complicates their handling and fabrication.

There are at least two general concepts of using plutonium as a reactor fuel. In one, plutonium is recycled in a thermal heterogeneous reactor.[1, 2, 3, 4] Although a power reactor can be designed to operate on natural uranium, there are advantages to enriching the core. Enrichment of a core extends the useful life of a fuel loading by increasing its initial reactivity; it also permits attainment of greater power densities per unit of core volume, and thus reduces the capital cost per unit of power produced. Plutonium can provide a limited amount of fuel enrichment in a self-sustaining operation with natural uranium feed, independent of isotope separation. A uniform enrichment implies that all fuel elements contain plutonium and that all elements must be fabricated under conditions dictated by the plutonium health hazard. Spike enrichment, in which some of the fuel elements of a loading contain plutonium dispersed in an inert matrix, requires a high through-put of the enriched elements. An intermediate possibility is zone enrichment, in which a uranium-plutonium mixture is used in selected regions of the reactor.

Spike enrichment has been used for some time in Canada.[5] The Hanford

---

* Work done under the auspices of the U. S. Atomic Energy Commission.

Laboratory has embarked on a program of developing technology for recycling plutonium economically[1]; and an experimental reactor, the Plutonium Recycle Test Reactor (PRTR), is being built as a part of this program.

The second concept is the plutonium-fueled fast reactor. It has been shown that although plutonium is slightly inferior to U^{235} as a thermal reactor fuel on the basis of its nuclear characteristics, it is markedly superior to U^{235} as a fast reactor fuel.[6]

The Los Alamos Fast Reactor,[7, 8] built in 1946 but now dismantled, was the first plutonium-fueled reactor and also the first fast reactor. Authors in the USSR have described three plutonium-fueled fast reactors, BR-1, BR-2, and BR-5.[9, 10] At Los Alamos, a medium-size plutonium-fueled fast reactor, the Los Alamos Molten Plutonium Reactor Experiment (LAMPRE),[11] is now under construction. Several fast reactors that eventually can be converted to use plutonium fuel are now being designed or constructed. These include EBR-II,[12] the Enrico Fermi Reactor,[13] and the Dounreay Reactor.[14]

The properties of plutonium have been reviewed by Coffinberry and Waldron,[15] by Konobeevsky,[16] and by Bagley[17] and others. A brief examination of these properties soon leads to the conclusion that unalloyed plutonium is unattractive as a straight replacement for uranium in a power reactor. The thermal expansion discontinuities resulting from the five solid state transformations of plutonium, and the high positive and negative expansion coefficients of some of the phases, create a severe problem of dimensional stability. The melting point of plutonium is relatively low (640°C) and the thermal conductivity is quite low (about 0.02 cal/cm/ sec/°C at room temperature).[18] These two properties seriously limit the power density that can be achieved.

In selecting elements to be used for diluting plutonium, the nuclear properties of these elements must be considered. Kiehn[6] has suggested that a good rule to guide metallurgists in making such selection would be to make the macroscopic neutron cross section of the diluent materials less than 10 per cent of the plutonium macroscopic fission cross section, if the absorber is not U^{238}. Thermal neutron cross sections should be used for thermal reactor designs, and fast neutron cross sections used for the design of fast reactors.

An analysis of the effect of alloy additions on the plutonium inventory requirement for the spherical core of a fast reactor has recently been published by Waber *et al.*[19] They have shown that at equivalent atomic per cent dilutions certain low density elements (e.g., strontium and barium) require large inventories of fissionable material, while other elements (e.g., cobalt and ruthenium) do not increase the inventory requirements by a large factor.

In designing a useful fuel element a number of engineering and economic factors must be considered. Most important are these five items:

1. *Simple Fabrication.* The simpler the fabrication as expressed in fabrication cost and in design reliability, the more acceptable the element.

2. *Dimensional Stability.* Dimensional changes produced by thermal cycling and/or radiation damage should be minimized in order to obtain a fuel element whose life is determined only by the loss of reactivity.

3. *Retention of Reactor Products.* Obviously, the hazardous fission products and transuranic elements which result from reactor operation must be kept under strict control.

4. *Compatibility With Can and Coolant.* Reaction between the fuel element and its container, under the most severe operating conditions of the reactor, must be minimized so that any reaction will not be a limiting factor in achieving maximum fuel burn-up. In the unlikely but possible occurrence of container failure, the coolant and fuel material must not react together catastrophically.

5. *Economical Reprocessing.* Unless the unused fuel can be returned to the reactor fuel cycle economically, the fuel element may not find acceptance.

CHRONOLOGICAL REVIEW OF PLUTONIUM-FUELED REACTORS

A number of reactors fueled either partially or completely with plutonium have been designed and built, or are under construction. Chronologically, in this section, brief descriptions of these reactors are presented; and, where available, some pertinent details of the fuel element fabrication are included. Further details may be found in the references cited.

The Los Alamos Fast Reactor (U.S.A.)

Operation of the Los Alamos Fast Reactor[7, 8] began in November of 1946 at a power of 10 kw, but was increased to 25 kw in 1949. This reactor was both the first fast neutron reactor and the first to be fueled with plutonium. The reactor core consisted of a number of steel-clad, stabilized delta-phase plutonium rods. Mercury was used as a coolant to remove heat from the core.

Fuel rods of stabilized delta-phase plutonium, each weighing approximately 450 g, were cast and then machined to dimensions. In order to minimize the health hazard in subsequent handling, these rods were plated with a 0.003-in. thick nickel coat by decomposition of nickel carbonyl. Dimensions of the plated rod were 0.647 ± 0.002 in. in diameter and 5.500 ± 0.005 in. long. Each plated rod was inserted in an annealed, mild steel can having a 0.020-in. wall thickness. A uranium wafer having a recess for fission gas accumulation was used to cover the end of the plated plutonium rod (see Figure 8-1) in order to prevent possible serious plutonium contamination of the weld during subsequent welding of the mild steel cap to the container. The rod and container assembly was sized through a die to insure a tight fit between can and fuel rod. The final can diameter was 0.687 inch. The sized can was then trimmed to length and the cap welded in place. The loading and welding operations were performed in a helium atmosphere.

The reactor was dismantled in 1953, one of the reasons being the failure of a fuel rod and the resulting contamination of the coolant.[20, 21]

The NRX Reactor (Canada)

The NRX reactor[22, 23] is a 30-Mw thermal reactor used for research purposes at Chalk River, Ontario. The heavy water moderator is contained in a tank, called a calandria, which is pierced by a large number of vertical tubes. These tubes contain aluminum-clad fuel rods, normally of natural uranium, and each is surrounded by a concentric channel for cooling-water circulation. A concentric air gap exists between the water-cooling channel and the calandria tube.

In 1951 it was decided to replace some of the uranium elements with elements containing plutonium in order to enrich or spike the reactor and to produce higher plutonium isotopes for reactor-physics studies. This program has continued,[5] and three successive models of the spike elements

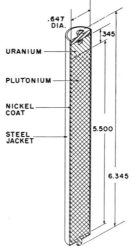

(*Courtesy Los Alamos Scientific Laboratory*)

Figure 8-1. Sketch of the fuel element used in the Los Alamos Fast Reactor.

have been evolved. In the first model, of which three assembly units were fabricated, plutonium-aluminum alloys were cast into aluminum cans which were sealed by casting aluminum plugs in place. Eleven cans were screwed together to make one assembly 300 cm (118 in.) long, and this assembly was jacketed in a standard, three-finned, aluminum fuel-element sheath. The approximately sine-squared distribution of the plutonium along the length of the rod was accomplished by using alloy compositions ranging from 0.5 to 20.8 w/o* plutonium in the various cans. The three fuel elements were irradiated to high burn-ups without incident.

In the second design, the dilute plutonium alloy, which contributed little excess reactivity and which was present at the ends of the element, was replaced by uranium. The central section was composed of a uniform aluminum alloy containing 20 w/o plutonium. Eighteen such composite elements were irradiated and several failed. Failure has been attributed to the inadequate transfer of heat between the doubly canned alloy and the coolant. The severe thermal gradients that were generated were accompanied by thermal ratcheting, melting of the alloy, and sheath distortions.

The third and current design attempts to minimize the aforementioned difficulties by (1) eliminating the can and placing the alloy directly in the fuel element sheath, and (2) reducing the plutonium content of the aluminum alloy to 3.7 w/o to correspond to a maximum heat-transfer flux of 190 watts/cm² (6×10^5 Btu/ft²/hr) across the aluminum-water interface. This design is illustrated in Figure 8-2.

Wauchope[24, 25] has described the fabrication of these elements. Using the method developed by Runnalls[26] plutonium dioxide is reduced in the presence of cryolite with sufficient excess aluminum to produce an alloy of the desired composition. These alloy reduction billets are then induction-melted in graphite crucibles. No fluxes or inert gas cover are used within the protective glove box. The melt is poured into a tilted, heavy graphite mold to form an ingot about 12 in. long by 1.41 in. in diameter and having about 2.5 in. of pipe. Each ingot weights about 765 g and contains approximately 27.2 g of plutonium. A variation of about 5 per cent in the plutonium concentration between top and bottom of the ingots has been noted. The cast slugs are machined to a diameter of 1.360 ± 0.002 in. and a length of 9.022 ± 0.005 inches. Compressed air, instead of carbon tetrachloride, is used as a coolant in the machining operations. Earlier, when carbon tetrachloride was used as the coolant, difficulties were experienced because of a reaction between the hot aluminum chips and the carbon tetrachloride. The finished slugs are cleaned with carbon tetrachloride and removed from the glove box into polyethylene bags. Radiographic inspection completes preparation of the slug.

* w/o = weight per cent, and a/o = atomic per cent.

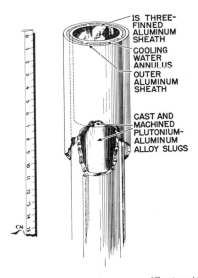

IS THREE-FINNED ALUMINUM SHEATH

COOLING WATER ANNULUS

OUTER ALUMINUM SHEATH

CAST AND MACHINED PLUTONIUM-ALUMINUM ALLOY SLUGS

(Courtesy Atomic Energy of Canada, Ltd.)

Figure 8-2. Cut-away drawing of the plutonium-alloy rod, canned in a single operation, used in the NRX reactor.

The inner end-pieces of aluminum and 12 alloy slugs are loaded into a finned, aluminum NRX fuel sheath in a chemical fume hood. The inner diameter of the sheath is 1.410 in. and the wall thickness is 0.080 inch. The inside of the open end of the sheath is decontaminated and closed with a one-hole rubber stopper into which a piece of copper tubing has been inserted. The assembly is evacuated by means of a mechanical vacuum pump, and is heated to 160°C where it is held for 4 hours to insure removal of traces of water vapor from the interior. After the element cools to room temperature, the rubber stopper is replaced with a felt wiper plug. The assembly is then transferred to a drawbench located in an open shop where it is drawn to give the sheath an inner diameter of 1.360 in. and insure that it is in close contact with the slugs. It has been found necessary to exert pressure on the slugs to prevent gaps being formed between them during the drawing operation. This has been accomplished most easily by having a strong man exert pressure on the wiper plug with a stout stick.

The sheath is then trimmed to length, the inside portion of the end is decontaminated, and closure is accomplished by spinning the end of the sheath over the inner end-pieces. Outer end-fittings are screwed in place and welded to the sheath. The element is evacuated through a vent and is checked with a mass spectrometer leak detector. Then the vent is closed by welding. As a final check on the integrity of the sheath, the element is placed in a "Pyrex" column partially filled with enough ethylene glycol to cover the element, and the air above the liquid is evacuated. Leaks can then be located by observing bubbles rising through the liquid. This type of element has performed satisfactorily for more than a year.

The Zero Energy Fast Reactor (U.K.)

The Zero Energy Fast Reactor (ZEPHYR)[27, 28] at Harwell is an experimental facility for the study of fast neutron systems. Operation of this reactor began in 1954. No provision has been made for cooling the core, and therefore the maximum operating power level is limited to a few watts. The core is composed of plutonium rods and natural uranium rods in a cylindrical assembly having a height and diameter of about 15 cm (6 in.). Each plutonium fuel rod[29] consists of two cylinders of plutonium placed end to end to form a single rod about the size of an ordinary lead pencil. These rods are sheathed in nickel.

The BR-1 Reactor (U.S.S.R.)

The BR-1 reactor[9, 30] is a small, 30-watt, fast neutron reactor which began operation in 1955 at the Russian Institute of Physics. The core, composed of plutonium rods and some uranium rods, is a cylinder of about 13 cm (5.1 in.) in height and in diameter. Because of the low power level no special cooling system has been provided. The plutonium fuel rods are 10 mm (0.395 in.) in diameter and 130 mm (5.1 in. long) These rods are sealed in stainless steel cans having outside diameters of 10.8 mm (0.425 in.). This reactor has been used in a large number of physics studies of fast neutron systems.

The Materials Testing Reactor (U.S.A.)

The Materials Testing Reactor (MTR)[31, 32] is a thermal reactor designed to provide a high neutron flux for experimental purposes. The original design power of the reactor was 30 Mw, but this has now been increased to 40. A plate-type fuel element[33] was developed especially for this reactor. In this element, the aluminum-clad, fuel-bearing plates are approximately 2.8 in. wide by 24 in. long. Eighteen plates are stacked, separated from each other by 0.11 in. clearance, and are brazed into solid aluminum side frames. The form of the element is an open-ended, long, rectangular box having an approximate 3-in. by 3-in. cross-sectional area. Adaptors are fitted to each end of the element. The elements are then stacked vertically in the reactor tank in a lattice array, and ordinary water is pumped upward through the elements to act as both coolant and moderator. This type of element is used with forced circulation in the MTR, and with convection cooling in the lower powered pool-type reactors.

In 1956 it became desirable to irradiate plutonium to form significant quantities of higher plutonium isotopes and transplutonic elements. To accomplish this irradiation in a reasonable length of time it was decided to fabricate a limited number of MTR type fuel elements in which plutonium replaced the enriched uranium normally used.

The first plutonium-bearing MTR fuel elements[34] were manufactured as a joint effort by the Los Alamos Scientific Laboratory and the Oak Ridge National Laboratory. The procedure used followed that developed at Oak Ridge for the uranium fuel elements as closely as the properties of plutonium would permit.

At Los Alamos an aluminum alloy containing 10 w/o plutonium was prepared by combination of the elements and was cast into a water-cooled copper mold in a vacuum furnace to form a slab ingot 2.5 in. by 6 in. by 0.75 in. thick. Chill casting was deemed necessary to minimize gravity segregation. After radiographic inspection of the ingot and chemical analysis of samples taken from the top and bottom of the casting, the scalped ingots were heated in a furnace operating at 550°C (1022°F) and were hot-rolled in air to a thickness of approximately 0.45 in. Reductions of about 50 mils per pass were made. The hot-rolled plates were then cold-rolled to a thickness of 0.370 in., following a rolling schedule of 5 to 7 mils reduction per pass. These cold-rolled plates were straightened and radiographed. Cores 2.10 in. by 2.19 in. by 0.370 in. were punched from the flawless areas of the plates with a conventional punch and die set. The density of each core was determined by the water displacement method in order to check the alloy composition. The operations to this point were performed in suitably equipped glove boxes.

Acceptable cores, within the composition limits 9.5 to 10.5 w/o plutonium, were cleaned in a nitric-hydrofluoric acid bath, rinsed with hot water and air-dried. The cores were then pressed into holes in aluminum core plates by means of a 20-ton press. These core plates had been prepared with the identical die set used later for punching the cores. The complete billet, consisting of a core, core plate, and top and bottom cover plates, shown in Figure 8-3, was assembled and clamped to hold it together for welding. The cleaning and assembly operations were performed in chemical fume hoods.

The periphery of the billet was manually welded in a closed room. Because of the chemically cleaned core surface, the low oxidation rate of the fuel alloy, and careful handling, no contamination was detected as a result of this operation. The billet fabrication was completed by leak checking of the billets with a mass spectrometer leak tester, and sealing the evacuation tube after pumping the billet assembly to a pressure of less than 1 μ while maintaining the temperature at 540°C (1004°F).

Fabrication of the billets into fuel elements was performed at Oak Ridge

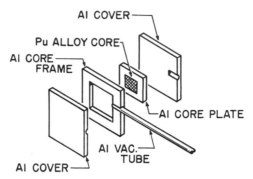

(Courtesy Los Alamos Scientific Laboratory)

Figure 8-3. Component parts of a billet assembly for making MTR-type fuel elements containing plutonium.

and followed rather closely the procedure[33] for uranium fuel elements. This procedure consisted of hot rolling the billet to 0.070-in. thickness to achieve a bond between core and aluminum cladding. Some of the excess cladding material was then sheared away. The plates were coated with a proprietary flux and annealed at 590°C to permit escape of entrapped hydrogen. The flux-annealed plates were rolled at room temperature to the final thickness, nominally 0.060 in. Plates were fluoroscoped to locate the core and to reveal any defects. Most of the excess cladding metal was sheared away and the final dimensions of the fuel plate were obtained by milling a stack of sheared plates. The plates were blister-tested in the conventional manner and, after being given the correct curvature, were assembled in suitable jigs. Furnace brazing of the assembly was the final operation.

These fuel elements have been used without incident in the MTR, some having been used to the extent that an estimated 70 per cent of the plutonium atoms have been consumed.

In 1957 it was decided to demonstrate the feasibility of operating the MTR entirely on plutonium. This has been recently accomplished[35] by using a loading of 27 elements fabricated at the Hanford Laboratories. The general procedure outlined above was used, but certain details[36] differed radically from those of previously used techniques. The nominal alloy composition was changed to 14 w/o plutonium. The alloying and casting were performed in an air-atmosphere glove box; first, aluminum was melted and then plutonium was added while the melt was stirred with a graphite rod. Cylindrical ingots 1¼ in. diameter by 8 in. long were cast by hand-pouring into tilted graphite molds, care being taken to maintain the pouring rate equal to the freezing rate. Samples for chemical analysis were taken from the top and bottom of each ingot. Analyzed ingots were sawed into disks, the size of the disks being adjusted so that each contained a nominal

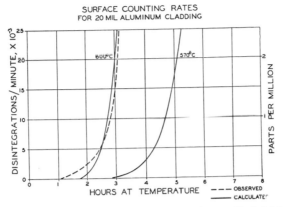

SURFACE COUNTING RATES
FOR 20 MIL ALUMINUM CLADDING

(Courtesy Hanford Laboratories Operation)

Figure 8-4. Diffusion of plutonium in aluminum.

weight of 8.16 g of plutonium. These disks were then press forged at 350°C under a load of 125 tons to form cores with tapered leading and trailing edges. The cores were thoroughly cleaned using both chemical and ultrasonic methods until a smear test for contamination was negative. Three sides of the evacuated billet assembly were joined using automatic welding equipment, an operation that takes 9 sec per pass. The evacuation tube and the fourth side were manually welded to finish sealing the enclosure.

During fabrication of the billets into fuel plates, difficulty was experienced with alpha contamination of the plates. The contamination was attributed to diffusion of the plutonium through the aluminum cladding at elevated temperature. Calculated and observed surface counting rates as a function of time at elevated temperature have been recently obtained in controlled experiments[40] and are presented in Figure 8-4. Difficulty with diffusion was eliminated by reducing the temperatures of the flux annealing and blister-testing cycles and reducing to a minimum the time that the plates were held at elevated temperatures.

A core of 27 elements was fabricated, including four control or shim elements. The shim elements differed from the bulk of the elements by having fewer fuel-bearing plates and by having a nominal composition of 12 w/o plutonium. The operation of the reactor on its plutonium loading is described by a report[37] now in preparation.

The BR-2 Reactor (U.S.S.R.)

A fast neutron research reactor, designated BR-2,[9, 10] began operation in 1956 at the Russian Institute of Physics. The power level of this reactor was nominally 150 kw, but could be increased to a maximum of 200 kw. The heat was removed by circulating mercury through the core. The core was similar to that of the BR-1 reactor. The plutonium fuel rods were 10 mm (0.395 in.) in diameter and 130 mm (5.1 in.) long. The rods were enclosed in sealed, stainless steel tubes having a wall thickness of 0.3 mm (0.015 in.). The core also contained depleted uranium rods similar in design to the plutonium rods. This reactor has now been dismantled to make room for the more powerful BR-5 reactor.

Zero Power Thermal Reactor Experiments (U.K.)

A large number of elements for zero power, thermal reactor experiments has been manufactured[38] at the Atomic Weapons Research Establishment at Aldermaston. These elements are made of an aluminum alloy containing 20 w/o plutonium and are in the form of strips 69.2 cm (27.2 in.) long, 2.93 cm (1.15 in.) wide, and 0.051 cm (0.020 in.) thick. Each strip is inserted in an aluminum sheath which has a 0.025-cm (0.010 in.) wall thickness, and which is flattened and welded at each end. Since there are no heat transfer requirements it is unnecessary to bond the core and sheath.

The elements are fabricated in an integrated series of glove boxes, in which some of the fabricating equipment is semiautomatic. Generally, air atmosphere is used in the glove boxes, except that argon is used in the casting operation to minimize oxidation of the plutonium.

Pure aluminum is melted in a graphite crucible placed in a resistance-heated pot furnace. At 900°C, plutonium rods are added one by one to the melt by means of a charging device operated by a servo mechanism. During the plutonium addition the melt is agitated violently by mechanical stirring. After the alloy is prepared, the temperature is reduced to 850°C and ten ingots 7 cm (2.75 in.) by 20 cm (7.88 in.) by 0.65 cm (0.25 in.) are cast from each heat by tapping the bottom of the crucible. Graphite molds, coated with "dag" and set upon a water-cooled copper base, are used. After the ingots are removed from the mold, the sprues are cut off with a mechanical saw, and the ingots are radiographed with Ir[192] in the arrangement illustrated in Figure 8-5.

The ingots are then hot-rolled to a thickness of 0.076 cm (0.030 in.) in a small, enclosed rolling mill. The hot-rolled strips are slit longitudinally with a shear and the resulting pieces are cold-rolled to a final thickness of 0.051 cm (0.020 in.). The finished strips are cut to width on a double-bladed shear and then to length on a similar shear. Each strip is inspected for dimension, cleaned with trichloroethylene, weighed, and then passed through an x-ray densitometer to determine the uniformity of the plutonium content. This device, illustrated in Figure 8-6, uses a double beam of monochromatic x-rays. One beam is transmitted through the moving strip over an area of 0.5 cm by 2.5 cm (0.2 in. by 1 in.), and the intensity of the transmitted beam is recorded from a scintillometer detection circuit. The other

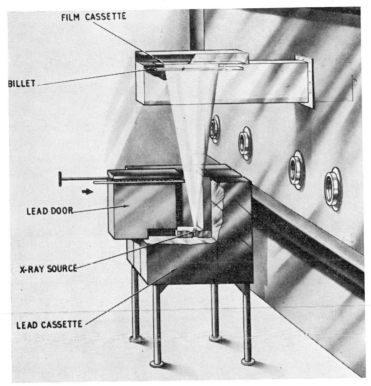

FILM CASSETTE

BILLET

LEAD DOOR

X-RAY SOURCE

LEAD CASSETTE

(Courtesy Atomic Weapons Research Establishment

Figure 8-5. Sketch showing the method used to radiograph plutonium-aluminum alloy billets at the Atomic Weapons Research Establishment, U. K.

beam is transmitted through a standard sample and is also recorded from a similar circuit. The difference between the two scintillometer outputs is a measure of the plutonium content of the strip.

The sheath is fabricated by drawing and flattening commercially pure aluminum tubing. One end is welded shut, and is tested by immersing the welded end of the pressurized tube in water. Sheaths which pass inspection are placed in the glove box train and are positioned in the loading machine. This machine inserts the plutonium alloy strip into the sheath, presses the sheath into contact with the strip to expel most of the air, and crimps the open end for welding. The loaded assembly is repositioned under the automatic welding head and the sheath is closed by argon arc welding. The integrity of the weld is verified by inserting the elements in groups of five into a glass vessel containing enough ethylene glycol to cover the elements, and evacuating the vessel. Bubbles in the liquid indicate the location of any leaks in the sheath.

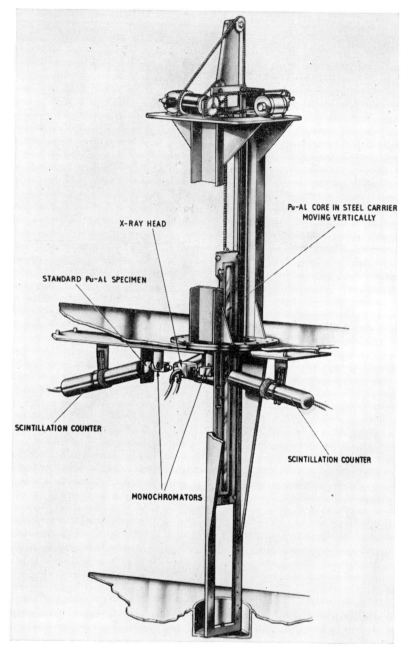

(*Courtesy Atomic Weapons Research Establishment*)

Figure 8-6. Sketch showing the x-ray equipment used to determine the uniformity of plutonium content in plutonium-aluminum alloy strip.

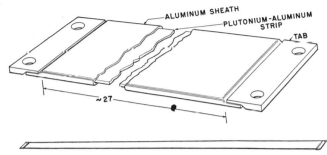

(*Courtesy Atomic Weapons Research Establishment*)

Figure 8-7. Cut-away sketch of the completed AWRE fuel element.

The elements are decontaminated by immersing them for 20 min. at 70°C in a bath containing a 1 per cent solution of complexing agents known as SDG3 powder. The elements are then washed in hot water for 20 min. and dried in hot air. The finished elements leave the glove box via an alpha-contamination inspection machine. Rollers move an element through a slit in the glove box and between two alpha-particle detection tubes. If the contamination level is below 50 disintegrations per minute (dpm), the element moves out of the box; if the count level exceeds 50 dpm, the machine reverses and rapidly withdraws the element into the box for recleaning. Four minutes are required for each element to pass through the exit counters. Figure 8-7 shows the completed element.

The BR-5 Reactor (U.S.S.R.)

The BR-5 reactor,[9] recently built to take the place of the now dismantled BR-2 reactor, is a medium-power fast reactor designed to operate at 5 Mw. It utilizes sodium at a maximum temperature of 500°C as a heat-transfer medium, and plutonium oxide as a fuel. This reactor will provide experience for the design of a pilot, industrial atomic-power station based on a fast reactor designated as BN-50. The BR-5 reactor has as its objectives (1) testing of fuel and shield elements, (2) gaining experience with a radioactive sodium heat-transfer system, and (3) nuclear and material-testing studies in a high fast-neutron flux.

The fuel element for this reactor is a stainless steel (designation IXI-8H9T) tube filled with briquettes of sintered plutonium oxide. The dimensions of the element are: 5 mm (0.195 in.) OD, 0.4 mm (0.016 in.) wall thickness, and 280 mm (11 in.) length of active material. A cavity 2 to 3 mm ($\sim$0.1 in.) in length is provided in the upper end of the tube to allow for thermal expansion. The tube is filled with helium to a pressure of one atmosphere absolute to improve the heat transfer properties. Plugs, welded in place at each end, seal the tube.

Nineteen elements are installed in a subassembly made from hexagonal stainless steel tubing. This tubing has a dimension of 26 mm (1 in.) across flats and a wall thickness of 0.5 mm (0.020 in.). The fuel elements are installed in grids fastened near the top and bottom of the subassembly. The bottom of the subassembly has a conical nozzle for centering in a hole in the reactor lattice, and the top of the subassembly has a cone fitted to engage a recharging mechanism. The reactor core is composed of 80 subassemblies.

Located around the core is an internal reflector composed of subassemblies loaded with uranium rods. These differ from the core subassemblies in that each contains seven uranium elements in 9-mm (0.354 in.) diameter cans, and that the thermal bonding medium is a sodium-potassium alloy. Heat is removed from the core and the internal reflector by pumping sodium upward through the subassemblies.

The Plutonium Recycle Test Reactor (U.S.A.)

The Plutonium Recycle Test Reactor (PRTR)[1, 39] is under construction at the Hanford Laboratories and is scheduled to be operational in 1960. Among its objectives are (1) direct investigation of long-term irradiation on plutonium reactivity, (2) irradiation testing of plutonium-bearing fuel elements, and (3) the production of prototype irradiated fuels for pilot plant reprocessing and refabrication studies. The PRTR is a 70 Mw thermal neutron reactor moderated by heavy water in an unpressurized calandria. Heat will be removed by circulating pressurized heavy water through process tubes running through the 85 vertical channels in the calandria. Fuel elements will be suspended in the process tubes from hangers located at the outlet nozzles.

The plans for the initial loading of the reactor call for 35 per cent of the fuel to be in the form of plutonium spike elements and the remainder to be natural uranium dioxide. Subsequent loadings may be uniformly enriched. The plutonium fuel elements are to have the 19-rod geometry illustrated in Figure 8-8. In this element, the rod cluster contains individual rods of fuel material, ½ in. in diameter by about 7 ft long, clad in Zircaloy-2. An aluminum alloy containing about 1.7 w/o plutonium will be used as the initial fuel material. Injection casting and extrusion are considered to be potential production methods for the fabrication of the rods. The fuel and cladding will be unbonded, and differential thermal expansion will be relied upon to provide an adequate heat-transfer path. A prototype element has been fabricated using foot-long rod sections prepared by precision casting,[40] but the details have not yet been published.

Some experience in fabricating this low-plutonium material has been reported[41] as a result of preparing test pieces for lattice tests in support of

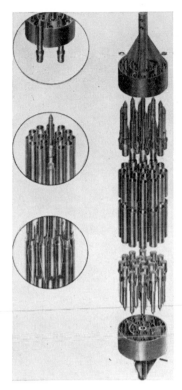

(*Courtesy Hanford Laboratory Operation*)

Figure 8-8. Drawing of the 19-rod cluster for the Plutonium Recycle Test Reactor fuel element.

the PRTR physics calculations. Rods, $\frac{1}{2}$ in. in diameter, of an aluminum alloy containing 1.7 w/o plutonium were vacuum-cast, machined, and then sealed in aluminum or Zircaloy tubes by welding end-plugs in place. The mold was designed so that eight 11-in.-long cylindrical cavities arranged in a circular pattern could be filled from a central pouring basin. A water-cooled chill plate, which had been provided on the bottom of the mold to promote directional solidification, was found to be unnecessary in avoiding centerline shrinkage in the rods. In casting, the alloy was found to be sensitive to hot tearing, but a taper of $\frac{1}{8}$ in./ft in the graphite mold eliminated this difficulty. In comparing the pure aluminum castings, which were made to prove the equipment, with the alloy castings, it was observed that the plutonium addition resulted in some grain refinement. A statistical analysis of the analytical chemistry results showed that the bottom ends of the rods were richer in plutonium than the tops by a difference of 0.035 w/o.

The Experimental Breeder Reactor II (U.S.A.)

The Experimental Breeder Reactor-II (EBR-II)[12] is, as the name suggests, a reactor designed to produce fissile material. This reactor of the Argonne National Laboratory, scheduled for operation at the Idaho Testing Station site in 1960, is a sodium-cooled, fast neutron reactor having a power rating of 62.5 Mw. A principal feature of this installation is a plant which will test not only a complete power cycle including reactor plant and power plant, but also a complete fuel cycle, including facilities to reprocess and refabricate the fuel for reloading the reactor. To avoid a prohibitively large fuel inventory, complete decontamination of the fuel by conventional aqueous methods will not be performed. Instead, pyrometallurgical reprocessing, resulting in partial decontamination, will be used. New methods suitable for remote control reprocessing and refabrication will be required to handle this intensely radioactive fuel.

The pyrometallurgical refining process consists of holding the metal in a drossing crucible at a sufficiently high temperature to oxidize the more reactive elements and to volatilize those elements having high vapor pressures. After repeated irradiation and reprocessing cycles, the refined metal is expected to reach an equilibrium composition determined by the amount of new fuel added in each cycle. For the plutonium-uranium alloy scheduled for the second or Mark II loading of this reactor (the initial or Mark I loading will not contain plutonium), the predicted equilibrium composition is shown in Table 8-1. With the exception of zirconium, the fission product elements are beneficial to the alloy, and the fuel material has been found to be comparatively resistant to irradiation damage.

The fuel element[42] for EBR-II will be an alloy pin 0.144-in. in diameter by 14.22 in long. This pin will be contained in a sealed, stainless steel tube

TABLE 8-1. CALCULATED EQUILIBRIUM FUEL COMPOSITION FOR
MARK II LOADING OF EBR-II

Element	Weight Per Cent
Zirconium	0.08
Niobium	0.01
Molybdenum	3.15
Technetium	0.96
Ruthenium	3.48
Rhodium	0.60
Palladium	1.35
Total fission elements	9.63
Uranium	70.37
Plutonium	20.00

0.174-in. OD and having a 0.009-in. wall thickness. Sodium in the annulus between pin and tube will provide a thermal bond. Ninety-one fuel elements will be placed in the core subassembly, illustrated in Figure 8-9 (see also Figure 4-12).

The method selected as most suitable for remote refabrication of the fuel pins is gas-pressure, injection precision casting. The mold tubes are precision-bore, high-silica glass tubes coated with a thin thoria wash and closed at one end. In this process the refined metal is induction melted under vacuum in a coated graphite crucible. A heated assembly of mold tubes, open end down, is suspended over the molten metal, and, at the selected casting temperature, the crucible is elevated by a ram, submerging the open ends of the tubes. The furnace is then pressurized with an inert gas from an accumulator tank. The rapid increase in pressure forces the molten

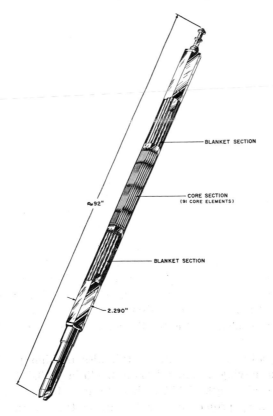

(Courtesy Argonne National Laboratory)

Figure 8-9. Drawing of the 91-rod fuel element for the Experimental Breeder Reactor-II.

metal into the molds where it solidifies. The crucible is lowered while the remainder of the metal charge is still molten. It appears that approximately 100 pins can be cast in a single operation, a limiting factor being the self heating of the cast array by fission product decay.

The molds are stripped from the pins by feeding them between roughened concave rolls to pulverize the glass. The cast pins are cleaned by moving them through an assembly of rotating wire brushes and then they are transferred to a double bladed shear which simultaneously crops both ends of the castings to make fuel pins 14.22 in. long. Various procedures, including weighing, eddy current inspection, and dimensional inspection complete the preparation of the fuel pins, after which they are loaded into a machine which pushes them into fuel jackets.

Much of the development work on the refabrication process has been performed with a uranium alloy containing nonradioactive additions to simulate the fission products. Since technetium was not available, 0.5 w/o molybdenum, plus 0.5 w/o ruthenium were added in its place. The Mark I loading of EBR-II is scheduled to be fabricated of this alloy, enriched with U^{235} and containing about 8 w/o simulated fission products. In the Mark II loading, plutonium replaces a portion of the uranium, as indicated in Table 8-1. Acceptable fuel pins of the plutonium alloy have been produced recently.[43]

The Los Alamos Molten Plutonium Reactor Experiment-I (U.S.A.)

The Los Alamos Molten Plutonium Reactor Experiment-I (LAMPRE-1),[11] now under construction, is designed to evaluate one type of plutonium-fueled fast reactor, and to test the concept of eliminating radiation damage to the fuel by maintaining it in a molten condition. The design power of the reactor is 1 Mw. The fuel, initially to be a plutonium alloy containing 9.5 a/o iron, will be contained in tantalum capsules and will operate at a calculated average temperature of 680°C. About 150 capsules will form a lattice array in a reactor vessel containing molten sodium. Heat will be dissipated to the molten sodium at a calculated maximum heat flux of 235 watts/cm² (740,000 Btu/ft²/hr) across the tantalum-sodium interface. The sodium coolant will enter the reactor vessel at 450°C and leave the reactor at 565°C.

The fuel capsules are deep-drawn thimbles of high purity, vacuummelted tantalum having a nominal ID of 0.375 in., a 0.024–in. wall thickness, and an over-all length of 8.75 inches. Figure 8-10 shows this container. An external locating projection is a feature of the integral bottom. The capsule is filled with fuel to a depth of 6 in., the empty portion of the capsule providing a volume for the accumulation of gaseous fission products. The capsule is closed by fusion-welding a cap in place. The pressure of the gas generated by fission will limit the life of these capsule "elements." It is felt, however, that this design will be most advantageous for evaluating the material compatibility and corrosion problems of the molten fuel system, and that, when these problems are minimized, a later reactor design of the calandria type will have the full advantages of the molten fuel concept.

THE HANDLING OF PLUTONIUM

A detailed discussion of the handling of plutonium-bearing materials is beyond the scope of this paper. Various viewpoints on this subject have been presented[44, 45] and this general topic has been the subject of a symposium.[46] It is pertinent, however, in a discussion of plutonium fuel elements to point out that equipment is needed which is more highly specialized than that required for the manufacture of uranium fuel elements of comparable design. Unless the plutonium being considered has a very high irradiation level or is incompletely separated from fission products, the primary requirement of the equipment is an airtight enclosure, to prevent the escape of even very minute quantities of plutonium, rather than the heavy shielding commonly associated with radioactive material processing.

In order to emphasize two main points concerning equipment for handling

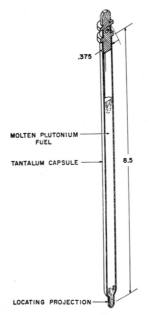

(Courtesy Los Alamos Scientific Laboratory)

Figure 8-10. Fuel capsule for the Los Alamos Molten Plutonium Reactor Experiment.

(Courtesy Atomic Energy of Canada, Ltd.)

Figure 8-11. Glove box line used at Chalk River for the preparation of plutonium-aluminum alloys.

(Courtesy Hanford Laboratories Operation)

Figure 8-12. Enclosed 20-in. Monarch tracer lathe used for machining operations at Hanford's Plutonium Metallurgy Operations.

(Courtesy Los Alamos Scientific Laboratory)

Figure 8-13. Photograph of enclosed equipment for rolling, swaging, wiredrawing and annealing in the Plutonium Metallurgy Research Group at Los Alamos.

plutonium, a series of illustrations, Figures 8-11 through 8-14 are presented below. These illustrations are photographs of equipment used in various laboratories to fabricate plutonium. The two principal points to be noted in these photographs are that (1) the working area of each item of equipment is completely enclosed, and all manipulations inside the enclosures are performed by mechanisms, or by operators using rubber gauntlets; and (2) the equipment pictured indicates that designers are accepting the challenge of plutonium handling and are effectively solving the problems.

THE PRESENT STATUS OF PLUTONIUM FUEL-MATERIALS DEVELOPMENT

A considerable amount of work is being undertaken to develop plutonium-bearing fuel materials, all of which has not as yet culminated in actual fuel elements. Taube[47] and Waldron *et al.*[48] have made the most extensive surveys of the possibilities of these materials. Since the field of plutonium fuel element manufacture appears to be destined for expansion, it seems appropriate to summarize briefly the status of various plutonium-containing materials. These fuels are most conveniently grouped into three general categories based on alloys, oxides, and other refractory compounds.

(*Courtesy Argonne National Laboratory*)

Figure 8-14. Photograph taken during the construction of the new Plutonium Fuel Fabrication Facility at Argonne National Laboratory.

Fuel Materials Based on Plutonium Alloys

Plutonium-Aluminum Alloys. The technology of the aluminum-rich plutonium alloys is probably more advanced than that of any of the other plutonium fuel alloys, as evidenced by the number of plutonium fuel elements prepared from these materials. The constitutional diagram has been worked out by various workers in the United States,[49] United Kingdom,[50] and U.S.S.R.[51] Although there is disagreement in some portions of the diagram, it confirms the principal features of the high aluminum end: (1) a two-phase region bounded by essentially pure aluminum and the inter-metallic compound $PuAl_4$, and (2) a eutectic point at 13 w/o plutonium and 640°C.

The usual metallurgical practice in alloy preparation is to add metallic elements to the solvent melt and this practice has been used in preparing aluminum-plutonium alloys.[34, 36, 38, 52] Runnalls,[26] on the other hand, has pioneered the preparation of these alloys through reduction of PuO_2 by aluminum in the presence of cryolite, a method which bypasses the preparation of plutonium metal from the oxide and promises considerable economic advantage. Workers at Hanford[53] have made this process semi-continuous and have attained a pilot plant production rate of 1 kg of 8.25 w/o plutonium master alloy per hour. Preparation of aluminum alloys by reduction of plutonium trifluoride has also been successful.[26, 52]

The effect of heat treatment on plutonium-aluminum alloys has been studied by Abramson *et al.*[52] They report that softening of the alloy and spheroidization of the $PuAl_4$ proceed more rapidly than the analogous phenomena in uranium-aluminum alloys of corresponding composition.

Mechanical properties of cast aluminum-plutonium alloys in the range 0 to 12 w/o plutonium have been reported by Gardner *et al.*[54] The yield strengths range from about 4,000 to about 8,000 psi, increasing approximately linearly with increased plutonium content. The ultimate strengths also increase linearly between 0 and 10 w/o plutonium, from 11,000 to 16,000 psi; but between 10 and 12 w/o plutonium they increase more rapidly to 22,000 psi.

Preliminary experiments[55] on alloys containing up to 12 a/o plutonium indicate that the thermal conductivity of these alloys is approximately proportional to the volume of free aluminum present, and that the thermal conductivity of the compound $PuAl_4$ is quite low.

The corrosion of high aluminum alloys (5 to 20 w/o plutonium) in high-temperature water—i.e., up to 340°C is being investigated by Jones[56] at Chalk River, and the corrosion rate has been found to be remarkably low, about one-tenth that of aluminum-nickel alloys that have been considered as fuel-sheath materials in pressurized water reactors.

Irradiation experience with plutonium-aluminum alloys has been favorable, and high burn-up has been attained.[8, 57] The most direct investigation of irradiation stability has been made in a Hanford experiment[36] where an aluminum alloy containing 1.67 w/o plutonium was irradiated to 60 per cent burn-up. This was accompanied by a uniform volume increase of 1.4 per cent and an increase in hardness from 46 to 101 on the Rockwell H scale.

Plutonium-Uranium Alloys. The plutonium-uranium system is one of obvious reactor interest, and it has been described by workers in the United States,[49] United Kingdom,[50] and the U.S.S.R.[51] The region of most interest to reactor engineers is at the uranium-rich end where alpha-uranium dissolves about 12 w/o plutonium at room temperature, and beta-uranium can dissolve up to about 18 w/o plutonium at 600°C. Increasing the plutonium content beyond the solubility limit in alpha-uranium introduces the zeta phase. Alloys containing even small amounts of zeta phase have poor properties:[58] the castings contain microcracks and are fragile, pyrophoric, and susceptible to radiation damage. Workers at Argonne[59, 60] and Harwell[48] have reported on the irradiation of uranium-plutonium alloys having compositions in the range from 4 to 20 w/o plutonium. The number of variables involved makes it difficult to summarize the results briefly, except to say that the results with these binary alloys are not encouraging.

Plutonium-Uranium-Molybdenum and Plutonium-Uranium-Fissium Alloys. Molybdenum is known to improve the radiation stability of uranium and is therefore an obvious choice to improve the properties of binary plutonium-uranium alloys. Partial isothermal sections at 800 and 900°C of the ternary alloy system have been published by workers at Harwell.[50] The preliminary irradiation results with molybdenum additions are not clear-cut. British results[48] for 28 a/o molybdenum additions to uranium alloys containing 7 to 18 a/o plutonium and irradiated in the temperature range between 500 and 700°C are not encouraging, but the results reported by Kelman[60] at Argonne National Laboratory for 5 w/o (11 a/o) molybdenum additions to a uranium alloy containing 20 w/o plutonium and irradiated in the temperature range between 190 and 340°C show considerable improvement, which is attributed to the molybdenum addition.

Molybdenum, ruthenium, and technetium with lesser amounts of palladium, rhodium, and zirconium, collectively called fissium, remain as alloying elements in the uranium or uranium-plutonium fuel after being processed by the pyrometallurgical method developed at Argonne National Laboratory. These fission elements, with the exception of zirconium, have a beneficial effect on the irradiation stability of uranium and uranium-plutonium alloys. Irradiation experiments of Argonne[60] have shown that a uranium alloy containing 20 w/o plutonium and 5.4 w/o fissium, irradiated at 500°C, and a similar alloy containing 10.8 w/o fissium, irradiated at 300°C, have been practically unaffected by irradiation damage. These alloys are the best uranium alloys yet tested at Argonne.

Plutonium-Thorium Alloys. The plutonium-thorium system has potential reactor interest and has been investigated in the United States,[49] United Kingdom,[61] and U.S.S.R.[51] The region of high thorium content is of greatest reactor interest. The solid solubility of plutonium in thorium is fairly extensive, the limits being approximately 20 a/o plutonium at room temperature and about 50 a/o plutonium at 600°C. These alloys are quite malleable and no pyrophoric tendencies have been observed.[62] Fabrication of thorium-plutonium reactor fuels presents no new problem in fabrication.[48] A thorium alloy containing 15 w/o plutonium has been irradiated at a temperature of 500°C to a 0.54 per cent burn-up of the plutonium atoms.[48] No gross distortion resulted, but a uniform 14 per cent increase in volume was observed.

Plutonium-Iron, Plutonium-Cobalt, and Plutonium-Nickel Alloys. Constitutional diagrams for binary plutonium alloys containing the iron group metals have been reported. The plutonium-iron system[16, 49, 63, 51] is comparatively simple, with only two compounds, $PuFe_2$ and Pu_6Fe, and little or no solid solubility being reported in the diagram. The plutonium-nickel[64, 16] and plutonium-cobalt[49] systems are more complex, six intermetallic compounds being reported for each system.

Iron, cobalt, and nickel all form low melting point eutectic alloys with

TABLE 8-2. COMPOSITION AND MELTING POINTS OF SOME
EUTECTIC PLUTONIUM ALLOYS

Fluxing Element	Eutectic Composition (a/o)	Melting Point (°C)
Iron.........................	9.5	409
Cobalt......................	12	405
Nickel.....................	12.5	465

plutonium as shown in Table 8-2, and are of interest as fuels for reactors of the molten metal fuel type such as LAMPRE.[11] However, the plutonium concentration in such eutectic composition fuels is too high to permit gaining attractive values of specific power, watts per gram of plutonium inventory, without encountering severe fabrication problems associated with providing adequate heat-transfer surfaces. Diluting the binary eutectic alloys with cerium does not raise the melting point of the alloys above 500°C. and thus may offer a solution to the heat-transfer problem.[65]

For the more dilute plutonium alloys that might be used for solid fuel elements, iron seems to be a favorable alloying element. It has been reported at Harwell[48] that high iron alloys can be fabricated in suitably designed glove boxes. The compound Pu_6Fe is reported by Russian workers[16] to be sufficiently plastic to allow its fabrication into wire at 350°C. In the ternary system, iron-uranium-plutonium, Ellinger[66] has reported continuous solubility between the compounds Pu_6Fe and U_6Fe, and between $PuFe_2$ and UFe_2.

Plutonium-Zirconium Alloys. The plutonium-zirconium constitutional diagram has been published by Russian[51] and British[50] workers. According to these diagrams beta-zirconium and epsilon-plutonium are completely miscible, and alpha-zirconium dissolves about 12 a/o plutonium. A two-phase field is reported between the temperatures of 415 and 630°C, where the two phases present are delta-plutonium containing about 70 a/o zirconium and alpha-zirconium containing about 12 a/o plutonium. At lower temperatures two-phase fields are reported to exist between the solid solution of plutonium in alpha-zirconium and the compound $PuZr_2$, and between $PuZr_2$ and Pu_6Zr. Foil has been fabricated[67] from an arc-melted zirconium-alloy button containing 5 w/o plutonium. The button was hot-pressed to a 0.120-in. thickness and was then cold-rolled 97.5 per cent to a thickness of 0.003 inch. British workers[48] report that a zirconium alloy containing 40 a/o plutonium, irradiated at 500°C to a total burn-up of 0.83 per cent, showed remarkably good irradiation stability.

Plutonium-Copper Alloys. Taube[47] has suggested that the plutonium-copper alloys might be suitable for reactor fuels. The binary constitutional diagram has recently been published by workers in the U.S.S.R.,[51] and their work confirms the early studies made at Los Alamos. The copper-rich end of this system consists of a two-phase field bounded by nearly pure copper and by the intermetallic compound $PuCu_6$. The upper boundary is the eutectic temperature of 885°C. The fabrication of fuel elements similar to those based upon the aluminum system but permitting higher operating temperatures would seem to be a possibility.

Plutonium-Bismuth, Plutonium-Lead, Plutonium-Tin, and Plutonium-Mercury Alloys. The solubility of plutonium in bismuth has been determined at Los Alamos,[68] and a partial diagram of this system has been reported by Schonfeld[49] and by Bochvar *et al.*[51] Plutonium is significantly more soluble in bismuth than is uranium, and a thermal reactor based upon a bismuth solution has been proposed.[69, 69a] Since a temperature of approximately 700°C is required in order to dissolve as much as 10 w/o plutonium, a fast reactor based on this system does not appear attractive.[70]

The plutonium-lead diagram has been reported by Schonfeld[49] and by Bochvar *et al.*[51] and the work of Poole on the solubility of plutonium in lead and in tin has been reported by Frost *et al.*[70] in discussing liquid fuel technology. The data reported show that the solubility of plutonium in lead is 0.055 w/o at 600°C and <0.01 w/o at 450°C; and the solubility in tin is 0.4 w/o at 600°C and 0.17 w/o at 400°C. The solubility in these systems is not sufficiently great to create much interest.

In the plutonium-mercury system there is a large temperature coefficient of solubility, 2.1 g of plutonium per liter of mercury at 25°C and 85.7 g of plutonium at 325°C, reported by Bowersox and Leary.[71] The low solubility (0.66 w/o plutonium at 325°) and the large inelastic scattering properties of mercury have not encouraged serious consideration of these alloys as reactor fuels.

Fuel Materials Based on Plutonium Oxide

Plutonia. As Taube[47] has pointed out, of the plutonium compounds suitable for refractory fuel elements, PuO_2 is the best understood at this time, and the technology associated with it is probably the simplest. A paper by Holley *et al.*[72] on the plutonium oxides includes a partial diagram of the condensed plutonium-oxygen system and most of the available information concerning PuO_2. Very few properties of PuO_2 pertinent to fuel element use have been reported in the literature. The material has the fluorite type of crystal structure isomorphous with UO_2 and ThO_2, and no allotropic forms are known to exist. The density, calculated from x-ray data, is 11.46 g/cm^3. From x-ray data, Mardon and Waldron[73] have estimated the average linear coefficient of expansion of PuO_2 to be $9.0 \pm 1.0 \times 10^{-6}/°C$ in the temperature range from 25 to 500°C. Although the Russians[9] report using PuO_2 as fuel for their BR-5 reactor, no details of fabrication technology have been reported by them. PuO_2 is difficult to dissolve in aqueous solvents, and for this reason it cannot be easily reprocessed in conventional fuel reprocessing plants.

Plutonia and Urania Systems. PuO_2 and UO_2 form a continuous series of solid solutions.[74] Difficulty was experienced in preparing the solid solution directly from the two oxides, but coprecipitation from soluble plutonium and uranium compounds followed by calcination in hydrogen at 1000°C was successful in preparing the complete solid solution series. A very important property of the solid solution is the rapid rate of solution of this material in nitric acid; PuO_2 alone is soluble only with great difficulty.

A fuel cycle based upon plutonia-urania has been studied at the Knolls Atomic Power Laboratory,[75] and a 5 to 1 mole ratio of UO_2 to PuO_2 seems to have attractive breeding characteristics for a power reactor. In this composition range PuO_2 improves the sintering characteristics of UO_2. Several irradiation experiments on dry-pressed pellets of the mixed oxides contained in stainless steel tubes have been conducted and have given encouraging results. Some sintering occurred and a central void was formed, but there was no evidence of melting. When lead was added to the oxide mixture to act as a thermal bonding agent, the heat transfer from the oxide pellet to the capsule wall was improved to the extent that little if any sintering occurred during the irradiation. An unbonded oxide pellet of mixed PuO_2 and UO_2, after being irradiated to 35 per cent burn-up, was still readily soluble in nitric acid. Preliminary experiments with the mixed oxide fuel cycle have been sufficiently encouraging to have the Atomic Energy Commission invite bids for the development and construction of a fast breeder reactor based on this fuel material.[76]

Plutonia-Thoria and Plutonia-Ceria Systems. An investigation by Mulford and Ellinger[77] of the x-ray lattice parameter-composition relationship for PuO_2-ThO_2 and PuO_2-CeO_2 solid solutions has shown that continuous series of solid solutions exist in these systems as it does in the PuO_2-UO_2 system. Mixed crystals of these oxides may be desirable in fuel elements for special situations. However, additions of CeO_2 or ThO_2 to PuO_2 do not have the favorable effect of making PuO_2 more readily soluble in nitric acid.

Plutonia and Other Metal Oxide Systems. Interest has been expressed[36] in mixtures of PuO_2 with other metal oxide diluents such as Al_2O_3, MgO, SiO_2, and BeO, but no information on these mixtures has been published. Considering the similarities that exist between PuO_2 and UO_2, one might make cautious predictions concerning such plutonium-containing systems by analogy to the information reported[78, 79] for high-temperature reactions of UO_2 with various metal oxides.

TABLE 8-3. EVALUATION OF PLUTONIUM DIOXIDE CERMETS[48]

Matrix	Observations
Mg	Reduction to Pu_2O_3 at 500°C. Traces of metallic plutonium at 600°C.
Al	Al_2O_3 film formed at interface at 600°C. No further reaction observed.
Th	Reduction to Pu_2O_3 starts at 800°C. Reduction to metallic plutonium occurs at 1000°C.
U	Reduction to Pu_2O_3 occurs at 800°C. No reduction to plutonium observed at 1000°C.
Zr	Reduction to Pu_2O_3, but not to metal, below 1200°C. Apparent reduction to metal above 1200°C.
Fe	Reduction to Pu_2O_3 at 1300°C. No reduction to metallic plutonium observed at 1350°C.
Graphite	No reduction observed at 850°C. Reduction to Pu_2O_3 at 1000°C. Conversion to PuC above 1200°C.[80]

Plutonia Cermets. Waldron *et al.*[48] have reported preliminary experiments to determine the stability of PuO_2 dispersed in various metallic matrices. On the basis of these experiments it would seem that at least a limited reaction between PuO_2 and the matrices investigated must be expected. The matrices used in these experiments included magnesium, aluminum, thorium, uranium, zirconium, iron, and graphite. In all experiments, except with zirconium, 50 w/o mixtures of −300 mesh PuO_2 powder and metal powder were compacted and held at temperature for a few hours. A 10 w/o PuO_2 mixture was used with zirconium in order to obtain suitable x-ray diffraction patterns. The results of these experiments are summarized in Table 8-3.

Fuel Materials Based on Other Refractory Plutonium Compounds

History has demonstrated that the operating temperatures of power-producing plants have an inevitable upward trend, and the brief history of nuclear reactors shows no exception to this trend. To achieve fuel stability in uranium-fueled reactors for higher temperature operation, the technology of UO_2 fuel elements has received impetus. Epremian[81] has described briefly the search for other uranium compounds that could compete with or supplement UO_2 as a reactor fuel. It seems pertinent to consider analogous plutonium compounds for use as high-temperature fuels.

Among the uranium compounds considered are the borides, beryllides, carbides, aluminides, nitrides and silicides. Information on the corresponding plutonium compounds is not well developed but enough features are known to permit speculation to be made as to the possible future of these materials in high-temperature reactors.

Borides of plutonium probably exist, but their preparation has not been reported. Neutron emission may complicate the handling of such alloys. In the plutonium-beryllium system, the sole compound is $PuBe_{13}$, which has a face-centered cubic structure,[66] a high melting point (1950°C), and is quite stable at room temperature. Experimental work with this compound has been limited because of the neutron emission (approximately 6.8×10^4 neutrons/sec/g of $PuBe_{13}$[82]) resulting from the α, n reaction. The primary use of this compound has been for neutron sources that are stable with respect to time.

Two carbides of plutonium, PuC and Pu_2C_3, have been identified, and there are indications of the existence of a higher carbide. Drummond *et al.*[83] report them to be more reactive than the corresponding uranium carbides. A carbide preparation, intended to be PuC, recently made at Los Alamos by combination of the elements, was found to contain about 20 per cent Pu_2C_3 and to melt incongruently at about 1750°C.[84] Plutonium nitride, PuN, is reported to have been prepared by Brown *et al.*[85] by reacting nitrogen and plutonium hydride. These authors state that "the most notable property of the nitride is the ease of hydrolysis by heat and moist air."

The aluminides of plutonium, $PuAl_2$, $PuAl_3$, and $PuAl_4$, are known to be quite brittle. Of these, $PuAl_2$ is high melting and is the only one, according to the constitutional diagram, that melts congruently. This compound is face-centered cubic and isostructural with UAl_2.[66] A recent determination at Los Alamos places the melting point in the vicinity of 1550°C.[86]

The plutonium silicon system has not been reported in detail but a number of silicides, $PuSi$, Pu_2Si_3, and $PuSi_2$ are known to exist.[66] The compound $PuSi$ is orthorhombic. The melting point, recently determined at Los Alamos, is approximately 1550°C.[84]

ACKNOWLEDGMENT

Helpful discussions with W. N. Miner and F. W. Schonfeld during the preparation of this paper are gratefully acknowledged.

References

1. Goldsmith, S., "Plutonium Recycling in Thermal Reactors," Chap. 8 of "Solid Fuel Reactors," J. R. Dietrich and W. H. Zinn (Editors), Reading, Mass., Addison-Wesley Publishing Co., 1958.
2. Greebler, P., Harker, W. H., Harriman, J. M. and Zebroski, E. L., "Plutonium Recycle in Power Reactors," Second United Nations International Conference on the Peaceful Uses of Atomic Energy, Geneva (1958) P/2000.
3. Greebler, P., Harker, W. H., Harriman, J. M. and Zebroski, E. L., "Recycle of Plutonium in Low-Enrichment Light-Water Reactors," Second United Nations International Conference on the Peaceful Uses of Atomic Energy, Geneva (1958) P/2167.
4. Pugh, S. F., "Plutonium Fuels for Power Reactors," Conference on the Metal Plutonium, Chicago (1957).

5. Runnalls, O. J. C., "Irradiation Experiencn with Rods of Plutonium-Aluminum Alloy," Second United Nations International Conference on the Peaceful Uses of Atomic Energy, Geneva (1958) P/191.
6. Kiehn, R. M., "Role of Plutonium in Nuclear Power," Conference on the Metal Plutonium, Chicago (1957).
7. Glasstone, S., "Principles of Nuclear Engineering," p. 832, Princeton, D. Van Nostrand Co., 1955.
8. Jurney, E. T., Hall, J. H., Hall, D. B., Gage, A. M., Godbold, N. H., Sayer, A. R. and Swickard, E. O., "The Los Alamos Fast Plutonium Reactor," Report LA-1679 (1954) declassified.
9. Leipunsky, A. I. *et al.*, "Experimental Fast Reactors in the Soviet Union," Second United Nations International Conference on the Peaceful Uses of Atomic Energy, Geneva (1958) P/2129.
10. Leipunsky, A. I. *et al.*, "The BR-2 Fast Neutron Reactor," *Atomnaya Energiya*, **2,** 497–500 (1957).
11. Kiehn, R. M., "LAMPRE, A Molten Plutonium Fueled Reactor Concept," Report LA-2112 (1957) unclassified.
12. Koch, L. J. *et al.*, "Construction Design of EBR-II, an Integrated Unmoderated Nuclear Power Plant," Second United Nations International Conference on the Peaceful Uses of Atomic Energy, Geneva (1958) P/1782.
13. Luntz, J. D., (Editor), "The Enrico Fermi Fast Breeder Reactor," *Nucleonics*, **15,** No. 4, 68–72 (1957).
14. Shaw, E. N., (Editor), "The Dounreay Fast Reactor," *Nuclear Eng.*, **2,** 230–244 (1957).
15. Coffinberry, A. S., and Waldron, M. B., "The Physical Metallurgy of Plutonium" Chap. 4 in "Progress in Nuclear Energy", Vol. 1, Series V, New York, Pergamon Press, 1956.
16. Konobeevsky, S. T., "Equilibrium Diagrams of Certain Systems on Plutonium Bases," Proc. Acad. Sci. U. S. S. R. on the Peaceful Uses of Atomic Energy, Chemical Science Volume, 362–367, Moscow (1955).
17. Bagley, K. Q., "Plutonium and its Alloys," *Nuclear Eng.*, **2,** 461–468 (1957).
18. Sandenaw, T. A. and Gibney, R. B., "The Electrical Resistivity and Thermal Conductivity of Plutonium Metal," *J. Physics and Chemistry of Solids*, **6,** 81–88 (1958).
19. Waber, J. T., Kline, M. R. and Johnson, L. K., "Effect of Alloying on the Critical Mass of a Plutonium Spherical Fast Reactor," *Nuclear Sci. and Eng.*, **4,** 341–353 (1958).
20. Jurney, E. T., "The Failure and Disassembly of the Los Alamos Fast Reactor," *Chem. Eng. Prog.*, Symposium Series No. 13, **50,** 191–199 (1954).
21. Jurney, E. T., "Failure and Disassembly of Los Alamos Fast Reactor," *Nucleonics*, **12,** No. 9, 28 (1954).
22. Glasstone, S., "Principles of Nuclear Engineering," p. 804, Princeton, D. Van Nostrand Co., 1955.
23. Shaw, E. N. (Editor,) "The NRX—National Research Experimental," *Nuclear Eng.*, **1,** data sheet facing 106 (1956).
24. Wauchope, K. L., "The Preparation of Plutonium-Aluminum Alloy Fuel Elements for the N. R. X. Reactor," Conference on the Metal Plutonium, Chicago (1957); Report CRL-52.
25. Runnalls, O. J. C. and Wauchope, K. L., "The Preparation and Sheathing of Plutonium-Aluminum Fuel Alloys for the N. R. X. Reactor," Symposium on Fuel Fabrication, Paris (1957); Report CRL-47; also TID-7546, Book 2, 778–788.

26. Runnalls, O. J. C., "The Preparation of Plutonium-Aluminum and Other Plutonium Alloys," Atomic Energy of Canada, Ltd., Chalk River (1958).
27. Glasstone, S., "Principles of Nuclear Engineering," p. 838, Princeton, D. Van Nostrand Co., 1955.
28. Shepard, L. R., Smith, R. D., Holmes, J. E. R., Rose, H. and McVicar, D. D., "Operational Features of ZEPHYR," *Chem. Eng. Prog.*, Symposium Series No. 13, 50, 1–4 (1954).
29. Ball, J. G. and Lord, W. B. H., "A History of the Early British Work on Plutonium Metallurgy," *J. Inst. Metals*, 86, 369–379 (1958).
30. Leipunsky, A. I. *et al.* "Studies in the Physics of Fast Neutron Reactors," Second United Nations International Conference on the Peaceful Uses of Atomic Energy, Geneva (1958) P/2038. See also Leipunskii, A. I., *et al.*, "Studies on the Reactor Physics of Fast Neutrons," *Atomnaya Energiya* 5, 277–293 (1958).
31. Weinberg, A. M., Cole, T. E. and Mann, M. M., "The Materials Testing Reactor and Related Research Reactors," *Proc. Intern. Conf. Peaceful Uses of Atomic Energy*, United Nations, 2, 402–419 (1955).
32. Huffman, J. R., "The Materials Testing Reactor," *Nucleonics*, 12, No. 4, 20–26 (1954).
33. Cunningham, J. E., and Boyle, E. J., "MTR Type Fuel Elements," *Proc. Intern. Conf. Peaceful Uses of Atomic Energy*, United Nations, 9, 203–207 (1955).
34. Tate, R. E., "Fabrication of Billets Containing Plutonium for the MTR Fuel Elements," Conference on the Metal Plutonium, Chicago (1957).
35. Luntz, J. D. (Editor) *Nucleonics*, 16, No. 9, 157 (1958).
36. Wick, O. J., Nelson, T. C. and Freshley, M. D., "Plutonium Fuels Development," Second United Nations International Conference on the Peaceful Uses of Atomic Energy, Geneva (1958) P/1776.
37. de Boisblanc, D. R., "Operation of the MTR on a Plutonium Loading," Report IDO-16508 (1959).
38. Lord, W. B. H. and Wakelin, R. J., "Fabrication d'éléments combustibles plutonium-aluminum pour piles atomiques," *Rev. Met.*, 55, 620–626 (1958).
39. Fryar, R. M., "Plutonium Recycle Test Reactor," *Nucleonics*, 16, No. 1, 62–63 (1958).
40. Wick, O. J., Hanford, private communication (1958).
41. Bailey, W. J., Koler, R. K. and Patterson, D. A., "Fabrication of Aluminum-Plutonium Fuel Elements for Lattice Tests in Support of PRTR," Report HW-51855 (1958), unclassified.
42. Shuck, A. B., "Manufacturing Methods for the Experimental Breeder Reactor II, Mark I and Mark II Fuel Loadings," Fuel Element Conference, Gatlinburg, Tenn. (1958); also Report ANL-FGF-112, unclassified.
43. Shuck, A. B., Argonne, private communication (1958).
44. Kelman, L. R., Wilkinson, W. D., Shuck, A. B. and Goertz, R. C., "Handling Alpha-Active Pyrophoric Materials," Part 1, *Nucleonics*, 14, No. 3, 61–65 (1956); Part 2, *ibid.*, No. 4, 65-71 (1956); and Part 3, *ibid.*, No. 5, 77-82 (1956).
45. Lord, W. B. H. and Waldron, M. B., "The Development of Handling Techniques for the Study of Plutonium Metal," *J. Inst. Metals*, 86, 385–392 (1958).
45a. Wick, O. J., and Thomas, I. D., "Design and Operation of Hanford's Plutonium Metallurgy Facilities", Second United Nations International Conference on the Peaceful Uses of Atomic Energy, Geneva (1958) P/1903.
46. Walton, G. N. (Editor), "Glove Boxes and Shielded Cells," London, Butterworths Scientific Publications, 1958.
47. Taube, M., "Plutonium Dioxide as a Nuclear Fuel," *Nukleonika*, 2, 465–478 (1957).
48. Waldron, M. B. *et al.*, "Plutonium Technology for Reactor Systems," Second

United Nations International Conference on the Peaceful Uses of Atomic Energy, Geneva (1958) P/1452.

49. Schonfeld, F. W., "Phase Diagrams Studied at Los Alamos," Conference on the Metal Plutonium, Chicago (1957); see also "Plutonium," *Nucleonics*, **16**, No. 8, 96–100 (1958).

50. Waldron, M. B. *et al.*, "The Physical Metallurgy of Plutonium," Second United Nations International Conference on the Peaceful Uses of Atomic Energy, Geneva (1958) P/71.

51. Bochvar, A. A., Konobeevsky, S. T., Kutaitsev, V. I., Menshikova, I. S. and Chebotarev, N. T., "Interaction between Plutonium and Other Metals in Connection with their Arrangement in Mendeleev's Periodic Table," *Atomnaya Energiya*, **5**, 303–309 (1958); also Second United Nations International Conference on the Peaceful Uses of Atomic Energy, Geneva (1958) P/2197.

52. Abramson, R., Boucher, R., Fabre, R. and Monti, H., "Quelques proprietes du plutonium et de l'alliage aluminum-plutonium," Second United Nations International Conference on the Peaceful Uses of Atomic Energy, Geneva (1958) P/327.

53. Lyon, W. L., "The Preparation and Reprocessing of Plutonium-Aluminum Alloy, A Power Reactor Fuel Material," Second United Nations International Conference on the Peaceful Uses of Atomic Energy, Geneva (1958) P/546.

54. Gardner, H. R., Bloomster, C. H. and Jefferes, J. M., "The Tensile Properties of Pure Plutonium and Some Aluminum-Plutonium Alloys," Second United Nations International Conference on the Peaceful Uses of Atomic Energy, Geneva (1958) P/1081.

55. Gibney, R. B., "Preliminary Report on Thermal and Electrical Conductivities of Some Plutonium-Aluminum Alloys," Report LAMS-1080 (1950) declassified.

56. Runnalls, O. J. C., Chalk River, private communication (1958).

57. Foote, F., "Production and Use of Plutonium," Chap. 4 of Part III "Nuclear Fuels," in "The Industrial Challenge of Nuclear Energy," pp. 123–132, Paris, The European Productivity Agency, 1957.

58. Chiswik, H. H., Dwight, A. E., Lloyd, L. T., Nevitt, M. V. and Zegler, S. T., "Advances in the Physical Metallurgy of Uranium and its Alloys," Second United Nations International Conference on the Peaceful Uses of Atomic Energy, Geneva (1958) P/713.

59. Kittel, J. H. and Paine, S. H., "Effects of Irradiation on Fuel Materials," Second United Nations International Conference on the Peaceful Uses of Atomic Energy, Geneva (1958) P/1890.

60. Kelman, L. R., "Fast Reactor Fuel Development at Argonne National Laboratory," Fuel Elements Conference, Paris (1957), Report TID-7546, Book 2, pp. 751–777.

61. Poole, D. M., Williamson, G. K. and Marples, J. A. C., "A Preliminary Investigation of the Plutonium-Thorium System," *J. Inst. Metals*, **86**, 172–176 (1957).

62. Imlah, K., Los Alamos, private communication (1958).

63. Mardon, P. G., Haines, H. R., Pearce, J. H. and Waldron, M. B., "The Plutonium-Iron System," *J. Inst. Metals*, **86**, 166–171 (1957).

64. Wensch, G. W. and Whyte, D. D., "The Nickel-Plutonium System," Report LA-1304 (1951) declassified.

65. Hall, D. B., "Plutonium Fuels for Fast Reactors," Second United Nations International Conference on the Peaceful Uses of Atomic Energy, Geneva (1958) P/2021.

66. Ellinger, F. H., "Review of the Intermetallic Compounds of Plutonium," Conference on the Metal Plutonium, Chicago (1957).

67. Foote, F. G., Schumar, J. F. and Chiswik, H. H., ANL Metallurgy Division Quarterly Report for July, August and September 1957, Report ANL-5797.
68. Lane, J. A., McPherson, H. G. and Maslan, F., "Fluid Fueled Reactors," p 725, Reading, Mass., Addison-Wesley Publishing Co., 1958.
69. Gurinsky, D. H., "Plutonium Liquid Metal Fuel Reactor," Conference on the Metal Plutonium, Chicago (1957).
69a. Miles, F. T., Sheehan, T. U., Gurinsky, D. H., and Kouts, H. J. C., "Liquid Metal Fueled Reactor with Recycled Plutonium," Second United Nations International Conference on the Peaceful Uses of Atomic Energy, Geneva (1958) P/461.
70. Frost, B. R. T. *et al.*, "Liquid Metal Fuel Technology," Second United Nations International Conference on the Peaceful Uses of Atomic Energy, Geneva (1958) P/270.
71. Bowersox, D. F. and Leary, J., "Solubility of Plutonium in Mercury," *J. Inorganic and Nuclear Chem.*, **9**, 108–112 (1959).
72. Holly, C. E. *et al.*, "Thermodynamics and Phase Relationships for Plutonium Oxides," Second United Nations International Conference on the Peaceful Uses of Atomic Energy, Geneva (1958) P/701.
73. Mardon, P. G. and Waldron, M. B., "An Estimate of the Thermal Expansion Coefficient of PuO_2," Report AERE M/M 171 (1957).
74. Mulford, R. N. R. and Ellinger, F. H., "UO_2-PuO_2 Solid Solutions," *J. Am. Chem. Soc.*, **80**, 2023 (1958).
75. Cashin, W. M., "Role of Plutonium in Nuclear Power—Mixed-Oxide Concept," Conference on the Metal Plutonium, Chicago (1957).
76. Luntz, J. D. (Editor), *Nucleonics*, **16**, No. 11, 25 (1958.)
77. Mulford, R. N. R. and Ellinger, F. H., "ThO_2-PuO_2 and CeO_2-PuO_2 Solid Solutions," *J. Phys. Chem.*, **62**, 1466 (1958).
78. Lang, S. M., Knudson, F. P., Fillmore, C. L. and Roth, R. S., "High Temperature Reactions of Uranium Dioxide with Various Metal Oxides," National Bureau of Standards Circular No. 568 (1956).
79. Budnikov, P. P., Tresviatsky, S. G. and Kushakovsky, V. I., "Binary Phase Diagrams UO_2-Al_2O_3 , UO_2-BeO, UO_2-MgO," Second United Nations International Conference on the Peaceful Uses of Atomic Energy, Geneva (1958) P/2193.
80. Seaborg, G. T. and Katz, J. J., "The Actinide Elements," National Nuclear Energy Series IV, **14A,** p. 395, New York, McGraw Hill Book Co., Inc., 1954.
81. Epremian, E., "Uranium Compounds for New High-Temperature Fuels," Fuel Element Conference, Paris (1957), Report TID-7546, Book 2, pp. 549–553.
82. Tate, R. E. and Coffinberry, A. S., "Plutonium-Beryllium Neutron Sources, Their Fabrication and Their Yield," Second United Nations International Conference on the Peaceful Uses of Atomic Energy, Geneva (1958) P/700.
83. Drummond, J. L., McDonald, B. J., Ockenden, H. M. and Welch, G. A., "Preparation and Properties of Some Plutonium Compounds, Part IV, Plutonium Carbides," *J. Chem. Soc.*, **(1957)** 4785–4789.
84. Mulford, R. N. R., Los Alamos, private communication (1958).
85. Brown, F., Ockenden, H. M. and Welch, G. A., "Preparation and Properties of Some Plutonium Compounds, Part II, Plutonium Nitride," *J. Chem. Soc.* **(1958)** 4196–4201.
86. Struebing, V. O., Los Alamos, private communication, (1958).

9. DEVELOPMENT OF FABRICATION TECHNIQUES FOR APPR FUEL PLATES

W. WEINBERGER

Sylvania-Corning Nuclear Corporation, Bayside, Long Island, N. Y.

As a means of preparing process specifications for the production of Army Package Power Reactor fuel element subassemblies, the program outlined in this chapter was initiated. Processing knowledge gained from this investigation was subsequently employed for the production of natural and slightly modified enriched fuel element subassemblies.

All work carried out on this program was based upon the dimensional specifications and tolerances presented in the report, "Specifications for Army Package Power Reactors (APPR-1) Fuel and Control Rod Components" (see Appendix I).

A fuel element subassembly was made up of a group of 18 fuel plates brazed into two grooved side plates which subsequently had end adapters machined and welded into position. Each fuel plate had a nominal core size of 0.020 x 2.54 x 22.00 in. and contained 28.62 g of U^{235} in the form of highly enriched UO_2 and 0.2685 g of B^{10} in the form of normal elemental boron powder.

Development work consisted of the preparation of samples for evaluation of core material, picture framing techniques, fuel plate fabrication, and subassembly fabrication employing both brazing and welding methods.

DEVELOPMENT WORK

Primary emphasis in this program was placed on the establishment of a dependable and economical industrial process for fabricating Army Package Power Reactor fuel elements. Each fuel element subassembly contains 18 fuel plates. Sixteen of the fuel plates are 23 in. long, while the two utilized as the top and the bottom plates of the assembly are 27 in. long. All 18 plates are 0.030 in. thick, 2.778 in. wide and contain cores 0.020 x 2.54 x 22.0 inches.

Early work was carried out using type 304 stainless steel throughout the fabrication process. As of January 1957, however, type 347 stainless steel was substituted for type 304 as a means of eliminating possible sensitizing

144

TABLE 9-1. EFFECT OF COMPACTING PRESSURE ON THE DENSITY AND STRENGTH
OF AS-PRESSED CORES

Compacting Pressure (tsi)	Density (g/cm^3)	Modulus of Rupture (psi)
33	6.15	1250
50	6.80	1825
65	6.90	3050

and subsequent intergranular corrosion of the fuel plates. In addition, the
core composition of the fuel plates was changed. Work carried out prior to
March 1957 utilized fuel plates containing cores of 17.94 w/o UO_2, 0.141
w/o boron, and the balance stainless steel. Since that time, however, cores
containing 23.025 w/o UO_2, 0.094 w/o boron and a balance of stainless
steel have been employed.

Preparation and Evaluation of Core Material

Effect of Compacting Pressure. For comparison purposes, sample
cores 0.125 x 2.4375 x 4 in. were compacted at 33, 50, and 65 tsi. These
cores were composed of 17.94 w/o UO_2 powder (as-received, steam oxidized), 0.18 w/o B_4C powder, and type 304 stainless steel (as-received,
−100 mesh) powder. After being compacted, the cores were evaluated for
density and for modulus of rupture. The results are shown in Table 9-1.

The samples pressed at 33 tsi were powdery on the edges and tended to
crumble upon being handled. Compacts pressed at 50 tsi could be handled
in the as-pressed condition without damage. As evidenced in Table 9-1,
samples compacted at 65 tsi had extremely high strength. Based on the results obtained, it was felt that compacts pressed at 50 tsi possessed adequate
strength and were much more desirable than those compacted at 33 tsi.
The additional strength obtained by a compacting pressure of 65 tsi was
considered impractical in view of the shortened die life expectancy at the
higher compacting pressures.

Effect of Stainless Steel and UO_2 Particle Size Variation. Earlier
work revealed that radiographic evaluation of as-compacted cores prior to
their fabrication was an excellent technique for determination of the homogeneity of a finished plate. It had also been noted that various combinations of UO_2 particle sizes yielded compacts having very poor to very good
UO_2 distribution.

As a means of resolving this phenomenon, four mixtures containing stainless steel, UO_2 and boron of various particle size combinations, were prepared. The actual particle sizes employed for each mixture are shown in
Table 9-2.

The 4 x $2\frac{7}{16}$-in. compacts were pressed at 50 tsi from each of the four

TABLE 9-2. STAINLESS STEEL-UO₂-BORON PARTICLE SIZE COMBINATIONS
INVESTIGATED FOR EFFECT ON UO₂ DISTRIBUTION

Mix Number	Stainless Steel Mesh Size	UO₂ Mesh Size	Boron Mesh Size
1	−100 +325	−140 +325	−325
2	−100 +325	−325	−325
3	−325	−140 +325	−325
4	−325	−325	−325

mixes. Subsequently, all of the compacts were radiographed as a means of evaluating homogeneity. Compacts produced from Mix No. 1 and Mix No. 2 appear to be badly segregated, while those produced from Mix No. 3 and Mix No. 4 exhibit excellent distribution. Similar results were obtained when the mixtures investigated contained either 17.94 or 23.025 w/o UO₂ in either a type 304 or type 347 stainless steel matrix. Based upon these results, it appeared desirable that −325 mesh stainless steel powder be employed for best oxide distribution.

Evaluation of these cores containing powders of various particle sizes was continued throughout all further fabrication processes to a finish-size plate. No appreciable effect was noted due to any subsequent fabrication process.

Effect of Sintering Upon Core Compacts. A careful investigation was conducted to determine whether the sintering of cores to high density resulted in any improvement in the properties or ability to be fabricated of fuel plates over the as-compacted cores. A series of compacts was prepared consisting of 17.94 w/o UO₂, the balance type 304 stainless steel. A second series of compacts consisting of 17.94 w/o UO₂, the balance type 347 stainless steel, was also prepared. All of these compacts were 4 x 2$\frac{7}{16}$ in. in size and were pressed at 50 tsi to yield green densities of 80 to 85 per cent of theoretical. After half of the compacts from each series had been sintered, it was found that densities had increased to about 95 per cent of theoretical. A sintering cycle of 1350°C for 16 hr in a dry hydrogen atmosphere was employed. All of the cores were then assembled into conventional "picture frames" and subsequently fabricated to finish-size.

No difference between the fabrication characteristics of the plates containing as-compacted cores and as-sintered cores was noted. Also, metallographic examination revealed no structural difference between the cores that had been sintered and those that were fabricated in the as-compacted condition.

Therefore, it was concluded that use of a sintered core rather than an as-compacted core was not necessary, since no ease in fabrication or improvement in plate quality was realized. Since the sintering of cores is a very costly operation, it was omitted from all future work.

Evaluation of Various Methods of UO₂ Preparation. During the fabrication of fuel plates, some very subtle effects based on the method of UO$_2$ preparation were noticed. It has been known for some time that a hard, high-fired type of UO$_2$ particle was required. Only in this investigation, however, were differences in fabricability observed in stainless steel fuel plates containing the so-called hard, high-fired oxide types from various sources. UO$_2$ in this category includes the hydrothermal (Geneva Oxide) as prepared at the Oak Ridge National Laboratory, the Mallinckrodt Commercial high-fired, and the Sylvania-Corning Nuclear Corporation's granulated material (a high-fired type containing 3 w/o CaF$_2$). The investigation described below explains some of the effects of two of these three UO$_2$ types. The use of the hydrothermal type has already been amply demonstrated by the Oak Ridge National Laboratory.

A series of 20 fuel plate assemblies, containing Mallinckrodt Commercial high-fired UO$_2$, was prepared for hot-rolling. Ten of the cores contained 23 w/o −325 mesh high-fired UO$_2$, while the remaining ten cores contained 23 w/o −140 +325 mesh high-fired UO$_2$. These 20 assemblies were fabricated at a preheat and hot rolling temperature of 1200 to 1220°C by the conventional five-pass hot-rolling schedule developed for the fabrication of plates containing granulated UO$_2$.

It was observed during the hot rolling of these plates that a high percentage of the cores tended to edge-crack very badly on the first pass; and, in some instances, these cracks became propagated through the cladding by the second pass. Further rolling appeared to have no adverse effects upon the quality of the plates. Since it was possible for a small percentage of these plates to be fabricated successfully, and since no cracks occurred after the first pass, it was concluded that if a technique could be worked out for the rolling of the plates through the first pass without cracks, this oxide type would be usable.

An identical investigation was carried out using granulated oxide instead of the high-fired oxide. No difficulties were encountered during fabrication of these plates. It was therefore concluded that granulated oxide should be utilized for all subsequent work on this program.

Evaluation of Boron Activities. Since type 347 stainless steel required a higher preheat and hot-rolling temperature than the type 304, it was necessary that a technique for the addition of boron in a form stable at temperatures of approximately 1200°C and higher be found. The following compounds of boron as well as elemental boron were considered:

a. TiB$_2$ (31.1 % boron)
b. ZrB$_2$ (19.2 % boron)
c. BN (43.6 % boron)
d. Elemental crystalline boron (99.12 % boron)

Five mixtures consisting of type 347 stainless steel powder containing the following boron compounds were subsequently prepared to yield a constant boron content of 0.14 w/o:

1. 0.18 w/o B_4C
2. 0.45 w/o TiB_2
3. 0.73 w/o ZrB_2
4. 0.33 w/o BN
5. 0.14 w/o B

Nine disks approximately 1 in. in diameter and 0.250 in. thick were compacted at 50 tsi from each of the five powder mixtures. One compact from each of the five mixtures was then fired for 16 hr in a dry hydrogen atmosphere at temperatures increasing in increments of 25°C from 1150 to 1350°C. Table 9-3 exhibits results of these tests as determined by metallographic examination.

It was noted during metallographic examination that all additives exhibited a similar structure in the reacted condition. Figure 9-1 exhibits a section of a stainless steel compact containing TiB_2 which was sintered at 1300°C for 16 hours. The black areas represent smoothly rounded holes, indicative of melting, which were filled with TiB_2 particles prior to the firing. For comparison, Figure 9-2 shows a microstructure of a sample containing elemental boron after being fired for 16 hr at 1350°C. The structure is essentially the same as that of ordinary stainless steel. In all probability boron in these quantities forms a solid solution and has no significant effect

TABLE 9-3. EFFECT OF TEMPERATURE UPON THE REACTIVITY OF
BORON COMPOUNDS IN STAINLESS STEEL

Temp* (°C)	B_4C	TiB_2	ZrB_2	BN	B
1150	stable†	stable	stable	stable	stable
1175	stable	stable	stable	partially reacted	stable
1200	partially reacted	stable	stable	reacted	stable
1225	reacted	stable	stable	reacted	stable
1250	reacted	partially reacted	partially reacted	reacted	stable
1275	reacted	partially reacted	partially reacetd	reacted	stable
1300	reacted	reacted	reacted	reacted	stable
1325	reacted	reacted	reacted	reacted	stable
1350	reacted	reacted	reacted	reacted	stable

* Compacted samples were fired for 16 hr in a dry hydrogen atmosphere at the temperature indicated.
† The term "stable" as used here means that no melting or change in shape or dimensions occurred. It does not necessarily imply that no solid solution reaction took place.

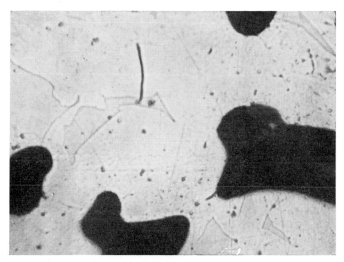

Figure 9-1. Typical section of type 347 stainless steel—0.45 w/o TiB_2 compact, sintered at 1300°C for 16 hr in a dry hydrogen atmosphere. (750×)

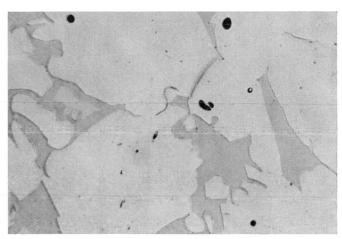

Figure 9-2. Typical section of type 347 stainless steel—0.14 w/o elemental boron compact, sintered at 1350°C for 16 hr in a dry hydrogen atmosphere. (750×)

on the structure or properties of the steel. Weight loss was determined and chemical analyses were made. These data showed that the small loss of boron which may occur during the heat treatment can be controlled.

Of the compounds tested, BN and B_4C are the least stable and cannot be used at temperatures greater than 1200°C. TiB_2 and ZrB_2 are somewhat more stable and could be used up to 1225°C. Elemental boron on the other hand showed no detrimental reaction at temperatures up to 1350°C, permitting the use of any hot-working temperature required as well as a higher temperature braze material than Coast Metals N.P. In addition, if fully sintered core material is required, elemental boron will withstand the sintering temperature.

Additional fuel plates containing cores in which elemental boron was added were fully processed with excellent results. The hot rolling was carried out at 1220°C (furnace temperature) with stability of the boron and excellent workability of the plates noted.

Fuel Plate Assembly

Simplified methods for fabrication of picture frames were evaluated in an effort to eliminate the frame punching operation and to minimize the stainless steel scrap which is involved. As seen in Figure 9-3, a typical simplified picture frame was assembled from stainless steel strips which were spot-welded to one of the cover plates. The core compact was then inserted in the frame cavity, the second cover plate put into place, and the entire assembly heliarc welded all around the edges but with the four corners left open for release of entrapped gases.

Upon the completion of a series of eight plates fabricated by means of sectional-type picture frames, all joints were radiographically inspected. No indication of unbonded joints could be noted. Since radiographic inspection will not distinguish mechanical contact from metallurgical bond, however, each joint on all eight plates, after being cold rolled to the finish thickness, was examined metallographically. Of the 32 joints examined, traces of the original butt joint were found on only six. The remaining 26 joints could not be detected during exhaustive metallographic examination.

Figure 9-3. Components of simplified picture frame assembly ready for the spot welding of top cover plate to frame.

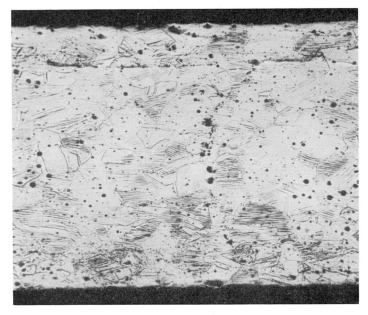

Figure 9-4. Cross section of butt joint (etched) of sectional-type picture frame. Joint exhibited is one formed parallel to the direction of rolling. (100×)

The six detectable joints had been joined both in the direction of rolling and transverse to it. Examples of the defective joints are exhibited in Figures 9-4, 5, 6, and 7.

Figures 9-4 and 9-5 show specimens secured from joints formed parallel to the direction of rolling, while Figures 9-6 and 9-7 show specimens secured from joints perpendicular to the direction of rolling. It is believed that defects such as those exhibited in Figures 9-4 and 9-5 are nothing more than slight oxide inclusions and that no possible leakage from the core of the plate could follow from these joints, as the oxide inclusions are of a non-continuous nature. Close examination of the etched specimen in Figure 9-4 reveals that grain growth progressed across the actual butt joint which indicates a good metallurgical bond. Figure 9-6 might be considered similar in most respects to Figures 9-4 and 9-5 even though the joint was formed perpendicular to the direction of rolling. Figure 9-7, however, contains a fractured joint, the fracture of which appears to be continuous and therefore would be cause for rejection.

In most cases the sectional picture frame was sound. Any failure, however, is a cause for rejection; and since there is no simple nondestructive method for testing the failure at these joints, the method is presently not applicable for production. Consequently, a conventional (single piece)

Figure 9-5. Cross section of sectional-type picture frame. Joint exhibited is one formed parallel to the direction of rolling. (100×)

Figure 9-6. Cross section of butt joint of sectional-type picture frame. Joint exhibited is one formed perpendicular to the direction of rolling. (100×)

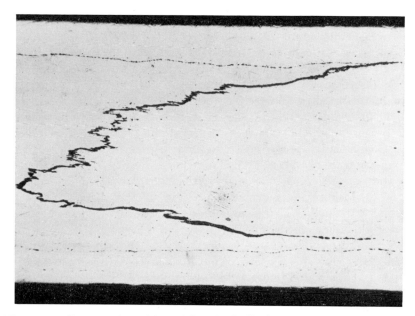

Figure 9-7. Cross section of butt joint (etched) of sectional-type picture frame. Joint exhibited is one formed perpendicular to the direction of rolling. (100×)

picture frame was employed for all subsequent work, since no difficulties were encountered.

Initially, the welding of the conventional picture frame assembly was carried out in a manner identical to that described for the sectional assemblies. The completion of a series of experimental plates showed that use of a minimum of 30 per cent reduction in thickness on the initial hot pass allowed sufficient core-to-clad bonding so that the conventional heliarc welding technique could be omitted and a simple spot-welding technique employed instead. This technique consists of the spot welding of each cover plate to the picture frame subsequent to insertion of the core compact.

Fuel Plate Fabrication

After the core compact was assembled into a conventional-type picture frame, the unit was preheated, hot-rolled, annealed, cleaned, and cold-rolled to the required finished condition.

Preheating and Hot Rolling. Early work on this program employed type 304 stainless steel only. It was found that satisfactory plates could be produced when a preheat and hot-rolling furnace temperature of 1150 to 1180°C was used. Subsequent work with type 347 stainless steel revealed that preheat and hot-rolling temperatures of 1150 to 1180°C were too low. Core material of plates rolled at these temperatures exhibited various defects, primarily cracks.

As a means of determining the optimum preheat and hot-rolling temperature to be employed for fuel plates composed of type 347 stainless steel, a series of plates was fabricated at preheat and hot-rolling furnace temperatures of 1180 to 1225°C. Observation during the processing and examination of the finished plates revealed that preheat and hot-rolling temperatures below 1200°C resulted in defective plates containing cracked cores. On the other hand, temperatures in excess of 1220°C resulted in torn cover plate stock because of the hot shortness of the stainless steel at these temperatures. Consequently, it was concluded that a preheat and hot-rolling furnace temperature of 1200 to 1220°C is required for plates composed of type 347 stainless steel, while 1150 to 1180°C is adequate for plates comprised of type 304 stainless steel.

Total hot reduction in thickness of these plates is dependent upon the required dimensions of the finished plate and the dimensions of the initial picture frame assembly.

While hot reductions per pass of approximately 15 to 40 per cent were evaluated, it was found that a reduction of about 30 per cent per pass was optimum. A reduction of this nature enabled core-to-clad bonding to take place on the first hot pass. It was noted that lesser reductions were not sufficient to attain good bonding on the first pass and greater reductions were responsible for distortion of the core end shape.

Annealing and Cleaning. After being hot-rolled, the plates were roughly edge- and end-trimmed as a means of squaring in order that any possible cambering which might occur during the cold-rolling would be minimized. Following this operation, the hot-rolled plates were bright annealed in a dry hydrogen atmosphere at 1150°C for one hour. In this manner, much of the surface oxide formed during the hot-rolling is reduced. Consequently, further cleaning operations are simplified. Annealing temperatures below 1150°C, while satisfactory for softening these plates, were not found to be very effective in reduction of surface oxides.

Subsequent to the annealing, some of the heavier deposits of surface oxide remain, which, if not removed, will become imbedded in the cladding during the cold-rolling. Rolled-in oxide of this nature might penetrate the cladding in such a manner as to be cause for rejection of the plate. These oxides can be removed by an acid pickle consisting of nitric acid (10 to 15 per cent by volume), and hydrochloric acid (2 per cent by volume) at 120 to 140°F.

Cold Rolling. Upon completion of the chemical cleaning, the fuel plates are cold-rolled to finish thickness, so that the finished plates will (1) have a good finish; (2) more readily meet dimensional specifications; and (3) be flat.

Since fragmentation and stringering of oxide particles increases as cold work is increased, it was believed necessary for the total cold work to be minimized. It was found that a minimum of about 20 to 25 per cent total cold reduction was required to yield a finished fuel plate satisfactory with respect to finish, dimensions, and flatness. Consequently, a minimum of about 20 per cent total cold reduction was maintained during all of the fuel plate processing. This consisted of a reduction of about 0.001 in. in thickness per pass in an effort to maintain flatness and to minimize camber. A light grade machine oil was employed as a lubricant for all cold-rolling operations.

Finishing. Subsequent to completion of the cold-rolling, the fuel plates were finished so that they might be utilized for subassembly fabrication.

Early in the program, the fuel plates were given a final flat-anneal prior to the finish-shearing operation. It was noted, however, that the plates contained badly burred edges which hindered assembly in the brazing jig. In order for this difficulty to be eliminated, all finish-shearing was carried out with the plates in the as-rolled condition. In this manner, a much cleaner, burr-free edge could be obtained.

After the fuel plates were sheared to finish size, they had to be fully annealed so that any possible distortion during the brazing due to relief of the stresses would be prevented. In addition to the annealing, it was essential that the plates be flat so that they might be readily fitted into the side plates. As a means of achieving these objectives, a flattening-annealing technique was worked out whereby the plates could be annealed and flattened in a simultaneous operation. In this process, the finish-sized dummy plates were coated with a slurry of levigated alumina and then stacked alternately between finish-trimmed fuel plates. This alternately piled stack was then placed between two, $5/8$-in. thick, $3\frac{1}{2}$-in. wide, and 30-in. long annealed steel plates and subjected to a temperature of 1150°C for 45 min. in a dry hydrogen atmosphere. Upon being cooled and removed from the furnace, the plates were found to be fully annealed, perfectly flat, and very clean and bright in appearance. Figures 9-8 and 9-9 are photomicrographs of typical longitudinal and transverse sections of two of these plates. These specimens were obtained from fully processed 0.030-in. thick fuel plates.

Subassembly Fabrication

In addition to the use of Coast Metals N.P. as a braze material for the production of APPR subassemblies in a manner similar to that employed at ORNL, other techniques which might yield a less costly operation or a more improved assembly were evaluated.

The subassembly methods primarily considered during this investigation were welding and the use of braze materials other than Coast Metals N.P.

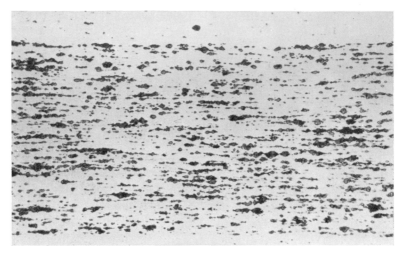

longitudinal section

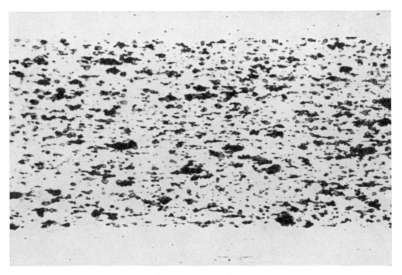

transverse section

Figure 9-8. Typical microsections of a 0.030-in. thick stainless steel-UO₂ fuel plate having a core composed of 25 w/o −325 mesh granulated UO_2 in a −325 mesh type 347 stainless steel matrix. (100×)

Welding. The fabrication of APPR subassemblies by welding was considered in order that the use of machined side plates necessary with the brazing technique could be eliminated. It was also believed that the welded assembly would be stronger and possess greater corrosion resistance than the brazed assembly.

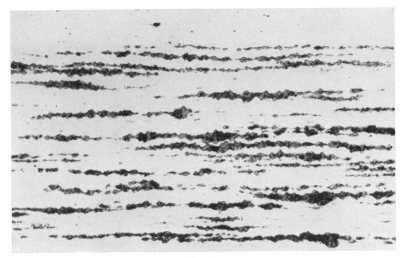

longitudinal section

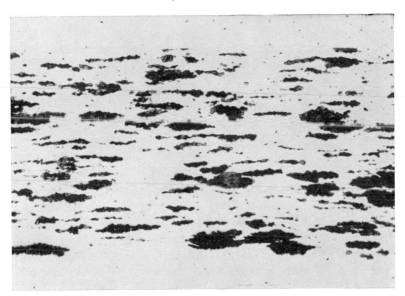

transverse section

Figure 9-9. Typical microsections of a 0.030-in. thick stainless steel-UO_2 fuel plate having a core composed of 25 w/o $-140 + 325$ mesh granulated UO_2 in a -325 mesh type 347 stainless steel matrix.

The welding techniques were evaluated with components such as those shown in Figure 9-10. The distance between plates was controlled by spacers of the desired width, spot welded to the edges of the plate. Work to date has been performed on dummy fuel plates and on subassemblies of full

Figure 9-10. Dummy APPR plate showing spot-welded side spacers and punched holes used for alignment prior to welding.

cross section and approximately half length. The required number of plates, with the spot-welded spacers, were assembled by the insertion of pins through the punched holes at the ends of the plate for alignment purposes. Copper plates of the same thickness as the spot-welded spacers were inserted between the fuel plates as an additional control over the plate spacing. They also prevented overheating of the fuel plate during the welding.

The welding operation was performed with a heliarc torch having a tungsten electrode. The torch was mounted on a carriage which automatically traveled parallel to the work piece. Diffusion weld beads were made in sequence on alternate sides of the assembly in order to minimize distortion which might arise from the welding. The arc length was adjusted semimanually, and the heat input was set to provide for a full penetration of the weld bead. A photograph of the fusion weld between the fuel plate and water channel spacer strip is shown in Figure 9-11. It is apparent from this figure that full penetration was achieved. No filler metal was used for this weld; and it can be seen that the weld material consisted of the fuel plate edge and the spacer strip. Upon completion of the welding of all joints, the copper spacer plates were removed from the assembly. A photograph of a welded assembly is shown in Figure 9-12.

While it has been established that it is feasible to make an APPR type

Figure 9-11. Photomicrograph showing full penetration of the weld bead at the intersection of fuel plate and water channel spacers. (15×)

Figure 9-12. Section of a welded APPR subassembly.

of assembly by a welding process, improvements are required in this technique to obtain a suitable assembly. As such, the welding procedure for assembly was set aside as a secondary effort, and the further development of subassembly fabrication by a brazing method emphasized.

Brazing. This work consisted of an investigation made in order to determine whether braze materials other than Coast Metals N.P. would fulfill the corrosion requirements and yield an improved, more readily obtainable braze. The materials evaluated, in addition to Coast Metals N.P., were electroless nickel plate (nickel-phosphorus alloy), 70Ni-20Cr-10Si (w/o) alloy powder, 57Ni-13Cr-30Ge (w/o) alloy powder, and an elemental powder mixture of the latter alloy.

Electroless Nickel Plate. The chief advantage of electroless nickel as a braze material for this type of assembly is the high uniformity and the ease of application. Work included the evaluation of various plate thicknesses, brazing temperatures, and brazing times in order to determine the optimum conditions.

Plating Technique. A standard practice was established for the electroless nickel plating of side plates as a means of depositing a braze material uniformly. In this process the plating operation was carried out at a temperature of 85 to 95°C in a rectangular "Pyrex" tank containing approximately 16 liters of plating solution. Heat was applied by a double-boiler technique. The Pyrex tank was immersed within a larger steel tank containing water heated by immersion heaters. Constant agitation of the plating bath was maintained by an electrically operated stirring mechanism.

In the first step, preparation of these plates for the plating bath, the grooved side plates in the as-received condition were degreased and painted with a levigated alumina slurry. The plates were subsequently bright flat-annealed in a dry hydrogen atmosphere for $\frac{1}{2}$ hr at 1150°C. After removal from the furnace, the plates were cleaned with soap and water to remove the alumina coating. The outside ungrooved surfaces of the side plates were next coated with United Chromium's stop-off lacquer No. 324 which prevents plating. After this coating had dried, the side plates were subjected to an electrolytic nickel strike for 2 min. at room temperature in a solution containing 244 g of nickel chloride and 84 ml of hydrochloric acid per liter of solution. Subsequently, the plates were given a cold water rinse.

The completely prepared plates were now ready to be plated. They were immersed in the plating bath which was contained in a rectangular Pyrex tank previously described. The bath was comprised of 30 g of nickel sulfate, 10 g of sodium acetate, and 10 g of sodium hypophosphite per liter of solution. The plates remained in this solution until no further reaction was noted, usually 2 to 3 hours. At this time, the plates were removed and the solution replaced with a fresh batch. It was found that 0.0012 in. of electroless nickel was deposited in the 3 hours that the solution was active. Consequently, the rate of deposition was approximately 0.0004 in. per hour.

The initial assemblies produced with electroless nickel plate as the braze material were destructively tested. It was found that use of a nickel plate thickness in excess of 0.0025 in. did not allow proper fit of the fuel plate into the grooved side plates. The poor fit so incurred caused many unbonded points and resulted in a finished subassembly which was greater in width than allowable tolerances.

Additional subassemblies fabricated with side plates containing a maximum nickel plate thickness of 0.0024 in. revealed many unbrazed zones upon destructive evaluation. Lack of braze material was believed to be the cause of these many voids. Since 0.0024 in. of nickel plate was not sufficient to yield good brazed joints, and since a nickel plate thickness in excess of 0.0024 in. would not allow proper fit of the fuel plates into the side plates, the feasibility of depositing an amount of nickel in excess of 0.0024 in. on the lands between the grooves, while the grooves were coated with less than 0.0024 in. of nickel plate, was evaluated. In this manner, it was believed that a good fit might be achieved without a sacrifice in the amount of braze material which was needed for bonding.

The plating procedure employed to carry out a two-step process of this nature consisted of deposition of a 0.001-in. thick electroless nickel plate on the entire grooved surface of the side plate. The grooves were subsequently coated with United Chromium No. 324 stop-off lacquer which inhibited further plating. An additional 0.004 in. of electroless nickel was then deposited on the lands between the grooves of the side plates. The finish-plated side plate contained a 0.001-in. thick plate in the grooves, allowing ample space for good fit of the fuel plates, and a 0.005-in. thick plate on the lands, insuring enough nickel for a satisfactorily brazed joint. It may be necessary for the grooves to be machined again after this plating procedure.

Brazing Technique. The component subassembly parts, consisting of 18 fuel plates, two combs, and two side plates containing a deposit of electroless nickel plate, were assembled in a brazing jig. This jig was comprised of two ¾-in. thick stainless steel side plates secured at the top and bottom between ¾-in. thick stainless steel channels. Subsequent to being assembled, the unit was brazed by means of the following steps:

1. Insertion of the unit in a hydrogen atmosphere furnace whose temperature is 815°C.
2. Gradual increase of the temperature from 815 to 1075°C over a period of 2½ hours.
3. Maintenance of the unit at 1075°C for 7 minutes.
4. Gradual decrease of the temperature from 1075 to 815°C over a period of 4 hours.
5. The withdrawal of the unit very slowly into a warm cooler.
6. Circulation of cold water to cool the cooling chamber and unit.
7. Removal of unit from cooler when it is nearly at room temperature.

Figure 9-13 shows a typical electroless nickel brazed joint of a side plate in a prototype APPR fuel plate assembly.

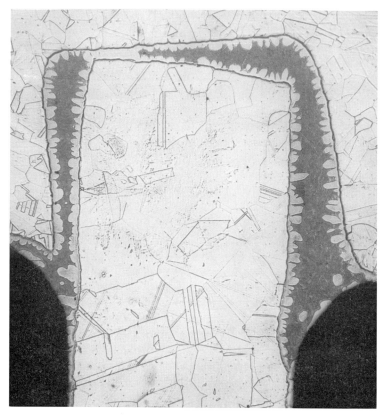

Figure 9-13. Typical electroless nickel braze joint of a side plate from a prototype APPR fuel plate assembly. (75×)

Coast Metals N.P. Preparation of the component parts of a subassembly to be brazed with Coast Metals N.P. was carried out in a similar manner to that described for the electroless nickel process. Because of the nature of the braze material, however, it was applied as a powder during the assembly of the unit into the brazing jig. The use of stop-off material was eliminated after several early assemblies, since excessive flow of the braze was not encountered. The brazing jig employed for the Coast Metals work was the same as that employed for the electroless nickel work. Subsequent to being assembled, the unit was brazed. The procedure used was identical to that followed with the electroless nickel plated samples except that: (1) the brazing temperature range extended from 815 to 1185°C; and (2) the unit was held at 1185°C for 4 minutes.

Figure 9-14 shows a typical photomicrograph of a side plate assembly joint, from a prototype APPR fuel plate, brazed with Coast Metals N.P.

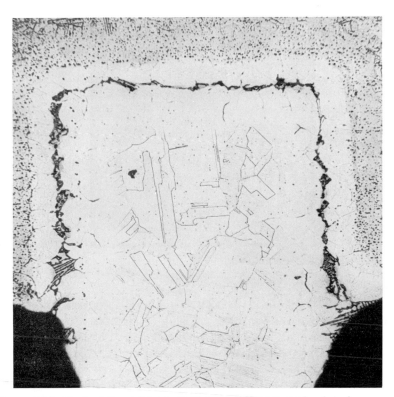

Figure 9-14. Typical Coast Metals N.P. braze joint of a side plate from a prototype APPR fuel plate assembly (75×)

Figure 9-15 shows a longitudinal section of a subassembly brazed by means
of Coast Metals M.P.

Other Materials. In addition to the evaluation of the electroless nickel
plate and Coast Metals N.P. as brazing materials, 57Ni-13Cr-30Ge (w/o),
and 70Ni-20Cr-10Si (w/o) materials were also investigated. Since these
two materials were in the form of a prealloyed powder, the problem of application was similar to that encountered for Coast Metals N.P.

As a means of overcoming the difficulty in the application of these powders, metallizing was evaluated. This process consisted of the spraying of
the braze materials in a powdered form onto the grooved side plates. Early
results indicated that the flow temperature of all the materials was elevated to over 1200°C as a result of the spraying. Since temperatures in this
range were considered too high, this technique did not appear to be feasible
for this operation.

In addition to evaluation of the 57Ni-13Cr-30Ge (w/o), the 70Ni-20
Cr-10Si (w/o), and Coast Metals N.P. materials, elemental mixtures of the

Figure 9-15. Typical section of an APPR subassembly brazed with Coast Metals N.P. braze.

Ni-Cr-Ge material were investigated. Owing to the extremely fine particle size of the germanium powder obtainable, spraying was not possible because the metering valve on the metallizing gun had become badly clogged. Further work on these materials was halted, since no advantages over Coast Metals N.P. were realized from their use.

Corrosion Testing. A static corrosion test was performed for the purpose of evaluating the corrosion resistance of electroless nickel plate, 57Ni-13Cr-30Ge (w/o), and 70Ni-20Cr-10Si (w/o), in comparison to Coast Metals N.P.

Specimen Preparation. A series of type 347 stainless steel disks $\frac{7}{8}$ in. in diameter were punched from a 0.030-in. thick sheet. Each of the braze materials under investigation was applied to a group of disks in the same manner as was employed in actual subassembly fabrication. The coated disks were subsequently fired with the same braze cycle being employed for each material that was used on a full-scale subassembly.

Test Procedure. Four specimens containing braze materials and four control-type 347 stainless steel disks were weighed and placed into autoclaves as follows:

1. Coast Metals N.P. and control disk.
2. 70Ni-20Cr-10Si (w/o) and control disk.
3. 57Ni-13Cr-30Ge (w/o) and control disk.
4. Electroless nickel plate and control disk.

All four autoclaves contained distilled water having a pH of 5.7 and a conductivity of 0.2 micromho/cm. The autoclaves were heated uniformly

TABLE 9-4. CORROSION RESULTS FOR VARIOUS BRAZE MATERIALS ON TYPE 347
STAINLESS SHEET TESTED IN 290°C DISTILLED WATER AT 1200 PSI

Braze Material	Weight Change From Time Zero (mg/cm^2)			
	175 hr	850 hr	1930 hr	3874 hr
Coast Metals N.P.	+0.05	−0.03	+0.05	+0.31
347 Stainless steel control	+0.52	+0.64	+0.82	+0.72
57 Ni-13 Cr-30 Ge (w/o)	+0.20	+0.46	+0.33	+0.44
347 Stainless steel control	+0.23	+0.38	+0.10	| 0.36
70 Ni-20 Cr-10 Si (w/o)	+0.31	+0.41	+0.28	+1.16
347 Stainless steel control	+0.31	+0.49	+0.33	+0.83
Electroless nickel plate	+0.28	+0.31	+0.44	+0.41
347 Stainless steel control	+0.46	+0.49	+0.82	+0.98

to a temperature of 290°C by means of a salt bath. The equilibrium pressure at this temperature is 1200 psi.

Results. Table 9-4 shows the weight change, in mg/cm^2, of the brazed specimens and controls after exposure in high temperature water for 175, 850, 1930, and 3874 hours. It was interesting to note that the Coast Metals N.P., 57Ni-13Cr-30Ge (w/o), and 70Ni-20Cr-10Si (w/o) all exhibited a weight loss early in this evaluation, while the electroless nickel did not show any weight loss until the 3874-hr examination. The 0.03 mg/cm^2 loss finally reported was relatively small when compared to losses reported for shorter exposures for the other materials under investigation. Also, it was equally interesting to note the excessive weight gain exhibited by the 70 Ni-20Cr-10Si (w/o) specimen after 3874 hr as compared to the other materials under investigation.

In conclusion, however, it can only be stated that the over-all results show all weight changes to be so minute that all of the braze materials evaluated can be considered to be quite corrosion resistant under the test conditions, and, therefore, satisfactory from the corrosion standpoint for use on the APPR fuel element subassembly.

Since none of the braze materials tested exhibited any greatly improved corrosion resistance in comparison to Coast Metals N.P., the Coast Metals N.P. was selected for use, because of the wealth of information available from work carried out by the Oak Ridge National Laboratory and Sylvania-Corning Nuclear Corporation.

FABRICATION OF NATURAL UO$_2$ FUEL ELEMENT SUBASSEMBLY

Finally, a complete APPR subassembly containing natural UO$_2$ was fabricated. This necessitated the fabrication of 18 natural UO$_2$ fuel plates by the technique proved to yield the highest quality product in the most economical manner. This technique was established from results of the aforementioned investigation. The actual procedure employed for production of the 18 natural UO_2 fuel plates is described below.

Powder Preparation. UO_2, prepared by the reduction of calcined ammonium diuranate, was granulated, and a $-140 + 325$ mesh particle size was obtained for use. The coarse oxide was selected for use rather than the fine, since it promoted higher green strength of the core compacts. In addition, radiation damage tests have indicated the coarser oxide particles to be superior to the finer particles. Subsequently, individual powder mixtures were prepared for each plate. Each mix contained 34.9 g of $-140 +325$ mesh granulated UO_2, 0.144 g of -325 mesh elemental crystalline boron, and 100.5 g of -325 mesh type 347 stainless steel powder. Each powder mixture was then dried for 20 min. at 250°C in dry hydrogen and subsequently blended for 2 hours.

Compacting. A come-apart compacting die having a 2.455 x 4-in. cavity was employed in the fabrication of the core compacts. Each individual blended powder mixture made up one die charge which was cold compacted at 50 tsi. The resultant core compact was 0.125 in. thick, 2.455 in. wide, and 4 in. long.

Picture Frame Assembly. The as-pressed core compact was placed into a punched stainless steel picture frame, 0.110-in. thick, which was spot-welded to a 0.031-in. thick cover plate. A second 0.031-in. thick cover plate was finally spot-welded to the open side of the picture frame, fully enclosing the core compact. The dimensions of the over-all assembly prior to its being rolled were 0.185 in. thick, $4\frac{7}{16}$ in. wide, and 7 in. long.

Hot Rolling. After the green compacts were assembled into picture frames, the units were preheated at 1220°C for 35 minutes. They were then hot-rolled by means of a four-pass schedule which reduced the unit from 0.185 to 0.042 in. in thickness, or a total reduction of 77.4 per cent. A reduction of about 31 per cent per pass was employed. After each pass, the pieces were heated in a hydrogen furnace at 1220°C for a period of 10 minutes.

Cold Rolling and Annealing. At the final hot-rolled thickness of 0.042 in., the plates were rough trimmed, bright annealed at 1150°C for 1 hr in dry hydrogen, and finally cleaned in an acid solution followed by a water rinse.

After being cleaned, the plates were cold-rolled to a finish thickness of 0.030 in. with a light grade machine oil being employed as a lubricant. Subsequently, it was necessary that the fuel plates be fully annealed and perfectly flat in preparation for subassembly fabrication. The flattening-annealing operation previously described was employed to prepare the plates for final subassembly.

Subassembly Fabrication. Subassembly fabrication of the 18-plate natural assembly was carried out in a manner similar to that previously described. Coast Metals N.P. was employed as the braze material. Upon completion, the finished subassembly was found to fulfill all required spec- ifications.

FABRICATION OF ENRICHED FUEL ELEMENT SUBASSEMBLY

In addition to the APPR subassembly containing natural UO_2, one modified APPR subassembly containing enriched UO_2 for radiation tests in the Materials Test Reactor, Idaho (MTR) was also required.

ENRICHED FUEL PLATE AND SUBASSEMBLY SPECIFICATIONS

1. Over-all plate thickness: $0.030'' \pm 0.001''$.
2. Core composition: weight percentages used in a standard APPR assembly.
3. Core thickness: adjusted for a loading of 0.030 g of U^{235} per sq cm of plate.
4. Total number of plates: 19.
5. Plate spacing: $0.116'' \pm 0.012''$.

Feasibility Work

Subsequent to receipt of specifications for the enriched fuel plates, feasi- bility runs were carried out with natural UO_2. While the enriched plates were to be of the same width, length, and thickness as the natural plates, the core was to be about 0.008 in. thick rather than 0.020 in. as specified for the natural plates. Consequently, the cladding was to be about 0.011 inch.

The first step was evaluation of the feasibility of compacting cores to the specification required for the enriched plates with the 2.455 x 4-in. com- pacting die. Because of the final core thickness required, compacts approxi- mately 0.050 in. in thickness had to be prepared. It was found that cores of this thickness could be prepared readily, but extreme caution was re- quired for subsequent handling because of the brittle nature of the com- pacts.

After assembly of the green compacts into 0.050-in. thick picture frames and the spot welding of the 0.065-in. thick cover plates into position, the units were ready for the preheating and rolling operations.

The fabrication procedure was identical to that employed for the nat- ural UO_2-containing fuel plates.

Work with Enriched Material

Based upon data obtained from the feasibility run and work performed on the natural assembly, fabrication of the enriched plates was initiated.

Plate Fabrication. Core compacts employed for the enriched fuel plates were produced in the same compacting die used for the natural plates. The charge, however, was altered to compensate for the reduced core thickness.

A total of 31 compact charges was prepared. Each one consisted of 14.4 g of highly enriched UO_2 (granulated and containing 3 w/o CaF_2), 36.26 g type 347 stainless steel, and 0.0576 g of elemental boron (99.12 purity). A compacting pressure of 50 tsi was employed and resulted in pieces 4 x 2.455 long and approximately 0.050 inch thick. Green thickness of each compact was not accurately determined because of the fragile condition of the extremely thin compacts.

Each as-pressed compact was subsequently assembled into a 0.050-in. thick picture frame and completely enclosed by means of 0.065-in. thick cover plates secured in position by spot welding.

Preheating, hot-rolling, annealing, cleaning, and additional finishing operations were carried out in a manner identical to that employed for the natural fuel plates.

Subassembly Fabrication. After completion of the enriched fuel plates, subassembly fabrication was carried out. Procedures identical to those employed for the assembly of natural UO_2 plate were followed. The side plates, however, had 19 grooves instead of 18, so that the additional fuel plate might be accommodated. Also, the outside surface of each of the side plates was marked with $\frac{1}{32}$-in. wide grooves approximately 0.005-in. deep and located equidistant between fuel plate grooves on the opposite side. These grooves were to be utilized as saw guides during the postirradiation examination.

Examination of the finish-brazed enriched subassembly revealed that the bottom plate had been slightly distorted during the cooling cycle. Measurement of the plate-gap spacing revealed that this distortion did not allow for the necessary clearance between the bottom fuel plate and its adjacent one. Since the water-gap spacing was specified to be 0.116 ± 0.012 in., and since the distorted fuel plate caused the spacing to be as narrow as 0.093 in. in six specific locations, it was believed possible that the plate could be straightened to some degree thus obtaining the required spacing. The technique employed for this straightening operation is outlined below.

As the first step, a low-temperature melting alloy was cast into the subassembly, so that the entire water-gap spacing was filled except for the one between the distorted bottom plate and its adjacent plate. The alloy employed for this purpose was "Cerrotru" which consisted of 58Bi-42Sn (w/o). This material has a melting temperature of 281°F and upon solidification has the unique characteristic of expanding very slightly rather than shrinking. In this manner all of the fuel plates of the subassembly, except the distorted plate, were rigidly supported.

Two mild steel spacers were prepared next. These were to be placed in the water-gap spacing between the distorted fuel plate and its adjacent plate. The spacers were about 31 in. long, $1\frac{1}{4}$ in. wide, and 0.116 in. thick. After the spacers were in position, a planishing hammer was employed to straighten the distorted plate which was cushioned by a liberal coat of oil. At intervals during the hammering, the spacers were removed and the water-gap spacing measured. This procedure was followed until the water-gap spacing fell within tolerance. Subsequently, the unit was placed in an air furnace at 300°F and the Cerrotru alloy was melted out. In order for all traces of the Cerrotru alloy to be removed completely, the unit was finally washed in a dilute nitric acid solution.

The completely cleaned subassembly was fully inspected and prepared for shipment to Oak Ridge for preirradiation evaluation.

Specifications for APPR fuel and control rod components are given in Appendix I.

10. TUBULAR-TYPE DISPERSION ELEMENTS

W. A. MAXWELL

Staff Engineer, General Nuclear Engineering Corporation
Dunedin, Florida

The tubular form is one of the more interesting configurations for fuel elements. A major advantage is that the tube is inherently a rigid structural member which can support itself and requires a minimum of extraneous structure in the core. Applications of the tubular element are shown in the photographs. Figure 10-1 depicts the concentric tubular elements used in the CP-5 reactor at Argonne National Laboratory. Coolant flow is vertical between the concentric tubes and the center is filled with the specimen thimble shown in the photograph. Figure 10-2 shows a full core of bundle-mounted tubular elements as produced and tested by the Martin Company. The expanded tube ends position the elements and the flutes divide the water flow inside and outside the tubes.

The fact that little or no structural support is required, in combination with the fact that all the surface area of a tubular fuel element covers fuel and constitutes high performance heat transfer area, makes it possible, when using enriched fuel and a good coolant, to design minimum size cores. Cores of minimum size permit important savings in shield weight—an item of special significance in transportable and propulsion reactors. With propulsion reactors this weight saving becomes of increasing importance as the total weight of the vehicle decreases.

The heat-transfer advantages of the tubular element make its use attractive when power reactor coolants with poor thermal properties are used. Gas cycle reactors are now undergoing intensive investigation and gases are notoriously poor conductors of heat. Among coolant gases, the best known and one of the poorer heat conductors is superheated steam. Tubular elements are therefore being seriously investigated for superheater reactors.

The tubular element has certain disadvantages, one of the more important being the present high cost. A great deal of this cost is the result of limited production. However, it is doubtful if tubular elements would ever be considered for a low power research reactor. For high flux research reactors and power reactors, increased performance can outweigh a cost dif-

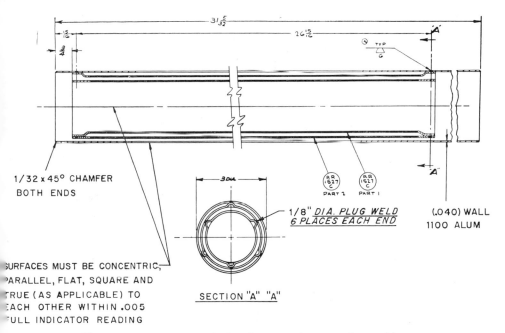

1/32 x 45° CHAMFER
BOTH ENDS

1/8" *DIA. PLUG WELD*
6 PLACES EACH END

(.040) WALL
1100 ALUM

SURFACES MUST BE CONCENTRIC,
PARALLEL, FLAT, SQUARE AND
TRUE (AS APPLICABLE) TO
EACH OTHER WITHIN .005
FULL INDICATOR READING

SECTION "A" "A"

Figure 10-1. The CP-5 tubular element: element subassembly.

ferential. Another characteristic, shared with other dispersed-type fuel elements, is that they are intended for enriched fuel. Dispersion elements are not considered for normal uranium reactors because of the tremendous amount of fuel that must be retained in the elements.

As shown in the first two figures, there are two basic configurations for tubular element assemblies. One of these, shown diagrammatically in Figure 10-3, is the bundle array in which small-diameter elements are mounted separately in square or hexagonal spacing. The cross section is shown with the fuel encased in the cladding. The second configuration employs elements of increasing diameter mounted concentrically as in Figure 10-1. The tubes themselves need not be perfectly cylindrical as they have always been produced to date, and the forms shown at the upper right in Figure 10-3 would increase both the heat transfer surface and the rigidity of the tubes. As shown, they might be difficult to manufacture but certainly some variation in the simple tube is possible. A modification which has been seriously considered is also shown. The core is not dispersion-type, but a thick-walled tube of stacked, low-enrichment UO_2 pellets. Such a form is a modification of the UO_2 pellet, gas heat-transfer, unbonded, stainless steel clad element. Center fuel temperatures should be lower with such an element than with the conventional pellet type, but there will be a problem of differential expansion between the inside and outside claddings.

(Courtesy Martin Corp., Nuclear Div.)

Figure 10-2. Full core mock-up for Martin Power Reactor.

To return to the dispersion elements, in a homogeneous tube the structural stiffness varies with the fourth power of the diameter and inversely with the cube of the length. There are, therefore, definite length/diameter ratio limitations in designing for tubular elements. With the concentric form, as shown in Figure 10-3, the smallest tube must be large enough in diameter to possess adequate stiffness. If smaller tubes were added to fill the vacancy a size would soon be reached at which the tube would not be rigid. For a research reactor this central hole is extremely convenient for test purposes, as was shown in Figure 10-1, as test capsules may be inserted down these channels in regions of maximum flux. Filling the hole with moderator has been considered in power reactor designs but usually the diameter is so small as to make the moderator ineffective.

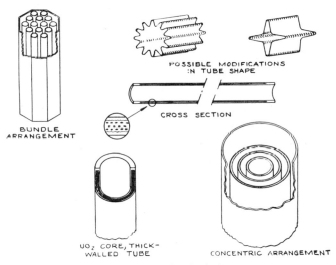

Figure 10-3. Tubular fuel elements.

Because of the comparatively large size of tube diameters, to get the coolant in and out of a concentric tube arrangement is comparatively simple. Mounting the large number of small diameter tubes in a bundle configuration is more difficult and presents an important problem. Methods of mounting and spacing which have been investigated are shown in Figure 10-4. Expanded tube ends can be either spot welded or brazed, and serve not only to locate the elements but also to divide the flow between in-tube and out-of-tube-passages. For pressurized water reactors, considerable work has been done on the effects of flow velocity, flow division, tube spacing, etc., (Refs. 1 and 2). Figure 10-5 from the work of Cushman[1] shows the variations possible in inside and outside hydraulic diameter for one configuration. The separation of the tubes by the expanded ends and the water separation by the flutes is shown at the top. The change in flute depth can vary the ratio of inside and outside equivalent diameters over a wide range.

Another important consideration is the effect of tube spacing on maximum element surface temperature. As developed by Ferrell and Lyon[2] and shown in Figure 10-6, a distinct optimum exists as regards surface temperature. For a given number of fixed-diameter fuel elements, for the configuration employed by the aforementioned authors and at constant coolant flow quantity, increasing the tube spacing would increase the core diameter, and through effects on coolant velocity would produce the pronounced effects shown in the curve.

The design background has been covered briefly, as the major concern of this chapter is with the fabrication and properties of the tubular element.

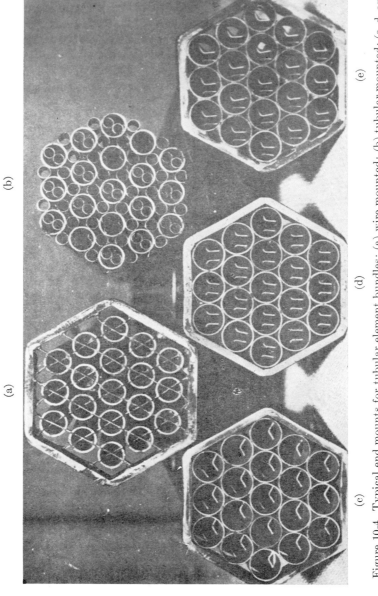

Figure 10·4. Typical end mounts for tubular element bundles: (a) wire mounted; (b) tubular mounted; (c, d, and e) flared and fluted ends of varying depths. (*Courtesy Martin Corp., Nuclear Div.*)

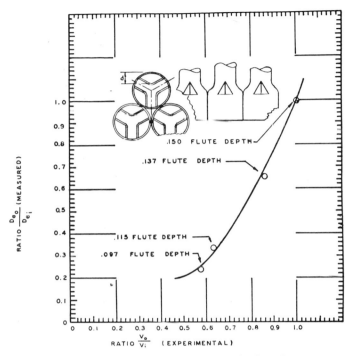

Figure 10-5. Plot of ratio of equivalent OD to equivalent ID *vs.* actual ratio of velocity outside tubes to velocity inside tubes.[1]

Tubular fuel elements can be produced by several methods. Coextrusion of the fuel containing core and cladding in a completely bonded, finished form is an attractive process and has been investigated both here and abroad. Aluminum tubular elements have recently been produced in France as reported by Montagne and Meny.[3] The tubes were 30 mm OD, 24 mm ID with a 0.4 mm cladding thickness and a core length of 300 mm. The core contained 43.5 per cent by weight UAl_4 which was prepared by vacuum melting of the compound or vacuum interdiffusion of the elements. As shown in Figure 10-7, the extrusion billet has a conical end, and the core material (UAl_4 plus 8μ lamellar aluminum powder) is canned in aluminum. Extrusion takes place at 500°C.

A multiple tube billet as employed by Nuclear Metals Inc. (Cambridge, Mass.) is shown in Figure 10-8, from which three zirconium-clad tubes can be extruded at once. The complex end-seal and core slug shapes, as developed by Kaufmann *et al.*[4] are necessary to produce reasonably square ends on the core and to main concentricity. If a rectangular billet containing a rectangular core is extruded, the motion of the outer parts of the billet

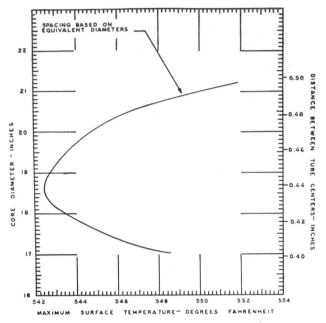

Figure 10-6. Effect of tube spacing on the maximum tube surface temperature.[2]

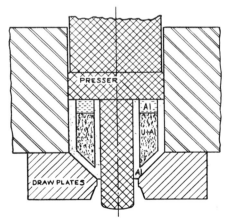

Figure 10-7. Tubular element extrusion; the arrangement before extrusion.[3]

will be much greater than that of the center and the core would be greatly elongated at the start and "fishtailed" at the end. This may be prevented to a large extent by proper curving of the core in the original billet. Slight differences in core length may occur but proper design of the billet and correct selection of materials will produce uniform cladding without "dogboning" or "whiskering."

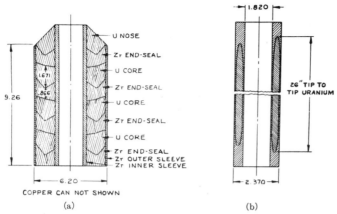

Figure 10-8. Zirconium-clad element coextrusion:[4] (a) billet assembly for extrusion of three uranium tubes clad inside and out with zirconium; (b) one coextruded tube as produced. Cladding 0.030 in.

With coextrusion, the area reduction ratios are so large that bonding on the top and bottom is assured; however, the extrusion process itself puts limitations on the materials which can be coextruded. For successful extrusion the core and cladding alloys must have approximately the same stiffness and resistance to deformation at the extrusion temperature. The extrusion constant K is given by the expression:

$$K = P/\ln R$$

where P is the extrusion pressure and R the ratio of initial cross-sectional area to the final cross-sectional area. Representative K values are:[4]

Material	Temp. (°F)	K-Tons/sq. in.
Uranium (0.04% C)	1100	17
	1200	15
Uranium	1600	3
Zirconium	1200	17
	1560	11.5
Copper	1000	15.5
Zircaloy-2	1200	25.0
	1600	16.5

These values of K can vary as much as 25 per cent when determined from experimental data. Alloys of divergent properties cannot be employed, although a certain amount of alloying might be employed to change the stiffness, and in some cases a temperature can be selected at which the K values match.

For the coextrusion of dispersion elements, the matrix alloy can well be the same as the cladding. At very low fuel loadings in the core the stiffness of the components would then be the same. The stiffness of the core cermet

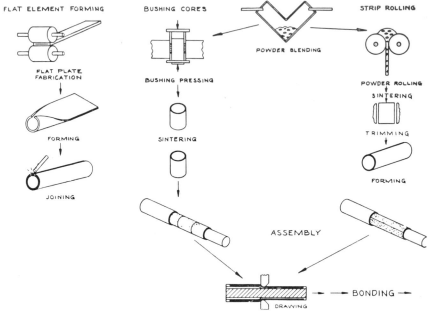

Figure 10-9. Tubular element fabrication methods.

will be affected strongly by the amount of dispersed fuel it contains, the particle size of the fuel, and its form: i.e., whether uranium is used in the form of UO_2, UAl_4, UC, etc.

Although the actual process of coextrusion is extremely rapid—in fact, with the impact extrusion of aluminum elements the action is too fast to be followed by the human eye—the preparation of the billet is complicated. It requires considerable data and experimentation on the extrusion characteristics of the materials used, and is also highly dependent on the experience and skill of the operators. However, once in production, the method should be economical, particularly for refractory metals.

Other techniques for the fabrication of tubular elements are shown in Figure 10-9. The most obvious way of making a tubular element is to form a flat-plate element, roll it into tubular shape, and weld it. Aside from possible welding difficulties, there is a loss of heat transfer area at the weld zone between the ends of the fuel. If the diameter of the tube is quite large, this loss is less important.

The other two techniques are among methods developed at the Martin Company. The "bushing" method is particularly applicable to heavy fuel loadings in the core and to refractory alloys. The core bushings can be produced on automatic presses but the wall thickness is probably limited to a minimum finished thickness of about 15 mils with no practical maximum.

Loadings as high as 65 per cent by weight of UO_2 in aluminum have been produced in fairly large quantities. After sintering, the bushings are strung on a preinspected cladding tube and covered with an outer tube. The fuel loading in the element may be varied over a wide range by changing the amount of fuel in each bushing. Fuel elements with properly controlled fuel distribution should make reactor power flattening possible.

After assembly the tubes are drawn down over a mandrel to a tight fit and are then diffusion-bonded by holding at the proper temperature. Precautions must be taken to prevent spreading of the bushings during bonding. Proper pressures must also be maintained in this operation and a high vacuum is employed when bonding aluminum.

Other promising methods have been described by Frank and Precht[5] but the discussion here will be limited to one of the most highly developed techniques, the so-called strip rolling process. As shown in Figure 10-9 the process consists of preparing a strip of UO_2-stainless steel cermet by rolling a mixture of the powders, sintering and trimming and then forming into a seamed tube which can be bonded to preinspected cladding tubes. As described by Shapiro and Galvez,[6] control of particle sizes and flow rates of the stainless steel and UO_2 is important. High-fired UO_2 of 44 to 88 μ particle size was employed. The hard particles resisted fragmentation during the fabrication process and provided discrete fuel particles in the matrix which would minimize radiation damage. The fuel elements were prepoisoned to permit increased burn-up. Boron carbide, boron nitride and zirconium boride were investigated for this purpose, and boron carbide was finally selected as the boron carrier. Although there is some difficulty with the evaporation of the boron during sintering, the major trouble is with the chemical analysis of boron. The boron content (approximately 0.1 per cent) was held with sufficient accuracy so that a full-scale, zero-power test of some 1700 elements went critical exactly as predicted.

In comparing the bushing technique with the strip rolling method, the latter is somewhat more limited in the fuel loading percentages which can be handled, as a certain amount of strength is required in the strip. There are also losses in trimming, and the UO_2 in the trimmed edges must be recovered. With the bushing process the bushings are produced to size. No ductility is required of the unsintered bushings, and only limited handling is necessary. However, separation of the bushings in the element must be prevented.

In both operations surface cleanliness is of the utmost importance for bonding, and the drawing operations indicated in Figure 10-9 not only produce tight contact but also introduce cold work which accelerates recrystallization bonding. The bonding temperature is slightly above the recrystallization temperature. Excessive grain growth is to be avoided. Typical

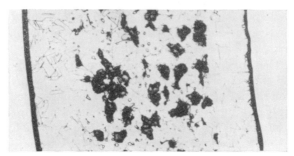

SS fuel element, transverse section, 230X

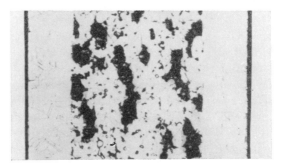

SS fuel element, longitudinal section, 230X

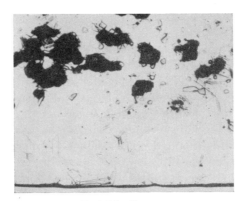

Typical bonding, 400X

Figure 10-10. Representative photomicrographs of tubular stainless steel-clad elements. (*Courtesy Martin Corp., Nuclear Div.*)

bonds are shown in Figure 10-10. Grain growth across the interface is evident and the interfaces are clean. Both processes, and particularly the bushing method, treat the fuel quite gently in that there is no rolling or drawing of the elements to large reduction ratios to achieve a bond. The fuel particles are therefore clean and unfragmented, particularly in the longi-

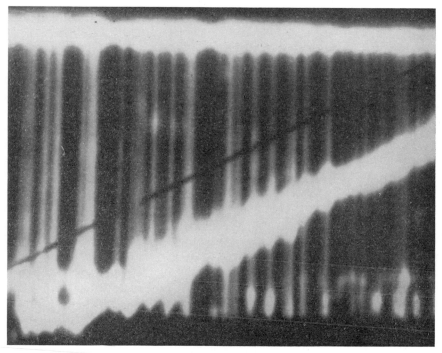

Typical B scan trace

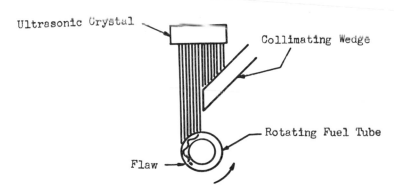

Arrangement of the specimen[7]

Figure 10-11. Ultrasonic testing.

tudinal direction. In an in-pile test after a burn-up of 41.7 per cent, with the element cooled in reactor coolant water, these structures were apparently unaffected, and no deleterious effects were apparent.

With the exception of research reactor elements, there are few performance data on tubular elements. Such data will have to await extensive and expensive in-pile tests under simulated operating conditions, or, preferably, the actual operation of reactors. However, the out-of-pile testing of tubular elements has undergone rather thorough investigation. Obviously many conventional testing techniques can be applied, such as radiography, dimensional checks, dye-penetrant methods, porosity checks by submersion in acid, etc. The degree of success recently obtained with such nondestructive testing techniques as ultrasonics encouraged investigation, even though the tubular geometry might not seem well suited for ultrasonic inspection.

Fulmer[7] has reported results based on the ultrasonic investigation of several hundred tubular elements and has correlated results of these nondestructive tests with those of destructive tests. An Immerscope and B-scan were used and the tubes were rotated while immersed. The general arrangement and a typical B-scan plot are shown in Figure 10-11. Unbonded areas were the most important defect sought. As shown in the traces, as a defect rotates away from the front surface, a diagonal line is produced, representing the distance of the defect from the front surface. The elements investigated, made by the strip-rolling technique, contained a seam which is shown on the trace but which is not deleterious. It was demonstrated that unbonded areas of 0.025 sq in. or smaller would be detected. Small distinuities or defects could be located with sufficient precision so that the elements could be sectioned and the defect examined under the microscope. All tubes rejected by the ultrasonic test failed in thermal shock when heated to 1000°C in a furnace and then immersed in cold water; tubes which passed ultrasonic inspection did not fail. It appears that the ultrasonic test technique can determine flaws so small that they probably would not be injurious under operation conditions.

In conclusion, it might be said that coextrusion and other techniques have been used to produce tubular fuel elements clad with aluminum and its alloys, zirconium and Zircaloy, and several stainless steels, in diameters from $\frac{1}{4}$-in. to greater than 3 inches. Core thicknesses vary from a minimum around 0.015 in. to a maximum probably greater than could be used. The lengths of tubular elements are probably controlled only by such practical considerations as furnace hot-zone lengths, etc. For dispersion-type cores, the maximum fuel loading depends to some extent on the fabrication technique but limitations imposed by the characteristics of the alloying diluent are more important in their effects. With aluminum, cores containing from 65 to 75 w/o of UO_2 can be produced, but with stainless steel the maximum UO_2 is between 30 and 45 per cent.

It would appear that the development of techniques for the production and nondestructive testing of tubular elements is well advanced and that the next important step is the design and operation of more reactors which employ tubular elements.

References

1. Cushman, R. A., and Cunningham, W. W., "Tubular vs Plate Fuel Elements: Heat Transfer and Flow Analysis," Reactor Heat Transfer Conference, New York, Nov. 1 and 2, 1956.
2. Ferrell, J. K., and Lyon, W. C., "Tubular Fuel Element Heat Transfer Analysis," American Nuclear Society, Pittsburgh, Jan. 10–14, 1957.
3. Montagne, R., and Meny, L., "Coextrusion Applied to the Fabrication of Solid Fuel Elements," Fuel Elements Conference, Paris, TID-7546, Book 1, p. 142 (Nov. 18–23, 1957).
4. Kaufmann, A. R., Klein, J. L., Lowenstein, P., and Sawyer, H. F. "Zirconium Claddings of Uranium and Uranium Alloys by Coextrusion," Fuel Elements Conference, Paris, TID-7546, Book 1, p. 157 (Nov. 18–23, 1957).
5. Frank, L., and Precht, W., "Techniques for Producing Tubular Fuel Element Cores," American Nuclear Society, Pittsburgh, June 10–14, 1957.
6. Shapiro, S., and Galvez, M., "A New Fabrication Technique for the Production of Stainless Steel-Oxide Dispersion Elements," Second United Nations Conference on the Peaceful Uses of Atomic Energy, Geneva, A/Conf. 15/P/784.
7. Fulmer, Glenn E., "Ultrasonic Testing of Small Diameter Tubular Stainless Steel Fuel Elements," ASTM (Nov. 1958).

11. FABRICATION OF THE ISNSE FUEL ELEMENT FOR LOW POWER RESEARCH REACTORS

H. BERGUA, R. FRIDDLE, J. DIAZ and J. BAIRD

International School of Nuclear Science and Engineering*
Argonne National Laboratory, Lemont, Ill.

Fabrication

The materials used for the preparation of this fuel element during the development work were U_3O_8 of natural isotopic content and commercial aluminum powder. Conventional equipment, which would normally be found in a metallurgical laboratory of a university, was used wherever possible.

Preparation of Powder. The as-received U_3O_8 powder was calcined before placing it in fabrication by heating it at 1,000° in air for 4 hours. The calcined powder was ball-milled in a porcelain ball mill for 12 hours to produce a −80 mesh powder. All transferring of U_3O_8 powders from one container to another was done in a chemical hood, which was loosely enclosed at the front, and the work was done through glove ports. There was a suction exhaust system connected to the hood so that there was a movement of air into the hood at the front. The air then passed through the prefilters in the back of the hood, through duct work to an absolute filter (Atomic Energy Commission) before being discharged to the atmosphere. There was no air-borne contamination in the laboratory, and none outside, because the absolute filters were very efficient.

The −100 mesh aluminum powder, which was used in the as-received condition, is commercially available as No. 120 atomized aluminum powder from Aluminum Company of America.

Weighing and Mixing of U_3O_8 and Aluminum Powders Required for One Fuel Plate. It is easy to give a physicist the exact amount of

* Messrs. Bergua and Diaz, Research Resident Associates from Spain, Junta Energia Nuclear. Messrs. Friddle and Baird, Instructors in the Metallurgy Section of the International School of Nuclear Science and Engineering, Argonne National Laboratory.

U^{235} in each fuel plate he desires because both the uranium content of the U_3O_8 and the isotopic content of the uranium are known. Since there are no inherent losses in subsequent fabrication, all of the U_3O_8 that is weighed out for a given fuel plate will be in that fuel plate after it is fabricated. In most of the experimental work, a mixture of 55 w/o U_3O_8 and 45 w/o aluminum powder was used. However, considerable work has been done with mixtures containing as high as 80 w/o* U_3O_8.

The required amounts of U_3O_8 and aluminum powder were weighed out and placed in a one-quart porcelain ball mill. A dozen small rubber stoppers (00) were put in with the powders to aid in the mixing. The porcelain balls were purposely omitted for the mixing operation because they produced an undesirable grinding action. The powders were mixed for 2 hr on a ball mill stand outside the chemical hood. The aluminum powder became uniformly distributed in the U_3O_8 powder, and the aluminum particles were bright and shiny and could be distinguished with the naked eye.

During the experimental work a more rapid method of mixing the powders was employed. The powders were placed in a wide mouth 500 cc Erlenmeyer flask and shaken vigorously by hand for 5 minutes. This quick method produced a mixture homogeneous to the eye. X-rays indicated that the finished fuel plates were of uniform density.

Encasing the Mixed Powders in Aluminum Foil. The mixture of powders was encased in 0.003-in. aluminum foil for ease in handling and to aid in the pressing and cladding operations. This was accomplished by transferring the powders from the ball mill directly into preformed foil boxes. The foil boxes were about 1 in. deep and were slightly smaller in cross section than the inside dimensions of the compacting die (2 x 2⅛ in.). They were easily formed by hand on a block of "Lucite." The transferring of mixed powders from the ball mill to the foil box was done in the chemical hood with great care taken to insure no loss of powders. The powders were uniformly distributed in the foil box by leveling with a flat spatula. A piece of 0.003 in. aluminum foil, 2 x 2 in. was placed on top of the loose powder. Then the edges of the foil box were folded over to completely encase the compact. The full foil box was then slipped into an empty foil box which was, in turn, folded over to doubly package the powders.

Pressing of Powders to Form a Compact. The use of aluminum foil made it possible to press the compacts outside the chemical hood without danger of air-borne contamination; it also prevented powder from adhering to the die walls. The compacting die was of 2 in. thick stainless steel and had a 2 by 2¼ in. cavity. The bottom ram fitted the cavity with about 0.003 in. clearance. The top ram was 1¹⁵⁄₁₆ in. x 2³⁄₁₆ in. The top two-thirds of the die cavity was lined with four pieces of 0.030-in. stainless steel sheet.

---

* w/o = weight per cent.

Figure 11-1. Uranium-aluminum compact before cast-cladding.

These four liners rested on top of the bottom ram and fitted around the top ram.

The foil-wrapped box of powder was placed into the die cavity so that it rested on the bottom ram. The top ram was inserted and the compact pressed at 30,000 psi. The pressed compact was ejected by an upward motion of the bottom ram. The four stainless liners moved upward with the compact until the bottom ram emerged from the die cavity, then they fell away from the compact. The aluminum foil was not ruptured during ejection, and there was no powder leakage. Compacts were usually about 0.600 in. thick. The thickness variation in any one compact was usually less than ±0.010 inch. The compacting was done on a 100-ton hand-operated Dake press. The press gave a double-action pressing to the compact because both the rams moved inward on the compact during pressing. The foil-clad compact was easy to handle and could be stored for several days before use. A typical compact is shown in Figure 11-1. Each compact is a core for one fuel element.

Cast-Cladding of the Compact to Make a Billet for Rolling. There were two methods considered for cladding the compact for rolling. One was the picture frame technique, which is widely used commercially and depends on roll-bonding of the solid aluminum; and the other was the cast-cladding technique, which has been developed and used successfully for 3 years in the metallurgy laboratory of the International School of Nuclear Science and Engineering at Argonne National Laboratory. It was decided to use the cast-cladding method because it was much more economical, and it permitted an investigation of cladding alloys.

The cladding mold had a cavity 1 in. thick x 3 in. wide x $4\frac{1}{2}$ in. deep. The mold frame, which formed the edges and bottom of the cavity, was made of 1 in. thick stainless steel. Then two stainless steel plates $\frac{1}{4}$ in.

thick x 4 in. wide x 6 in. high were clamped onto the frame, one on each side, to form the faces of the mold cavity.

The stainless steel locating pins were threaded into the frame and extended with long tapered points into the cavity. Two of the locating pins held the compact on one edge near the top and bottom, and the third pin held the opposite edge at the mid-point. The compact was uniformly centered with respect to the face plates so as to give uniform thickness of cladding on each face. The locating pins lay in a plane which was parallel to the rolled surfaces of the finished plate.

It was necessary to set up a steep temperature gradient in the mold to obtain a sound casting. Preheating the top of the mold with a gas ring burner for 5 min. set up a temperature gradient that caused solidification to progress from bottom to top and produced sound castings. The aluminum cladding alloy was held at about 800°C in a separate furnace. The molten alloy was ladled from the furnace, skimmed, and poured rapidly into the mold. Care was taken to keep the stream of molten metal from impinging on the compact. Complete solidification in the cladding mold took from 1 to 2 min., depending on the amount of preheating. Immediately after casting, the ring burner was raised so it heated only the very top of the mold where it served as a hot top. Thus, the molten metal was always available to feed the casting. The bottom of the cladding mold rested on a water-cooled copper block. As soon as the casting solidified, the locating pins were withdrawn, the cover plate removed, and the casting cooled so that it could be removed from the cladding mold. The nominal dimensions of the casting were 1 in. thick x 3 in. wide x $4\frac{1}{2}$ in. long. The core was completely clad on all surfaces except for the three holes on the edges of $\frac{1}{32}$ in. diameter, which were left when the locating pins were withdrawn. Figure 11-2 shows a cast billet ready for rolling.

Figure 11-2. Cast-clad U-Al billet, ready for rolling.

The cladding alloy most commonly used was 98 % aluminum, 1 % iron, 1 % nickel. Its hot working characteristics closely matched those of the 55 w/o U_3O_8 , 45 w/o Al core. When using 80 w/o U_3O_8 in the core, it was necessary to stiffen the cladding alloy by the addition of up to 10 per cent silicon to match the hot working characteristics of the core. The use of aluminum-silicon alloys made it necessary to scalp the billet in order to obtain a good finish. Also, it was necessary to control rolling temperatures more closely when working with the aluminum-silicon alloy.

Rolling the Cast-Clad Billet into a Fuel Plate. The billets were preheated at 500°C for 1 hr prior to rolling. Rolling was done in a 15-hp Stanat rolling mill with 5 in. diameter rolls 8 in. wide. The billets were hot-rolled with heavy passes to near finish size. Reheating was necessary after each two or three passes. The last few passes were made cold to produce a cold-worked fuel plate. The hot-rolling was effective in welding shut the small holes from the locating pins.

Inspection and Evaluation. The rolled plates were x-rayed to determine the location of the core. This was followed by an ultrasonic inspection check for defects in the cladding and a lack of bond between core and cladding.[1] In the early part of the development program, plates were blister-tested at 500°C. This was soon discontinued when McGonnagle and his associates showed that the ultrasonic test was more sensitive and more reliable than the blister test. Also, the ultrasonic test was recorded on electrosensitive paper, which gave a permanent visual record for later comparison studies. Furthermore, by eliminating the blister test, it was possible to keep the finished plates in the cold-rolled condition, which is more rigid and is highly desirable for spot welding into assemblies.

The cladding was of uniform thickness. The U_3O_8 was uniformly distributed in the core as determined by x-ray and metallographic examination. The core was bonded to the cladding and blended into the cladding. Claddings as thin as 12 mils have been produced on plates rolled with a 10 to 1 ratio. In general, it is easier to produce a 20 mil cladding with a 10 to 1 reduction in rolling because it is easy to cast a good 200 mil cladding over the core. The sidespread of the core was less than 5 per cent. No trace of the holes from the locating pins could be found by x-rays or ultrasonic testing.

In the 55 w/o U_3O_8-45 w/o Al alloy, no problems were encountered with "dog boning" at the end of the core when using the aluminum cladding alloy containing 1 per cent nickel and 1 per cent iron. In working with the 80 w/o U_3O_8 , the ends of the cores came up through this alloy cladding. Plates containing cores of 80 w/o U_3O_8 were satisfactorily fabricated when silicon up to 10 per cent was added to the cladding alloy. It was difficult to evaluate the quality of plates containing cores with 80 w/o U_3O_8 because sound waves could not readily penetrate the highly concentrated U_3O_8. The tapering of the ends of the core was less than $\frac{1}{2}$ in. at each end for a 24-in. long core, which was rolled 10 to 1. This compares favorably with the tapering encountered in fuel plates fabricated by the picture frame technique using U-Al alloy cores.

Some Advantages of the ISNSE Fuel Element

Economy and Small Capital Investment. The manufacture of the ISNSE fuel element is based on the conservation of raw materials by using powder metallurgy techniques for the core and an aluminum casting for the cladding. The required equipment is as follows: (1) ball mill and stand (2) 1 kg balance (3) rolling mill (4) heating furnace (1,000°C) (5) chemical hood with an exhaust system employing prefilters and absolute final filters (6) a 60-ton press (7) an aluminum melting pot (8) compacting die (9) casting mold (10) x-ray facilities (11) trimming shear.

Conservation of Fissionable Material. The powder metallurgy techniques make it possible for all of the fissionable material to end up in the finished fuel plate. This is in contrast to making aluminum-uranium alloy where there are inherent losses to the slag in melting, as well as chip formation from sawing and machining operations on the cast uranium-aluminum ingot and rolled core stock. Recovery of U^{235} from aluminum-uranium slag also is expensive.

Guaranteeded Fuel Content—No Need for Chemical Analysis. The U^{235} content of every batch of enriched U_3O_8 is furnished by the supplier. When the proper amount of U_3O_8 has been weighed out to give the desired U^{235} content for one fuel plate, there is no need for analytical work because there are no inherent losses in fabrication. With reasonable handling, all of the initial U_3O_8 will end up in the finished fuel plate. The U_3O_8 is uniformly dispersed through the core of the finished plate. By eliminating chemical analysis, there is a saving in both manpower and U^{235}, as well as prevention of speculation as to just exactly how much U^{235} is in each fuel plate.

Ease of Cast-Cladding. The described method eliminates the stamping dies for making the picture frame pieces and does away with the furnace brazing that precedes the roll bonding operation. Also, with cast-cladding, there is no waiting for delivery of sheet stock of a certain thickness. Fuel with any thickness of cladding within reason can easily be fabricated.

Ease of Varying Cladding Composition. Cast-cladding makes it possible to readily vary the composition of the cladding alloy to match the hot-working characteristics of the core material.

At this time, most of the MTR type fuel elements have been made with a cladding of 2S aluminum. This alloy is easy to roll-bond, but becomes quite soft at the hot-working temperatures. The use of the cladding alloy of 2S aluminum plus 1 per cent nickel gave rise to many problems in making the Argonne Low Power Reactor fuel plates because this alloy would not roll-bond satisfactorily by the conventional techniques of picture framing. This was overcome by Noland and Walker[2] with silicon pressure bonding, as described in detail in Chapter 4. They placed fine silicon powder between the plates to be bonded, then applied temperature and pressure and achieved the desired bond before rolling. The rolling was then only a sizing operation.

Uniformity of Uranium Content. The U_3O_8 is uniformly dispersed in the mixing operation and remains well dispersed during fabrication. In making U-Al alloys there is a constant problem of segregation of the alloy in the mold during solidification even when using a water-cooled mold. This segregation problem becomes more pronounced as the uranium content increases because at 33 w/o U-67 w/o Al, there is a freezing range of about 300°C. It is the length of time that it takes the alloy to cool from complete liquid to complete solid that governs the severity of the segregation.

Flexibility — Can Make Wide Range of Compositions. These fuel elements are prepared individually. It is as easy to make a number of fuel plates of different U^{235} content according to specifications as it is to make all of the plates to the same U^{235} content. This is of importance in research reactors where fuel elements of varying uranium content may be desirable for flux peaking.

Better Control Over Quality of Aluminum Cladding. A fuel element fabricator can melt and cast his own aluminum alloy cladding for the ISNSE fuel element. He would be able to control the quality of the aluminum so as to yield satisfactory results. Even when a fabricator purchases the best available aluminum plate for use in the picture frame method, he has no guarantee that the aluminum plate will not blister if heated to 500°C. Blisters which result from annealing finished fuel plates at 500°C have been found to occur within the aluminum plate as well as at the bond lines between the cladding-to-cladding or cladding-to-core.

Higher Uranium Concentrations. It can be shown that by using 80 w/o U_3O_8 and 20 w/o Al powder there can be $2\frac{1}{2}$ times as many uranium atoms per cm^3 as there are in the conventional 33 w/o U-67 w/o aluminum alloy. This is important when making fuel elements for research reactors where fabricators are limited to 20 per cent enriched uranium. Even with 55 w/o U_3O_8-45 w/o Al, there are 1.4 times as many atoms of uranium per cm^3 as in the 33 w/o U-67 w/o aluminum alloy.

Could be Fabricated in a University Metallurgical Laboratory. The ISNSE fuel element could be made in a university metallurgical laboratory without contaminating equipment which is used for teaching or experimental work. The only special equipment required would be a chemical hood with an exhaust and filter system. The dies for compacting and cast-cladding can be easily made. It is presumed that a metallurgical laboratory has a heating furnace and rolling mill as well as means for ball milling powders and melting aluminum. Even the pressing of the powders can be done in a simple welded frame of channel iron using portable hydraulic jacks.

Possible Disadvantages of the ISNSE Fuel Element

There is only limited information available as to the irradiation stability of this fuel element. It has not been used in a reactor at the present time.

There has been no study made of its heat-transfer characteristics. The ultrasonic testing can penetrate the 55 w/o U_3O_8 cores, but cannot get through the 80 w/o U_3O_8 cores. Ultrasonic testing simulates to a certain extent heat-transfer conditions.

The cladding alloy of 98 per cent Al, 1 per cent Ni, and 1 per cent Fe probably does not have good corrosion resistance in high temperature water because it is slow-cooled during the cladding operation. According to Ruther[3] it is necessary to chill this alloy rapidly to obtain a very fine dispersion of the nickel. It is the fine dispersion of nickel aluminum compound that gives the alloy its excellent hot water corrosion properties. However, this alloy will give excellent service in 100°C water even when slow-cooled. If one wishes to use the ISNSE fuel in the water at 250°C, considerable corrosion testing should be done to determine its suitability.

Irradiation Damage Studies on Dispersions of U_3O_8 in Aluminum Powder

There have been no irradiation damage studies made on the finished ISNSE fuel element. However, irradiation studies on the Argonaut fuel element by Kittel, Reinke and Horak[4] have been most encouraging. The Argonaut fuel, which is 20 per cent enriched, is a dispersion of 39 w/o of U_3O_8 in aluminum powder with a thin cladding of aluminum. It is made by coextrusion of core and cladding to produce a 0.095 in. thick core with a few mils of cladding. Nine samples of the Argonaut fuel were irradiated to burn-ups of the U^{235} from 3.9 to 27.0 w/o of the U^{235} in the fuel. The center temperatures ranged from 55°C for the 3.9 w/o burn-up to 130°C for 27.0 per cent burn-up. They reported that there was a small increase in density on all samples except one. This unexpected increase did not appear to be a function of the amount of irradiation. Also, the samples showed slight weight gains. All of the specimens were in excellent condition and apparently could have been taken to much higher burn-ups without damage.

Recent Fabrication Improvements

The sides and bottom of the cavity of the compacting die are lined with a box with open corners made from one piece of .030 in. soft 2S aluminum sheet. The four liners of .030 in. stainless steel are omitted from the die cavity. The foil-wrapped box of powder is placed inside the aluminum box. The top ram also fits inside the box, and the first pressing at 15,000 psi compacts the powders. The bottom ram is then moved up to bring the top of the compact level with the die, and the sides of the box are folded over to cover the foil box. Then it is pressed at 30,000 psi.

The compact is heated at 550°C in air for 30 min. and then is quickly centered in a cold cladding mold with locating pins. It is then cast-clad with an aluminum alloy of 1 % Ni, 1 % Fe, and 5 % Si. The aluminum box prevents any possible loss of U_3O_8 content by erosion during casting and makes it possible to use a cold mold. It eliminates preheating of the mold and gives the casting a good surface for rolling and should improve corrosion resistance of the alloy. The top of the casting just above the compact is puddled with a stainless steel rod during solidification to permit entrapped gasses to escape in order to yield a sound casting. The casting is then heated to 600°C for 1 hr and the top edge chamfered by hammering to permit easy entry into the rolling mill.

ACKNOWLEDGMENT

The authors wish to thank Warren McGonnagle and his non-destructive testing group for performing all the x-ray and ultrasonic testing.

References

1. McGonnagle, W. J., "Non-destructive Testing of Reactor Fuel Elements," *Nuclear Sci. Eng.*, **2**, No. 5, 602–616 (Sept. 1957).
2. Noland, R. A., Walker, D., Argonne National Laboratory, private communication.
3. Ruther, W., Metallurgy Division, Argonne National Laboratory, private communication.
4. Horak, J. A., Kittel, J. H., Reinke, C. F., Metallurgy Division, Argonne National Laboratory, private communication.

General References

Weber, C. E., and Hirsch, H. H., "Dispersion-Type Elements," *Proc. Intntl. Conf. on Peaceful Uses of Atomic Energy, Geneva*, **IX,** 196 (1956).
Beaver, R. J., "Irradiation Testing of Geneva Conference Reactor Fuel Elements," ORNL—1988.
Waugh, R. C., and Beaver, R. J., "Recent Developments in the Powder Metallurgy Application of Uranium Oxides to Aluminum Research Reactor Fuel Elements " ORNL, 57–9.

12. HIGH TEMPERATURE FUEL ELEMENTS

A. STRASSER

Nuclear Development Corporation of America, White Plains, N.Y.

APPLICATIONS

A number of incentives exist to obtain nuclear heat at temperatures above the range 800 to 900°C. The applications can be divided into several categories such as power reactors, propulsion reactors, process heat reactors, and reactors to produce chemical reactions. More so than in the case of any other reactor, the high temperature reactor depends on the development of a reliable fuel element. Very little is known about high temperature fuel elements compared to elements designed for moderate temperatures. A large number of conceptual designs exist for high temperature reactors; however, very few have reached the construction phase.

It is of interest to note some of these designs, as they give us an insight as to what we may expect in the future. High temperature power reactors are proposed for closed-cycle gas turbine systems. The high thermal efficiency of such plants (up to 40 per cent) may lower power cost.[1] In addition, compact gas turbine plants may provide power in locations, to which the transportation of fossil fuels is not economical. A summary of a number of the proposed power plants is given in Table 12-1.

A number of chemical processes require high temperatures; nuclear process heat[15, 89] may be an economical solution in the future. The NDA experimental results reported on p. 209 were a result of a fuel element development program for a process heat reactor to produce ~1370°C helium coolant. Economies may be enhanced if the nuclear radiation is utilized to propagate chemical reactions, as well as to supply heat or power. Examples of such processes are nitrogen fixation, nitric acid production, ammonia synthesis, hydrazine synthesis and hydrogen production.[16, 17, 89]

Propulsion reactors have been proposed for aircraft and rockets. Aircraft reactors are tied to a gas turbine system, but rockets need not be. Aircraft gas turbines operate at 760°C and up. Rocket temperatures are much higher; hydrogen coolant temperatures of 2200°C have been suggested.[18] Los Alamos' nuclear rocket development (Project Rover) requires materials with melting points above 2000°C,[19] to achieve a coolant temperature of at least 1650°C.[11]

TABLE 12.1. SOME POWER REACTORS WITH FUEL ELEMENTS WITH A POTENTIAL TO OPERATE AT HIGH TEMPERATURES

Originator	Application	Coolant	Coolant Temp. (°C)	Fuel Element Materials	Fuel Element Dimensions	Ref.
F. Daniels	Power (gas turbine cycle)	He Bi (boiling) Air	1500–2000 1450 1450	Graphite, uranium carbide Graphite, uranium carbide BeO-UO_2, unclad	2 in. diam. spheres	2
F. Daniels	Power (gas turbine cycle)	He, 225 psi	730	UC_2 clad in 3 in. long impervious graphite cartridges	4 fuel channels per 12 coolant channels in graphite moderator block	3
L. Brewer	Power breeder		~2400	UC_2 and ThC_2 in graphite matrix coated with Zr or Nb carbide, plan on releasing fission products		4
ORNL	Power breeder	He	760	Graphite impregnated with U, unclad	1 in. diam. sphere	5
U. of Michigan	Power (gas turbine cycle)	He, 1360 psi	730	25 w/o UO_2 dispersion in SS, clad with SS	0.030 in. core 0.10 in. clad } plates	6
B.B.C. & Krupp	Power	He	1000	Uranium carbide cylinder sealed in graphite sphere	2 in. sphere	7
Sanderson & Porter, Alco	Power breeder	He, 950 psi	760–810	Several types including UC-graphite clad with graphite (10 w/o fuel), ThO_2 in blanket	1½ in. sphere	7, 8
Los Alamos ("Turret")	Power (gas turbine cycle)	N_2, 500 psi	650–810	Fueled graphite tubes, unclad 90% enriched U	Tubes ¾ in. OD, ½ in. ID, 6 in. long	9

General Dynamics (HTRDA)	Power breeder	He	547	UC-ThC metal-clad		10
Los Alamos* ("Kiwi")	Rocket propulsion experiment	He	750 >1650	UC-ThC graphite-clad		11
General Electric* (HTRE-1,2,3)	Aircraft propulsion experiment					
U.S. Bur. Mines	Coal gasification	He	~1370	Several types of spheres, including SiC, graphite	1½ in.-2 in. diam. spheres	12
NDA (HOTR)	Process heat experiment	He	1370	Several types, primarily graphite, refractory metals	Plates, rods, spheres	13
AERE, Harwell (HTGCR)	Power breeder	He	750	UC-ThC, graphite-clad; fission products bled off	Hexagonal rods ~2 in. across flats. 1 in. diam. fueled core, 4 ft active and 8 ft total length. 7 rods per subassembly.	14

* Already constructed

TABLE 12-2. REQUIREMENTS OF HIGH TEMPERATURE FUEL ELEMENTS
Low absorption cross section (for thermal reactors)

* Resistance to corrosion by the coolant.
  Sufficient mechanical strength to resist: thermal stresses,* internal fission prod-
    ucts, external stresses, differential expansion of components.
* Inertness between fuel and matrix or cladding.
* Retention of fuel and fission products (not required in some designs).
  Resistance to radiation.
  Good thermal conductivity, and high heat transfer area.
  Ease of fabrication.
  Low cost.

   * The unusually high temperatures and heat generation rates emphasize some of the problems which
are not considered as serious at lower temperatures.

The coolants for the above reactors are almost exclusively gaseous. Liquid metals such as Na, NaK, Li, Bi and Sn may serve the temperature range of 800° to about 1200°C; above this temperature, however, only gases are sufficiently stable heat-transfer media. The gas coolants most frequently considered are air, N_2, CO_2, He and H_2. These are the media in which high temperature fuel elements will have to operate.

REQUIREMENTS

The requirements of high temperature fuel elements are summarized in Table 12.2. Corrosion resistance becomes crucial even in helium and hydrogen, as small amounts of impurities can have serious effects on high temperature materials such as graphite, molybdenum, tantalum, niobium, etc. The British estimate that the oxygen level of the helium coolant in their HTGCR will have to be kept below 1 ppm to minimize oxidation of graphite surfaces operating at about 1000°C.[14] Thermal stresses limit the allowable heat flux in cladding materials. The poor thermal conductivity and high modulus of elasticity of many high temperature materials often limit the safe heat generation rate.[59] Undesirable reactivity between fuels and other materials is greatly aggravated by temperature. Fission gas retention is very difficult at high temperatures and requires a completely dense cladding. (Chemical reactivity and fission gas retention are discussed in greater detail later on.)

Development programs have to solve these problems before high temperature reactor design can proceed very far. To a limited extent design can be used to circumvent some of the difficulties. A number of the proposals plan to release fission gases to the coolant and provide a coolant purification system.[49] The necessity of a fission product cladding is then removed; however, the development of a coolant clean-up system is required.

MATERIALS AVAILABLE FOR HIGH TEMPERATURE SERVICE

Fuels

The first requirement of a high temperature element is a high temperature fuel. Fortunately, a number of highly refractory uranium and plutonium compounds exist. A summary of the high melting point compounds is given in Table 12-3. Uranuim oxides are some of the most stable compounds, and considerable technology has been developed for them in the past few years, as described in Chapter 13. The good resistance of UO_2 to some gaseous and liquid metal coolants and the ability to burn up a large percentage of the fuel atoms without fatal effects on the fuel element make UO_2 one of the "standard" high temperature fuels.

At present the uranium carbides are enjoying new attention because of their high density, good thermal conductivity, good stability under radiation,[26] and compatibility with liquid metal coolants and such matrices as graphite.

Uranium nitride should be a good high temperature fuel, but little is known concerning it. On melting, it appears to decompose; this would be a serious disadvantage if the fuel were to operate close to its melting point.

Of the uranium silicides, the highest density silicide, U_3Si, has been investigated the most thoroughly. The adverse effect of radiation on dimensional stability of silicides has been a disadvantage. Good resistance to liquid metals such as Na may revive the interest. Little is known about the lower density, higher melting point silicides. Much less experience is available with the remaining compounds; their formation, structure, and fabrication is being investigated.[66]

Cladding and Matrix Materials

High temperature materials that may be useful as cladding and matrix materials will be mentioned only very briefly. Metals, intermetallic compounds, ceramics and cermets can be used for either cladding or matrix.

Metals. The advantages of metals are that they can be fabricated and "sealed" more easily than intermetallics and ceramics, and their thermal conductivity and thermal shock resistance is better. Some high-melting-point metals are summarized in Table 12-4. Niobium and molybdenum are two of the most promising high strength materials. Unfortunately, they are very sensitive to small amounts of impurities in the coolant; oxygen is a particularly offensive impurity. An oxidation-resistant alloy or coating is required, or else the maximum operating temperature of the materials will be determined by the purity of the coolant. Effects of radiation on metals are expected to be minimized because of the annealing effect of the high temperatures.

Table 12-3. Summary of High Melting Point Uranium and Plutonium Compounds

Fuel Compound	Melting Point (°C)	Density (g/cc)	Comments on Stability	Ref.
UO_2	2750	10.96	Stable in He and H_2 to melting point. Oxidizes at low temp. Stable in Na to high temp.	28, 29
UN	2650	14.32	Probably poor oxidation resistance.	
UC_2	2470	11.68	Poor resistance to oxygen, nitrogen. Dissolves in H_2O at 100°C. Stable in Na, NaK to 1300°F. UC_2 less stable than UC.	51c
UC	2370	13.63		
US	>2000		Probably poor oxidation resistance	29
UBe_{13}	2000	4.37	Poor resistance to nitrogen at about 500°C.	38
$CaUO_4$			At 1800°C stable in air, O_2. At 1615°C decomposed in He.	28
$SrUO_4$			At 1800°C decomposed in air. At 1655°C stable in O_2. At 1335°C decomposed in He.	28
U_2C_3	1775 (decomp)			
$MgUO_4$			At 1750°C decomposed in air. At 1700°C decomposed in O_2. At 1540°C decomposed in He.	28
$BaUO_4$			At 1700°C stable in air.	28
U_3Si_2	1665	12.2	Forms protective oxide films to at least 400°C; better oxidation resistance than U, but still poor. Reaction rate with N_2 greater than between U and N_2.	30, 38
βUSi_3	1650	8.15		
USi_2	1600	8.98		
USi	1600	10.40	Poor oxidation and nitriding resistance; worse than U.	30, 38
Na_2UO_4	1635			28
K_2UO_4	1620			28
UAl_2	1590	8.14	Protective film in O_2 to at least 400°C.	30
UB_2	1500	11.75	Poor oxidation resistance, poor nitriding resistance (better than U silicides).	29, 38
UB_4	1500	7.94		
UNi_5	1300	11.31		29
$UO_2 \cdot P_2O_5$	1260			28
UFe_2	1235	8.98		29
PuO_2	~2240	11.46		39
PuN		14.2		87
PuC		13.6		
Pu_2C_3	~2200	12.7		37
PuO	~1850	13.95		87
$PuBe_{13}$	1700	4.36		37
Pu_3Si_2				
Pu_2Si_3		10.15		37
PuSi	1550			
$\alpha,\beta PuSi_2$		9.1		
$PuOs_2$	1500			37
$PuAl_2$	1480			37
PuTe				
Pu_2Ge_3				
$PuGe_2$			Probably high melting point.	37
$PuGe_3$				

TABLE 12-4. HIGH MELTING POINT METALS

Metal	Melting Point (°C)	Thermal Neutron Absorption Cross Section σa (barns)	Comments on Stability in Various Coolants[42, 84, 85]
W	3380	19.2	Poor oxidation resistance. Good stability in hydrogen to high temp., Hg to 600°C, Pb-Bi to 500°C, Na and NaK to 800°C.
Re	3180	84.4	Poor oxidation resistance.
Ta	3000	21.3	Poor oxidation resistance. Good stability in Pb-Bi, Na, NaK, Li to 900°C, Pb to 1000°C. Poor resistance to Hg
Mo	2620	2.5	Poor oxidation resistance. Good stability in hydrogen to high temp., Hg to 600°C, Li, Na, NaK to 900°C, Bi to 1000°C.
Nb	2468	1.1	Poor resistance to oxygen, hydrogen. Good resistance to Bi to 800°C, Pb, Li, Na, NaK to 1000°C.
V	1900	5.1	Poor resistance to oxygen, hydrogen. Good resistance to Na, NaK to 500°C, Pb-Bi to 650°C
Cr	1875	2.9	Good oxidation resistance to 700°C. Alloys with more than 30% Cr good to 1000°C. Probably good resistance to Hg to 500°C, Bi to 800°C, Na, NaK to 900°C.
Zr	1852	0.18	Poor resistance to oxygen, nitrogen, CO_2 above 450°C. Poor resistance to hydrogen, Hg. Good resistance to Pb, Na, NaK to 600°C.
Th	1700		Poor oxidation resistance in air. Poor resistance to Bi, Pb. Good resistance to Na, NaK to 600°C.
Ti	1668	5.6	Good resistance in air, to 600°C, nitrogen to 1000°C. Poor resistance to hydrogen. Good resistance to Pb, Na, NaK to 600°C.

Intermetallic Compounds. Some of the known intermetallic compounds are summarized in Table 12-5. The potential of this group of materials has not been exploited. They are as difficult to fabricate as ceramics; however, they should have better thermal conductivity and thermal shock resistance.

Ceramics. Many potentially useful ceramics are summarized in Table 12-6. Major limitations of ceramics are their poor thermal conductivity, poor thermal shock resistance and poor resistance to thermal stresses. Materials with good thermal conductivity are then of prime importance. Of these some of the most promising are graphite, silicon carbide, zirconium carbide and beryllium oxide. Aluminum oxide, though not having as good a thermal conductivity, is promising because of its low absorption cross section and known technology. Again, the effects of radiation will be less pro-

TABLE 12-5. HIGH MELTING POINT INTERMETALLIC COMPOUNDS

Intermetallic Compound	Melting Point (°C)	Stability in Various Coolants
Zr_2Ge	2275	
CrAl	2160	Fair oxidation resistance in 1100°C air.
Mo_3Al	2150	Good oxidation resistance 100 hr, at 1150°C air.[40] Poor oxidation resistance at 1100°C.[41]
Zr_2Sb	1900	
$ZrBe_{13}$		
$ZrBe_9$	~1840	
$ZrBe_7$		
$CrBe_2$	1840	
Cr_3Si	1730	
MoAl	1700	
$ZrCr_2$	1675	
V_5Al_8	1670	
Ti_3Sn	1663	
NiAl	1640	Good oxidation resistance in 1150°C air.
$ZrAl_2$	1640	Poor oxidation resistance in 1100°C air.[41]

nounced at high temperatures than at low temperatures, because of thermal annealing. A recent review of low-temperature radiation effects is given in Ref. 53. Effects of radiation on graphite are discussed in Ref. 55–57.

Graphite deserves a special mention as one of the most useful high temperature fuel element materials. It has good strength at very high temperatures (to 2500°C), excellent thermal conductivity, thermal shock resistance, and nuclear properties. For this reason the majority of the high temperature reactors plan to use graphite-base fuel elements (see Table 12-1). Carbide coatings being developed for graphite (ZrC, TiC, SiC, NbC) will tend to make graphite a useful material in a variety of atmospheres.[46, 48, 49, 52]

Cermets. Of the large number of cermets made to date, Al_2O_3-Cr and SiC-Si have been suggested and tested for fuel elements.[54]

FUEL-MATRIX COMBINATION CONSIDERATIONS

Reactivity of Fuels with Matrix or Cladding

Fuels are dispersed in a matrix to increase thermal conductivity of the elements, to dilute enriched fuel, and to strengthen the element mechanically. The function of the cladding is to prevent fuel and fission product diffusion, and to protect the fuel from corrosion. At high temperatures the chemical reactivity of the fuels with respect to matrix and cladding increases and imposes some limitations on fuel-matrix combinations.

Very little information is available on the reactivity of fuels with refractory metals. UO_2 probably does not react with niobium and molybdenum. Tests on a UO_2-Nb diffusion couple for 5 days at 1370°C (2500°F) did not

TABLE 12-6. HIGH MELTING POINT CERAMICS

Ceramic	Melting Point (°C)	Stability in Various Coolants[42, 84-86]
Graphite and Carbides		
4TaC·ZrC	3930	In general carbides have poor oxidation re-
TaC	3880	sistance to air; exceptions are SiC to
ZrC	3530	about 1600°C and Cr_3C_2 to 1000°C. Car-
Graphite	3500*	bides should be stable in hydrogen;
NbC	3500	graphite probably forms hydrocarbons at
TiC	3140	high temperatures. The resistance of
WC	2870	graphite to CO_2 is better than to air, but
VC	2830	still limited to less than 900°C. Be_2C is
Mo_2C	2690	not resistant to moisture and nitrogen.
ThC	2630	TiC and NbC are stable in nitrogen to
SiC	2200	to 2500°C. Graphite is resistant to liquid
Be_2C	2150	Bi. TiC is resistant to Na, NaK.
Cr_3C_2	1890	
Nitrides		
TaN	2980	Nitrides generally have poor oxidation re-
ZrN	2980	sistance. Si_3N_4 appears to be an excep-
TiN	2950	tion; it has good oxidation resistance to
ThN	2360	1400°C. The nitrides should be stable in
AlN	2230	hydrogen and nitrogen. ZrN has good
Be_3N_2	2200	resistance to liquid Bi and probably al-
Ba_3N_2	2200	kali metals as well.
NbN	2030	
VN	2030	
Si_3N_4	1900*	
Oxides		
ThO_2	3300	Oxides in general are the most stable ma-
$SrO·ZrO_2$	2700	terials in air; some exceptions at high
$BaO·ZrO_2$	2700	temperatures are CaO, NiO, TiO_2, BaO,
ZrO_2	2680	SrO, Cr_2O_3. Oxides are generally stable
CeO_2	2600	in hydrogen; some exceptions are: MgO,
CaO	2600	CaO, SiO_2, CeO_2, Cr_2O_3, NiO, TiO_2.
BeO	2550	Some oxides are sensitive to water vapor:
$3BeO·2ZrO_2$	2540	MgO, BeO. The poor thermal conduc-
$ZrO_2·SiO_2$	2420	tivity of oxides would not make them a
SrO	2420	logical choice for use with high heat re-
Y_2O_3	2410	moval capacity coolants such as liquid
$CaO·ZrO_2$	2345	metals.
Cr_2O_3	2265	
$CaO·Cr_2O_3$	2160	
$MgO·Al_2O_3$	2140	
$2CaO·SiO_2$	2120	
Al_2O_3	2020	
$NiO·Al_2O_3$	2020	
$SrO·Al_2O_3$	2010	
$BaO·Al_2O_3$	2000	
NiO	1950	

TABLE 12-6.—(*Continued*)

Ceramic	Melting Point (°C)	Stability in Various Coolants [42, 84-86]
Oxides—Continued		
BaO	1920	
BeO·Al$_2$O$_3$	1870	
TiO$_2$	1840	
3Al$_2$O$_3$·2SiO$_2$	1830	
2BeO·SiO$_2$	1750	
SiO$_2$	1730	
Silicides		
Ta$_5$Si, Ta$_5$Si$_3$	2500	The silicides generally have good oxidation
Nb$_5$Si$_3$	2480	resistance by virtue of the formation of a
W$_3$Si$_2$	2340	protective SiO$_2$ film. MoSi$_2$, TaSi$_2$ are
Zr$_3$Si$_2$ to Zr$_6$Si$_5$	2210–2250	good in air to 1500°C. NbSi$_2$, ZrSi$_2$ and
TaSi$_2$	2200	VSi$_2$ are said to have promising oxidation
Mo$_3$Si$_2$	2190	resistance. Considering the limited resis-
WSi$_2$	2170	tance of SiO$_2$ to reducing atmospheric and
V$_5$Si$_3$	2150	water vapor, one would not expect sili-
Ti$_5$Si$_3$	2120	cides to be resistant to such atmospheres.
MoSi$_2$	2030	
NbSi$_2$	1930	

* Decomp.

show a significant reaction.[36] Reaction between UO$_2$ and zirconium becomes significant above 500°C.[60] The reaction between UO$_2$ and UC with beryllium starts above 600°C.[32] The reaction between UC and zirconium requires 1000°C;[32] at this temperature it appears to proceed rapidly.[51a]

A number of phase diagrams have been determined for uranium compounds and other refractories. These are summarized in Figure 12-1. There is no solubility of uranium compounds with BeO, MgO, and Al$_2$O$_3$. Partial solubility exists in the CaO, SrO systems, and large or complete solubility exists in the ZrO$_2$ and ThO$_2$ systems. The solidus-liquidus lines for the yttria and ceria systems are not available; however, x-ray measurements indicate a continuous series of solid solutions for CeO$_2$,[22] and a large range of solid solubility (up to 78 mole per cent) for Y$_2$O$_3$.[23]

UO$_2$ would generally not be expected to be stable in carbides at high temperatures. There is a reaction between UO$_2$ and graphite to form UC and CO; the rate of reaction increases rapidly with temperature, particularly above 1200°C.

The relationships between UC and refractory materials are even less well known than those for UO$_2$. Complete solid solutions are formed with ZrC, ThC, TaC, and NbC.[61, 63] Incomplete x-ray examinations showed partial solubility with TiC, VC, Cr$_3$C$_2$, Mo$_2$C, WC and Be$_2$C.[33, 61] No mutual solubility was found in the UC-SiC and UC-Cr system.[63] Both UC and UC$_2$

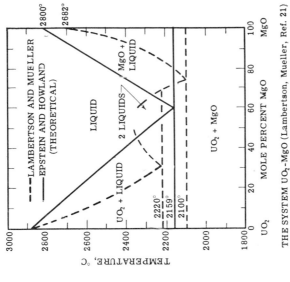

THE SYSTEM UO₂-MgO (Lambertson, Mueller, Ref. 21)

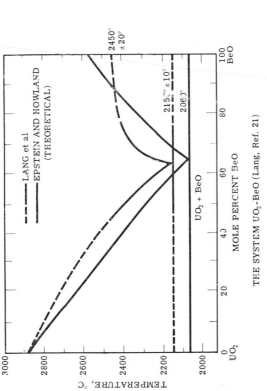

THE SYSTEM UO₂-BeO (Lang, Ref. 21)

Figure 12-1. Some phase diagrams of uranium compounds.

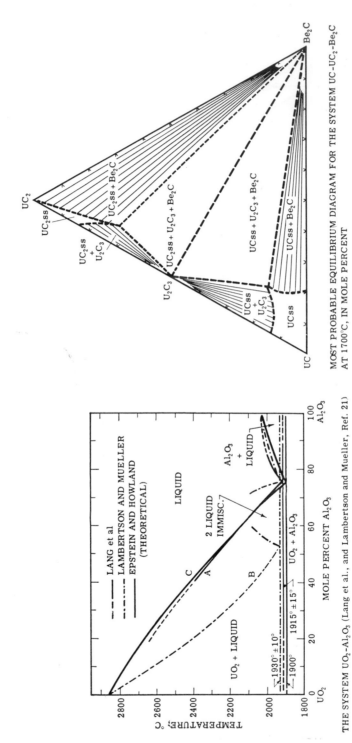

MOST PROBABLE EQUILIBRIUM DIAGRAM FOR THE SYSTEM UC-UC₂-Be₂C
AT 1700°C, IN MOLE PERCENT

THE SYSTEM UO₂-Al₂O₃ (Lang et al., and Lambertson and Mueller, Ref. 21)

Figure 12-1. (Cont.)

204

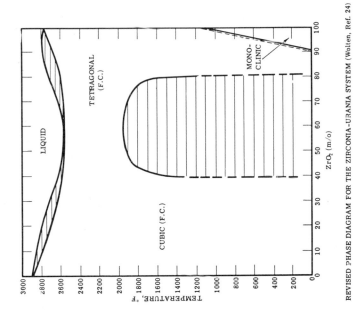

REVISED PHASE DIAGRAM FOR THE ZIRCONIA-URANIA SYSTEM (Wolten, Ref. 24)

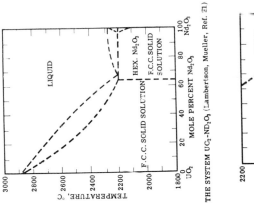

THE SYSTEM UO_2-Nd_2O_3 (Lambertson, Mueller, Ref. 21)

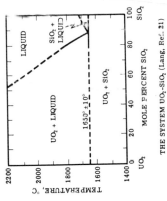

THE SYSTEM UO_2-SiO_2 (Lang, Ref. 21)

Figure 12-1. (Cont.)

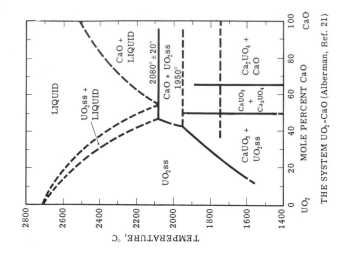

THE SYSTEM UO₂-CaO (Alberman, Ref. 21)

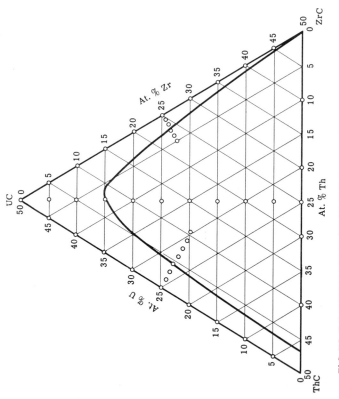

ThC-UC-ZrC SYSTEM PHASE STATE (O.S. Ivanov and T.A. Badajeva, Ref. 23)

Figure 12-1. (Cont.)

206

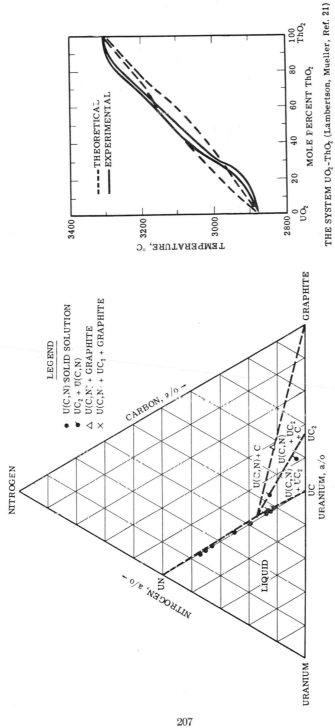

THE SYSTEM UO$_2$-ThO$_2$ (Lambertson, Mueller, Ref. 21)

LEGEND

- U(C,N) SOLID SOLUTION
- UC$_2$ + U(C,N)
△ U(C,N) + GRAPHITE
× U(C,N) + UC$_2$ + GRAPHITE

TERNARY SECTION OF U-C-N$_2$ SYSTEM AT 1800°C IN ARGON ATMOSPHERE

Figure 12-1. (Cont.)

207

have good stability in graphite; UC_2 is the stable form in graphite above about 2000°C. The volume change occurring in the UC to UC_2 transformation is small.

The ternary UC-UC_2-Be_2C has been studied at 1700°C by the National Bureau of Standards,[33] and the UC-ThC-ZrC was established for ambient temperatures by Soviet investigators.[23] Both are shown in Figure 12-1.

Metal infiltration of UC has been tried with aluminum, magnesium, iron, copper, silver, titanium, and zirconium.[34] Only iron infiltration appeared to be satisfactory without preliminary additions of metal to the porous UC compact. The experience with UN is limited to the fabrication of dispersions. UN did not react with molybdenum and niobium during powder metallurgy fabrication of 30 v/o UN compacts which involved sintering at 1200°C for 4 hr, followed by annealing at 1200°C. A slight reaction with vanadium was noted.[51d]

PuO_2 dispersions in thorium, zirconium, and graphite have been studied.[48] In thorium, a reaction to form βPu_2O_3 starts at 800°C. The oxide is reduced to metal in 100 min. at 1200°C. Reactions have been noted with zirconium at 1260°C. PuO_2 reacts with graphite at about 1850°C to form PuC and Pu_2C_3 .

Properties of Fuel-Matrix Combinations

As mentioned previously, one of the reasons for dispersing fuel in a matrix is to increase thermal conductivity and mechanical strength. The thermal conductivity of a number of fuel matrix combinations is given in Figure 12-2. Some improvement over solid UO_2 can be noted by BeO additions. The thermal conductivity of UC appears particularly promising.

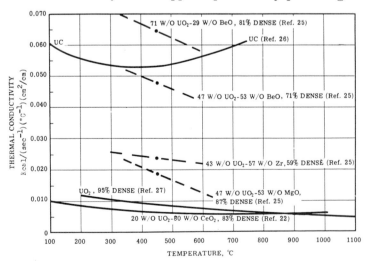

Figure 12-2. Thermal conductivity of some high temperature fuels.

Battelle Memorial Institute studied the effect of BeO, SiO_2, ZrO_2, CeO_2, SiN, Si, and Be on the strength and thermal shock resistance of UO_2.[64] BeO additions were the most effective in increasing thermal shock resistance. The AERE at Harwell found that, of silicon, zirconium, ZrH_x, and thorium additions, only thorium helped thermal shock resistance.[65] The effect of niobium, molybdenum, and zirconium metal fibers on thermal shock resistance of thoria-base ceramics was studied at Argonne National Laboratory and Armour Research Foundation.[47] Molybdenum fibers were found to be very effective in improving thermal shock resistance. Niobium was not as effective, and the addition of zirconium showed little improvement.

HIGH TEMPERATURE FUEL ELEMENT DEVELOPMENT

Table 12-1 describes some of the fuel elements being proposed for high temperature reactors. One cannot speak of proved products, only of development.

Graphite-Fuel

Justifiably so, the largest development effort has been expended on graphite-base fuel materials. Graphite and fuel have been combined by a number of methods. Uranium oxide and carbide have been placed in graphite "crucibles" in massive form.[43, 49, 66] To obtain uniform distribution of uranium throughout a graphite matrix, carbon has been mixed with uranium compound and binder and fired.[56, 67] Graphite has also been impregnated with uranium solutions such as uranyl nitrates.[68, 69, 78] Uranium oxides or carbides can be formed in the impregnated graphite by subsequently being heated to various temperatures.[66b]

The development of methods to make high temperature graphite-to-graphite joints is vital for sealing the cladding. Reimpregnation of a threaded joint with a carbonaceous material is suggested by Boettcher in the element described in Chapter 15.[43] Titanium or zirconium carbide seals have also been made, but not evaluated.[45, 46]

The diffusion of uranium from unclad graphite bodies proceeds by both volume and pore diffusion, pore diffusion accounting for the major percentage. North American Aviation[70] and Battelle Memorial Institute[76] have studied the problem using reactor grade graphites of about 75 per cent theoretical density. Diffusion was measured at temperatures in the 1100 to 2400°C range up to 1000 hours. The diffusion rates are sufficiently high to warrant the use of dense graphites and diffusion barriers for reactors that are to operate for extended periods of time. Surface coatings on graphite have decreased fuel losses at 1650°C.[66a]

Fission product diffusion through unclad porous graphite is high. The majority of the tests were made by low temperature irradiation and out-of-pile reheating. North American Aviation tests[72] showed that, in uranium carbide-impregnated AUF graphite, 50 per cent of the xenon escaped in 1 hr at 1000°C, and 75 per cent of the xenon escaped in $3\frac{1}{2}$ hr at 1500°C. Tests[73] at higher temperatures showed that 60 per cent of the total fission product activity diffused out in 4 hr at 1880°C, and 85 per cent of the total fission product activity diffused out in 4 hr at 2200°C. Tests of fission product diffusion from unclad uranium-graphite slugs were made by Los Alamos at 1600 to 2600°C, for periods of 30 sec to 5 minutes.[77] Diffusion rates for a number of fission products were measured. Elements which form stable carbides, such as zirconium and molybdenum, did not diffuse. The retention of elements like ruthenium, rhodium, and europium was fair; however, gases and alkaline earths diffused rapidly. About 70 to 80 per cent of the gamma activity was lost after 5 min. irradiation at 2600°C. Battelle concluded[66a] that fuel and fission product diffusion can be reduced by placing the fuel into the graphite in massive form and cladding it with graphite.

Oak Ridge National Laboratory[49] has fabricated samples consisting of a cylinder of UO_2 clad with dense graphite and coated in turn with a SiC-Si coating. Such a sample has survived an air blast of near sonic velocity at 1000°C for more than 1000 hours. Of two subsequent samples, one has survived a 1100°C air blast for more than 300 hours.

SiC-Fuel

SiC does not have the good thermal conductivity and high temperature potential of graphite; but, among oxidation resistant materials, it is one of the best thermal conductors and has good thermal shock resistance.

Early fabrication efforts were concerned with unclad SiC-UO_2 plates. A satisfactory dense material was not obtained.[78] Silicon metal-bonded SiC was used by Oak Ridge[50] as a matrix and cladding for UO_2 and USi_3. Fission product retention was examined by low temperature irradiation and out-of-pile reheating at 900°C. Samples were irradiated in quartz glass envelopes. They were reheated with one end of the envelope cooled by liquid nitrogen. The gaseous fission products were condensed in this end on glass wool. The cold end was pinched off and counted by a scintillation counter. Fission product release from samples was compared to release from UO_2 powder standards. About 0.1 to 0.01 per cent of the total activity diffused from the SiC-Si clad samples in 24 hours; however, some of the USi_3 had diffused to the surface. High temperature irradiation[79] of improved specimens was carried out at 870 to 950°C. Plates $\frac{1}{2} \times \frac{1}{8} \times 1\frac{1}{2}$ in. containing 4 w/o U^{235} generated 120 watts/in.[2] The plate was dimensionally stable and resistant to thermal cycling. Fission gas release was limited to 0.001 per cent of the total xenon produced.

At the laboratories of Nuclear Development Corporation[35] fueled and

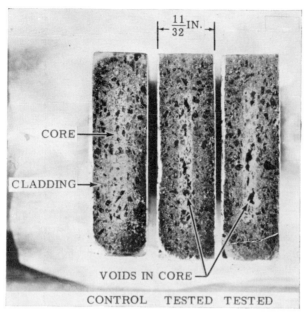

Figure 12-3. KTSiC-clad KTSiC-UO₂ matrix samples sectioned along diameters showing central fueled cores and voids in cores.[35]

clad self-bonded silicon carbide (KTSiC*) has been tested. This material is SiC with approximately 3 per cent free silicon, a small amount of SiO_2 and free carbon. The samples were $1\frac{1}{4}$-in. diameter by $1\frac{1}{32}$-in. thick slugs with a $\frac{1}{16}$-in. thick, central-fueled core fabricated by the Carborundum Co. The core was initially UO_2, but heating to 2000°C during the fabrication process caused a reaction of some of the fuel to form USi_3. Very small amounts of fuel were also detected on the surface of the fabricated samples, indicating some fuel diffusion during fabrication. Out-of-pile heating at 1370°C for 120 hr caused further reaction and diffusion of fuel, leaving some voids in the center of the specimen as shown in Figure 12-3. A photomicrograph of the core of the tested sample is shown in Figure 12-4. Fuel diffusion was measured qualitatively by exposing the cross section of the sample to an alpha-particle sensitive emulsion, developing the emulsion and counting the alpha tracks in the emulsion. A view of such tracks is shown in Figure 12-5. Figure 12-5A shows an exposure made by the core; Figure 5B, by the core-cladding interface; and Figure 5C, by the sample surface.

Fission product retention of one sample was tested by irradiation for 10 days at a thermal flux of about 2×10^{11} n/cm²-sec at a temperature of about 150 to 200°C. The sample was reheated out-of-pile in a slowly flowing

* Commercial product of the Carborundum Co., Niagara Falls, N.Y.

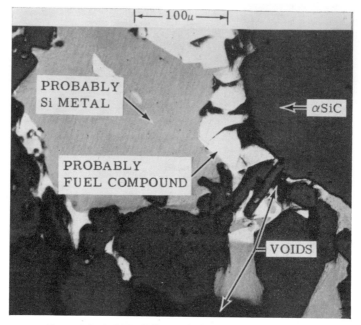

Figure 12-4. Core of fueled KTSiC sample heated 120 hr at 2500°F in helium, unetched.[35]

helium atmosphere at 1370°C and the released activity was counted downstream in a filter by a gamma-ray scintillation detector. Figure 12-6 shows a photograph of some of the equipment. The furnace which can be seen was used to heat the unirradiated samples. A similar furnace was in the isolation area, with the addition of the filter and counter between the exit of the furnace tube and the nitric acid traps. Figure 12-7 shows a plot of the counts per minute *vs.* time, for the SiC specimen. Two large bursts of activity were noted. Subsequent gamma counting showed that approximately 6 per cent of the gamma activity of the sample was released.

Al_2O_3-Fuel

Alumina has excellent oxidation resistance and does not react with UO_2, as can be seen from the phase diagram. Its thermal conductivity and thermal shock resistance are not as good as that of SiC or BeO.

Al_2O_3-clad UO_2 samples were tested[35, 36] in a manner similar to the SiC samples. All but one of the samples were fabricated by the Norton Company by pressing and sintering at 1750°C. The cladding was nearly fully dense; a small amount of closed porosity existed within grains. No visual change or fuel diffusion was noted after out-of-pile heating for 120 hr at 1370°C. Fuel diffusion was again measured by alpha-particle sensitive emulsions. Thin

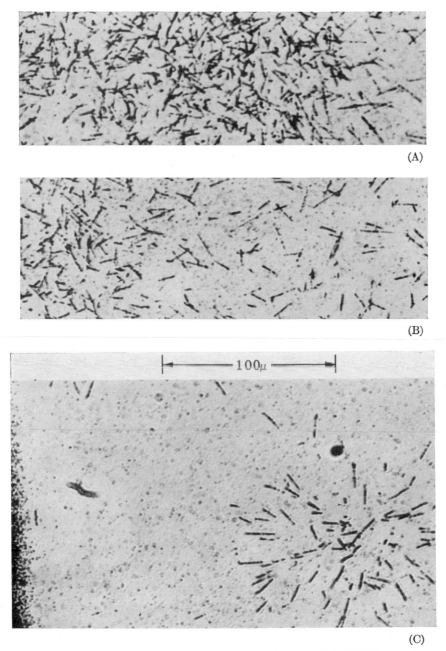

Figure 12-5. Nuclear track plate autoradiographs of fueled KTSiC sample, as fabricated. (A) fueled core; (B) core-cladding interface; (C) clad surface of sample. These patterns are typical of tested and untested samples.[35]

Figure 12-6. Control panels and equipment. A—fission product retention test isolation area; B—helium purifiers; C—furnace; D—vacuum pump; E—gamma ray counting equipment; F—furnace temperature controls; G—nitric acid traps.[35]

sections ($\sim$30 μ) were also examined by transmitted light. Figure 12-8 shows a macroscopic cross section of the specimens. Figure 12-9 shows a photomicrograph of the core-cladding interface.

Fission product retention was measured on four specimens. The specimens were irradiated at a thermal flux of 10^{11} n/cm²-sec for 10 to 12 days at 150 to 200°C. They were reheated out-of-pile in a slowly flowing helium atmosphere to 1370°C, and the released activity was counted as before. Figure 12-10 shows the measure of fission product release *vs.* time of four specimens. Three specimens made by one fabricator lost, respectively: zero; less than 0.1 per cent; and 0.3 per cent of the fission product activity. One specimen made by the second fabricator released 2 per cent of the fission product activity. The sample which did not release any detectable fission product was cycled between 1370°C and 1100°C several times during the

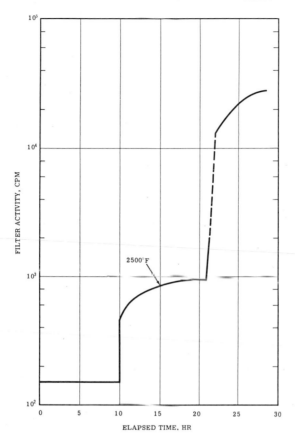

Figure 12-7. Fission product activity at filter *vs.* elapsed time. KTSiC-clad KTSiC-UO$_2$.[35]

fission product diffusion test. The results on the Al$_2$O$_3$-UO$_2$ samples were very encouraging.

To reduce the porosity of alumina cladding even further the use of a single crystal of alumina or sapphire was suggested.[35] Such an element is shown in Figure 12-11. The crucible was diamond-ground from a single crystal bar. To give an idea of the cost of such material, centerless-ground, ⅛-in. diameter single crystal bar is approximately 62 cents/in; ⅜-in. diameter rod is closer to $7/inch. The major problem, of course, is the high temperature joint between the cover and the crucible. A preliminary examination of the problem was made by attempting to "solder" single crystal disks together. Three bonding materials were tried: aluminum, titanium hydride and chromium. Aluminum was tried because it could be fused easily and oxidized after fusion to form an Al$_2$O$_3$ bond between the two Al$_2$O$_3$

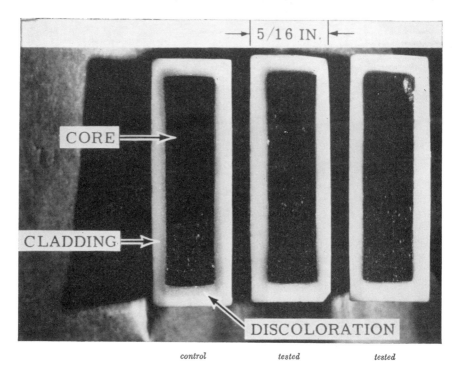

control   tested   tested

Figure 12-8. Al_2O_3-clad Al_2O_3 matrix samples sectioned along a diameter, showing fueled core.[35]

crystals. Titanium hydride was tried because it had been used successfully on nonmetallic joints, including sapphires. Chromium was tried because Cr_2O_3 forms a continuous solid solution with Al_2O_3. The metals were vacuum-deposited on the surfaces to be joined, to a thickness of about 1500 Å. The titanium was hydrided prior to joining. The surfaces were pressed together at 50 to 100 psi in a vacuum at elevated temperatures for about 15 minutes. A joint was achieved by heating the aluminum surfaces to 770°C. This joint was translucent to light indicating there was no metallic aluminum left. The properties of the joint were not evaluated. The other joining methods failed due to experimental difficulties rather than to the principle of the joint.

Al_2O_3-Cr-Fuel

Cermets of 30 per cent Al_2O_3 and 70 per cent Cr were developed for nonnuclear high temperature applications some time ago. The material has been used by the Oak Ridge National Laboratory[50, 54] to make plate-type, clad fuel elements. Oak Ridge had previously tested their fission product retention by low-temperature irradiation and out-of-pile reheating. At

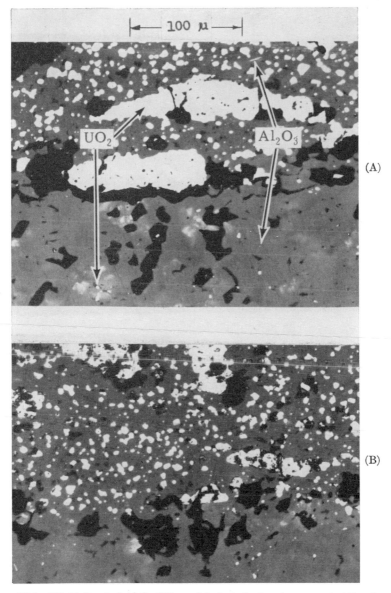

Figure 12-9. (A) Al₂O₃-clad Al₂O₃-UO₂ as fabricated, showing core-cladding inter-face.[35] (B) Al₂O₃-clad Al₂O₃-UO₂ heated for 120 hr at 2500°F in helium.[35]

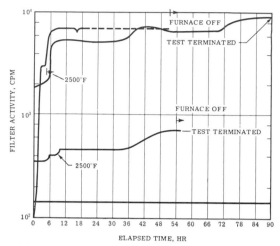

Figure 12-10. Fission product activity at filter *vs.* elapsed time. Alumina-clad Al_2O_3-UO_2 .[36]

Figure 12-11. Fueled, single-crystal Al_2O_3 (sapphire) sample. (Sapphire can ⅜ in. OD x ¼ in. ID x ⅝ in. long.)[35]

900°C, 0.02 to 0.04 per cent of the fission product activity diffused in 24 hours; at 1000°C, 0.15 per cent and 24 per cent of the activity was diffused. The majority of the activity was identified as W^{187} picked up from a tungsten carbide ball milling operation during fabrication.[50] At NDA, samples fabricated at ORNL with a ceramic ball mill were tested.[36] Low temperature irradiation and out-of-pile reheating to 1370°C resulted in 2 to 7 per cent activity loss, as shown in Figure 12-12. In this case a large fraction of the activity was Sb^{124}, again a product of cladding impurity rather than a fission product.

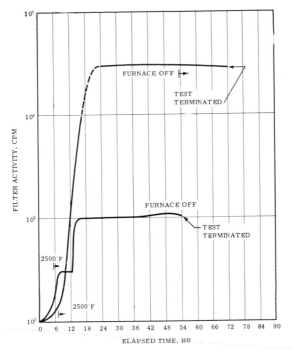

Figure 12-12. Fission product activity at filter *vs.* elapsed time. Chrome alumina-clad UO_2.[36]

ORNL[49] irradiated a similar plate at 1000 to 1050°C at a power of 150 watts/in.[2] of plate, to a 14.7 per cent U^{235} burn-up. The irradiation lasted 2800 hours. Fission gas evolution was measured after irradiation to be 5×10^{-5} per cent of the available Xe^{133} and 9.3×10^{-3} per cent of the available Xe^{135}. Some porosity developed in the cladding, and a thin layer of Cr_2O_3 formed on the surface. The plate did not crack or rupture.

BeO-Fuel

BeO is a good high-temperature fuel element material because of its good nuclear properties, thermal conductivity and thermal shock resistance compared to other oxidation resistant materials. The Daniels Pile proposed BeO fuel elements;[2] however, the elements fabricated at the time[58] did not possess the required thermal shock resistance, and theoretical analysis showed[59] that thermal stresses would rupture the proposed fuel tubes. Since then, BeO fabrication techniques have been developed to produce a highly dense (99.5 per cent of theoretical) improved material.[80] Attempts to produce clad fueled tubes have been made. Clad tubes of $1\frac{1}{4}$ in. OD, $\frac{1}{2}$ in. ID, 1 in. long, with 5 per cent UO_2 have been thermally cycled to 1000°C, and irradiated without any mechanical damage to the tubes.[81]

MgO-Fuel

The high melting point, oxidation resistance, and low thermal absorption cross section of MgO are attractive. It has notably poor thermal conductivity and thermal shock resistance.

Los Alamos[77] reported fission product diffusion from a MgO matrix at 1600 to 2000°C. As in the case of their work with graphite, the diffusion rates were high for a number of the fission products. In 240 sec at 1950°C, 40 to 80 per cent of the iodine, tellurium, antimony, lead, silver, tin, cadmium, and arsenic activity had diffused, while less than 10 per cent of zirconium, barium and molybdenum diffused. It was noted that fission products which form low stability carbides diffuse rapidly from graphite, and fission products which form low stability oxides diffuse rapidly from the MgO matrix.

MgO-Ni-Fuel

The fission product retention ability of a 34 % MgO-66 % Ni cermet was tested by Oak Ridge National Laboratory[50] by low-temperature irradiation and reheating at 1000°C for 24 hours. 0.2 to 0.3 per cent of the fission product activity diffused from the sample.

CaO·ZrO$_2$-Fuel

Some samples of CaO·ZrO$_2$-clad UO$_2$ were tested.[35] The core was 50 w/o UO$_2$ and 50 w/o CaO·ZrO$_2$. The samples were made at the Carborundum Company by hot-pressing at 1500°C. Figure 12-13 shows the severe cracking and shrinkage that occurred by heating at 1370°C for 120 hours.

Glass-Fuel

Successful attempts have been made to incorporate fuel into silica and glass.

Knolls Atomic Power Laboratory[82] incorporated UO$_2$ into SiO$_2$ by mixing, pressing and fusing a compact. Porous "Vycor"* was infiltrated with uranyl nitrate hexahydrate (UNH) and subsequently fired to U$_3$O$_8$. The fuel content was 5 to 10 w/o. Quenching the Vycor sample into water from 1200°C and thermal cycling 500 times between room temperature and 900°C did not affect the sample. Fueled Vycor samples 1 × 1 × 0.4 cm were irradiated at 0.75 × 10^{14} thermal neutrons/cm^2-sec for 3 weeks at 100°C. Power generation was 420 watts, and the uranium burn-up was 6 per cent. The samples were in a capsule with Pb-Bi eutectic coolant. All samples were badly cracked; however, no detectable amounts of fission products were detected. The cracking was attributed to the reaction of coolant and glass, and the nonuniform distribution of fuel in the sample.

* Vycor is the trade name of Corning Glass Works, for a high silica glass.

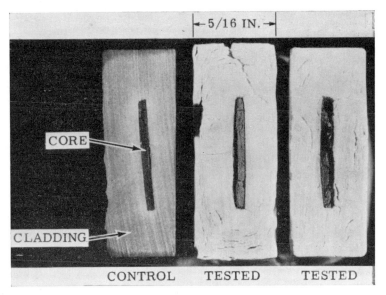

Figure 12-13. CaO·ZrO$_2$-clad matrix samples sectioned along diameter showing fueled core, and cracking and shrinkage caused by heating to 2500°F.[35]

Fuel has been incorporated into glass fibers at Rensselaer Polytechnic Institute.[83] One of the advantages of such an arrangement is that the recoil energy from the fissioning process is available to the environment around the fibers. Measurements have shown that as high as 60 to 90 per cent of the total recoil energy may be available, depending on the nature of the environment. In addition, the heat transfer surface is extremely large. The fueled fibers are made by addition of fuel oxide to the glass melt prior to processing it into fibers. Fibers with softening points between 600 and 1000°C have been made with uranium contents up to 10 per cent. Natural and 90 per cent enriched, 1 μ diameter fibers have been irradiated in a thermal neutron flux of 3×10^{12} n/cm^2-sec for 10 days, at temperatures in the range of 175 to 300°C. There was no evidence of change. Some of the fibers were reported to have sintered together, probably due to poor heat dissipation in the test. Larger diameter fibers, 25 μ, were irradiated at the same flux and time at 400°C, without sintering. Some loss in strength and surface corrosion was noted.

MoSi$_2$-Fuel

MoSi$_2$ is an oxidation resistant material which has been used successfully for heating elements up to 1600°C. Compacts of MoSi$_2$ containing 30 w/o UO$_2$ have been fabricated by pressing and sintering.[66a] Exposure to 500°C air for 9 hr did not appear to harm them. Exposure to 1260°C air for 100 hr decreased the modulus of rupture somewhat, and caused some surface corrosion. Fuel near the surface is particularly subject to oxidation under such conditions; for this reason cladding would be required.

Cermets-Fuel

In addition to the SiC-Si and MgO-Ni cermets previously mentioned, Oak Ridge National Laboratory[50] has also tested 80 per cent ZrC-20 per cent Fe and 80 per cent TiC-20 per cent Ni cermets. Specimens containing UO_2 distributed throughout the sample were tested for fission product retention by low-temperature irradiation and out-of-pile reheating to 1000°C for 24 hours. 1.5 to 3.3 per cent of the activity diffused from the ZrC cermet and 6 to 10 per cent of the activity diffused from the TiC cermet. Some of the diffusion products were identified as xenon, iodine, and tellurium.

Metal-Fuel

Since wrought metallic cladding is dense compared to ceramic cladding, fission product retention is not generally considered a problem. Some UO_2 pellets were clad in niobium tubing, then sealed by welding; the specimen

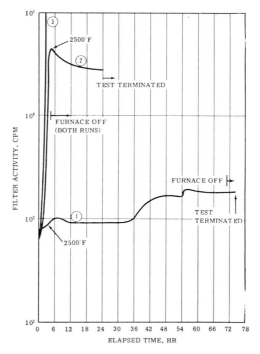

Figure 12-14. Fission product activity at filter *vs.* elapsed time. (1) Niobium-clad UO_2. (2,3) NiAl-clad UO_2.[36]

was irradiated and reheated out-of-pile at 1370°C.[36] Figure 12-14 shows the activity at the filter *vs.*time. It is estimated that 0.2 per cent of the activity was released. The same figure shows activity release rates for some hot-pressed, NiAl-clad UO_2 specimens; the release rates are considerably higher due to porosity in the powder metallurgy product.

SUMMARY

In summary, it is apparent that high temperature fuel element technology is in its infancy. Sufficient test results are not available to point out any one fuel element as the most promising.

Of the fuel compounds, the uranium oxides and carbides have an established future. For cladding and matrix materials, metals, intermetallic compounds, and graphite have particular potential based on their intrinsic properties rather than on tests as fuel element components. Tests by NDA show aluminum oxide to have some desirable properties as a fuel element component.

Additional work is much needed and some has been proposed.[88]

ACKNOWLEDGMENT

The NDA experimental studies reported here were performed under contract to the U.S. Atomic Energy Commission. The efforts of J. DeFelice, B. Minushkin, W. Arbiter, and P. Pinto all contributed to the results reported.

References

1. American Turbine Corp., Design Study—60 Mw Closed Cycle Gas Turbine Nuclear Power Plant, ATC-54-12 (Dec. 1954).
2. Daniels, F., "Suggestions for a High Temperature Pebble Pile, MUC-FD-8" (Oct. 1944).
3. Daniels, F., "Small Gas-Cycle Reactor Offers Economic Promise," *Nucleonics* **14,** No 3, 34–41 (Mar. 1956).
4. Brewer, L., "A Self Purifying High Temperature Breeding Power Reactor," Ceramic Information Meeting, ORNL, October 1 and 2, 1956, TID-7530, Pt. 1 (Oct. 1956).
5. Schuck, A., *et al.*, "Gas Cooled Pebble Bed Reactor for a Large Central Station," CF-57-8-12 (Aug. 1957).
6. Hammitt, F., and Ohlgren, H., "Nuclear Powered Gas Turbines for Light Weight Power Plants," *Advances in Nuclear Engr.*, **II**, Pt. 2 (1957).
7. *Nucleonics* **16,** 24, 26 (Aug. 1958).
8. *Nucleonics* **15,** 19 (June 1957).
9. Hammond, R., *et al.*, "Turret—A High Temperature Gas Cycle Reactor Proposal," LA-2198 (Jan. 1958).
10. *Nucleonics* **16,** 18 (Dec. 1958).
11. *Nucleonics* **17,** 29 (Jan. 1959).
12. McGee J., Bur. Mines, Morgantown, Va., personal communication, 1956.
13 Davidson, L., DeFelice, J., Klapper, J., "Design of an Experimental Reactor for High Operating Temperatures," NDA 64-101 (Sept. 1965).

14. Shepherd, L., *et al.*, "The Possibilities of Achieving High Temperatures in a Gas Cooled Reactor," Second United Nations International Conference on the Peaceful Uses of Atomic Energy (1958) P/314.

15. Davidson, L., and Strasser, A., "Process Applications and Construction Materials for a High Temperature Nuclear Reactor for Chemical Processing," Meeting of the A.I.Ch.E., Chicago, Ill., Dec. 1957.

16. Dawson J., *et al.*, "The Possibility of the Direct Application of Fission Recoil Fragment Energy to Industrial Chemical Processes," Second United Nations International Conference on the Peaceful Uses of Atomic Energy (1958) P/76.

17. Harteck, P., and Dondes, S., "Producing Chemicals with Reactor Radiations," *Nucleonics* **14,** No. 7, 22–25 (July 1956).

18. Levoy, M. M., and Newgard, J. J., "Rocket Reactor Design," *Nucleonics* **16,** No. 7, 66–68 (July 1958).

19. Schreiber, R., "Los Alamos Project Rover," *Nucleonics* **16,** No. 7, 70–72 (July 1958).

20. Albrecht, W., and Koehl, B., "Reactivity of Uranium Compounds in Several Gaseous Media," Second United Nations International Conference on the Peaceful Uses of Atomic Energy (1958) P/710.

21. Lang, S., *et al.*, "High Temperature Reactions of Uranium Dioxide with Various Metal Oxides," NBS-568 (Feb. 1956).

22. Ploetz, G., Mucigrosso, A., and Krystyniak, C., "Properties of Urania-Ceria Bodies for Fuel application," KAPL-1918 (Apr. 1958).

23. Ferguson, I., and Fogg, P., "The System Uranium Dioxide-Yttria," *J. Chem. Soc.* **1957,** 3679–81 (Aug.).

24. Wolten, G., "Solid Phase Transitions in the UO_2-ZrO_2 System," NAA-SR-2538 (June 1958).

25. McCreight, L., "Thermal Conductivity Data for Some Nuclear Fuels," KAPL-822 (Oct. 1952).

26. Rough, F., and Smith, C., "The Physical Properties of Uranium Monocarbide," ANS Meeting, Detroit, Mich., Dec. 1958.

27. Hedge, J., "Thermal Conductivity of UO_2," ARF-GO22D3 (1954).

28. Wisnyi, L., and Pijanowski, S., "Determination of the Melting Points of UO_2 and Other Reactor Refractories," Ceramic Information Meeting Held at ORNL, Oct. 1–3, 1956, TID-7530 (Pt. 1) (Apr. 1957).

29. Loch, L., "Survey of Refractory Uranium Compounds," BMI-1124 (Aug. 1956).

30. Snyder, M., and Duckworth, W., "Properties of Some Refractory Uranium Compounds," BMI-1223 (Sept. 1957).

31. Austin, A., and Gerds, A., "The Uranium-Nitrogen-Carbon System," BMI-1272 (June 1958).

32. Murray, P., and Williams, J., "Ceramic and Cermet Fuels," Second United Nations International Conference on the Peaceful Uses of Atomic Energy (1958) P/318.

33. Burdick, M., *et al.*, "An X-Ray Study of the System UC-UC_2-Be_2C," *J. Research NBS*, **54,** No. 4, 217–29 (Apr. 1955).

34. Kieffer, R., and Sedlatschek, K., "Uranium Alloys Prepared by the Powder Metallurgical Infiltration Process," Second United Nations International Conference on the Peaceful Uses of Atomic Energy (1958) P/1443.

35. Minushkin, B., and Strasser, A., "Evaluation of High Temperature Reactor Fuel Element Materials," NDA 64-102, (Sept. 1956).

36. diRende, J., "An Experimental Study of High Temperature Materials for HTTR Fuel Elements," NDA-43(Del.) (Sept. 1957).

37. Bochvar, A., *et al.*, "Interaction Between Plutonium and Other Metals in Connection with Their Arrangement in Mendeleev's Periodic Table," Second United Nations International Conference on the Peaceful Uses of Atomic Energy (1958) P/2197.

38. Albrecht, W., and Koehl, B., "Reactivity of Uranium Compounds in Several Gaseous Media," Second United Nations International Conference on the Peaceful Uses of Atomic Energy (1958) P/710.

39. Holley, C., Jr. *et al.*, "Thermodynamics and Phase Relationships for Plutonium Oxides," Second United Nations International Conference on the Peaceful Uses of Atomic Energy (1958) P/701.

40. Wachtell, R., *Powder Met. Bull.* **6,** No. 3, 99–104 (Apr. 1952).

41. "Fundamental Properties of Metal-Ceramic Mixtures at High Temperatures," NR-032-022, Alfred University, 1955.

42. Campbell, I., "High Temperature Technology," New York, John Wiley & Sons, Inc., 1956.

43. Boettcher, A., Schulten, R., and Wirths, G., "Fuel Elements for a High Temperature Reactor," Second United Nations International Conference on the Peaceful Uses of Atomic Energy (1958). P/1005.

44. Boettcher, A., and Schneider, G., "Some Properties of UC," Second United Nations International Conference on the Peaceful Uses of Atomic Energy (1958) P/964.

45. Aves, R., *et al.*, "High Temperature Graphite Joints," AERE R/M 165 (Apr. 1958).

46. Ohlgren, H., American Metal Products Co., personal communication, 1958.

47. Arenberg, C. A., Baskin, Y., and Handwerk, J., "Thoria Base Metallo-Ceramics," Ceramic Information Meeting Held at ORNL, Oct. 1–3, 1956, TID-7530 (Pt . 1) Apr. 1957.

48. Blocher, J., Jr., and Campbell, I., "Carbide Coatings for Graphite," Second United Nations International Conference on the Peaceful Uses of Atomic Energy (1958) P/1428.

49. Solid State Division, Annual Progress Report for Period Ending August 1958, ORNL-2614, Nov. 1958.

50. Moody, W., Jr., Taylor, A., and Johnson, J., "Preliminary Investigation of the Fission Product Retention Ability of Cermet Compacts," ORNL 1778, (July 1955).

51. *Reactor Core Materials*, Supt. of Documents, U.S. Govt. Printing Office, Washington, D.C.; (a) Vol. I, No. 1, Mar. 1958; (b) Vol. I, No. 2, May 1958; (c) Vol. I, No. 3, Aug. 1958; (d) Vol. I, No. 4, Nov. 1958.

52. Jones, M., "Graphite Based Materials for High Temperature Applications," WADC-TR-57-602 (Feb. 1958).

53. Crawford, J., Jr., and Wittels, M., "Radiation Stability of Nonmetals and Ceramics," Second United Nations International Conference on the Peaceful Uses of Atomic Energy (1958) P/679.

54. Johnson, J. R., "Ceramic Materials for Nuclear Reactors," *J. Metals* **8,** 660–4 (May 1956).

55. Woods, W., Bupp, L., and Fletcher, I., "Irradiation Damage to Artificial Graphite," First United Nations International Conference on the Peaceful Uses of Atomic Energy (June 1955) P/746.

56. Eatherly, W., *et al.*, "Physical Properties of Graphite Materials for Special Nuclear Applications," Second United Nations International Conference on the Peaceful Uses of Atomic Energy (1958) P/708.

57. Davidson, H., and Losty, H., "The Effect of Neutron Irradiation on the Mechanical Properties of Graphite," Second United Nations International Conference on the Peaceful Uses of Atomic Energy (1958) P/28.

58. Brittain, R., and Sibbitt, W., "Beryllium Oxide," M-3752 (1947).

59. Sibbitt, W., and Etherington, H., "Analysis of Maximum Thermal Stresses Generated in the Fuel Tubes During Steady State Operation of a High Temperature Pile," Mon N-292 (1946).

60. Mallett, M., et al., "The Zr-UO₂ Reaction," BMI-1212 (July 1957).

61. Nowotny, H., et al., "Zur Kenntnis der Teilsysteme: UC-TiC, -ZrC, -VC, -NbC, -TaC, -Cr₃C₂, -Mo₂C, und -WC," *Monatsh. Chem.*, **88**, No. 3, 336–43 (June 15, 1957).

62. Witteman, W., Leitnaker, J., and Bowman, M., "The Solid Solubility of UC and ZrC," LA-2159 (April 1958).

63. Ivanov, O., and Badajeva, T., "Phase Diagrams of Certain Ternary Systems of Uranium and Thorium," Second United Nations International Conference on the Peaceful Uses of Atomic Energy (1958) P/2043.

64. Bowers, D., et al., "Effect of Ceramic or Metal Additives in High UO₂ Bodies," BMI-1117 (July 1956).

65. Williams, L., et al., "A Preliminary Study of Three Cermets Based on Uranium Oxide," AERE M/R 1934 (May 1956).

66. Monthly Progress Reports, Battelle Memorial Institute:
    a. BMI-1035 (Aug. 1955).
    b. BMI-1128 (Aug. 1956).
    c. Progress Reports Relating to Civilian Applications.

67. Schofield, H., Slyh, J., and Loch, L., "Fabrication of Urania-Bearing Graphite," BMI-T-26 (May 1950).

68. Kanter, M., "Impregnation of Graphite with Uranium Compounds for Use as Fuel Rod Materials," ANL-4118 (Feb. 1948).

69. Sanz, M., "Impregnation of Porous Graphite with Uranuim," NAA-AL-93 (Rev.) (Jan. 1947).

70. Loftness, R., "The Diffusion of Uranium Carbide in Graphite," NAA-SR-64 (Aug. 1950).

71. Smith, C., and Young, C., "Diffusion of Fission Fragments from Uranium Impregnated Graphite," NAA-SR-72 (May 1951).

72. Cubicciotti, D., "The Diffusion of Xenon from Uranium Carbide Impregnated Graphite at High Temperatures," NAA-SR-194 (Oct. 1952).

73. Young, C., and Smith, C., "Preliminary Experiments on Fission Product Diffusion from Uranium Impregnated Graphite in the Range 1800°–2200°C," NAA-SR-232 (June 1953).

74. Doyle, L., "High Temperature Diffusion of Individual Fission Elements from Uranium Carbide Impregnated Graphite," NAA-SR-255 (1953).

75. Zigrang, D., and Bennet, G., "Preparation of Fuel Elements for the NAA Homogeneous Graphite Research Reactor," NAA-SR-240 (Aug. 1953).

76. Loch, L., Gambino, J., and Duckworth, W., "Diffusion of Uranium through Graphite," *A.I. Ch.E. Journal*, **2**, 195–8 (June 1956).

77. Cowan, G., Orth, C., "Diffusion of Fission Products at High Temperatures from Refractory Matrices," Second United Nations International Conference on the Peaceful Uses of Atomic Energy (1958) P/613.

78. Balint, L., et al., "Silicon Carbide as the Basis Material for Plate-Type Fuel Elements," TID-10044 (Sept. 1953).

79. *Power Reactor Technology*, Vol. I No. 2, February 1958. Supt. of Documents, U.S. Govt. Printing Office, Washington, D.C.
80. Hyde, C., Quirk, J., and Duckworth, W., "Preparation of Dense Beryllium Oxide," BMI-1020 (July 1955).
81. Miller, H., "Method of Making a Refractory Material," U.S. Patent 2,818,605 (Jan. 1958).
82. Cashin, W., and Sowman, H., "Silica-Uranium Fuel Systems," KAPL-1475 (Feb. 1956).
83. Harteck, P., and Dondes, S., "Glass Fibers—A New Form for Reactor Fuels," *Nucleonics*, **15,** No. 8, 94–98 (Aug. 1957).
84. "Ceramic Materials for Reactors," *Nucleonics*, **11,** 20 (July 1953).
85. "Liquid Metal Handbook," NAVEXOS P-733 (June 1952).
86. Schwarzkopf, P., *et al.*, "Refractory Hard Metals," New York, Macmillan Co., 1953.
87. Seaborg, G., Katz, J., and Manning, W., "The Transuranium Elements," New York, McGraw-Hill Book Co., Inc., 1949.
88. Strasser, A., "Development Program for High Temperature Reactor Materials," NDA 64–104 (Sept. 1956).
89. "Conference on the Utilization of Heat from Nuclear Reactors," AERE CE/R 2257 (Jan. 1957).

13. URANIUM DIOXIDE FUEL ELEMENTS

O. J. C. RUNNALLS

Head, Fuel Development Branch, Atomic Energy of Canada Limited
Chalk River, Ontario, Canada

Since 1955, when the decision was made to use uranium dioxide fuel elements for the core of the Pressurized Water Reactor at Shippingport, Pennsylvania, the interest in uranium dioxide has spread to most of those countries in the world with power reactor development programs. This interest has arisen primarily because of the dimensional stability of UO_2 during long irradiations and its compatibility with most liquid or gaseous coolants.

A wide variety of reactors now being designed or under construction will use uranium dioxide fuel sheathed in zirconium alloys, stainless steel, beryllium or aluminum alloys. Proposed coolants include light and heavy water, organic liquids, steam, carbon dioxide, helium and liquid sodium.

It seems appropriate, therefore, to attempt an assessment of our present knowledge of uranium dioxide elements by reviewing the data available on pertinent chemical and physical properties of UO_2, fabrication and sheathing methods, and irradiation behavior.

Properties of UO_2

An extensive summary of the properties of uranium oxides was published in 1951.[1] Since then, much additional work has been reported, particularly by Lustman and co-workers.[2, 3] It is the intention in this paper to refer only to those properties that are considered of special interest in the design of uranium dioxide fuel elements.

Composition Range. The results of many investigators who have studied phase relationships in the system UO_2-U_3O_8 have been reviewed recently by Belle and Lustman.[2] These are summarized in the phase diagram shown in Figure 13-1. The phase boundaries appear to be reasonably well-established in the UO_2 to U_4O_9 region, although in a recent Geneva paper Roberts *et al.*[7] briefly reported that the UO_{2+x} phase extended to at least $UO_{2.28}$ at 1077°C, in marked disagreement with the data shown in Figure 13-1. The composition limits of the U_3O_8 phase are still in some doubt, as described in detail by Belle and Lustman.[2]

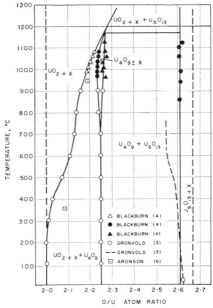

Figure 13-1. The system UO_2-U_3O_8 .[2]

The tetragonal U_3O_7 phase which is formed by the oxidation of UO_2 powder or pellets below 300°C was not shown on the phase diagram because it appears to be a nonequilibrium structure. Perio[8] found, for example, that samples in the composition range from $UO_{2.00}$ to $UO_{2.25}$, which consisted of a mixture of cubic and tetragonal phases, transformed to cubic UO_2 and U_4O_9 after 4 months at 140°C.

The calculated density of $UO_{2.00}$, determined from Gronvold's measured lattice constant of $a = 5.4704$ Å, is 10.96 g/cm³.[5] Cubic U_4O_9 has a higher density, 11.30 g/cm³, indicating that the excess oxygen atoms are accommodated interstitially in the UO_2-like structure.[5] From Gronvold's high-temperature studies on the UO_{2+x} phase, where it was observed that the lattice constant decreased when the O:U ratio was increased, a similar conclusion can be drawn; i.e., the excess oxygen atoms must occupy interstitial positions. This is confirmed, as Belle has pointed out,[3] by magnetic susceptibility and electrical conductivity measurements, and from a comparison of chemical, x-ray and pycnometric analyses.

Chemical Stability. Uranium dioxide powder is readily oxidized by air, even at room temperature. The extent of oxidation depends on the particle size and on the surface area exposed. According to Anderson *et al.*,[9] room-temperature oxidation proceeds until the outer 50 Å are oxidized, the oxygen absorbed being 0.8 cm³ per square meter of surface exposed

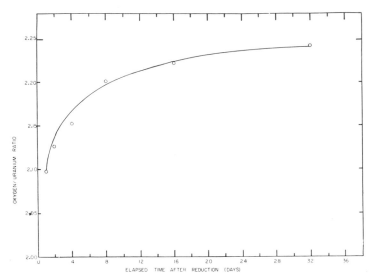

Figure 13-2. Spontaneous oxidation of ammonium diuranate-type UO_2 in air at room temperature.[10]

at normal temperature and pressure. Finely divided powders with particle sizes of 0.1 μ, such as are obtained by the hydrogen reduction of ammonium diuranate at 900°C, oxidize to a composition approaching $UO_{2.25}$ after standing for one month in air at room temperature[10] (see Figure 13-2). Coarser powders with a particle size of 1 μ are much more stable, oxidizing to only $UO_{2.02}$ under similar exposure conditions.[11] Once UO_2 powder has been sintered, at for example 1650°C in hydrogen, its oxidation rate becomes immeasurably slow. Thus, sintered UO_2 pellets may be stored for long periods in air at room temperature with no fear of oxidation.

Sintered UO_2 is stable in deoxygenated, high-temperature water. Belle and Lustman reported[2] that pellets showed only a slight dulling of their surfaces after more than 300 days of exposure in degassed water at 343°C or steam at 400°C at neutral or high pH. When 1 to 3 cm³ of O_2/kg were added to the water, however, a loose scale of hydrated oxide, $UO_3 \cdot 0.8H_2O$, formed and the pellets lost approximately 15 per cent of their weight after an exposure of 8 days at 343°C. In water-cooled power reactors, traces of hydrogen are likely to be present in the coolant stream due to the reaction of the water with structural metals. Thus, uranium dioxide should be stable in such systems. However, a steep temperature gradient will exist across the oxide radius, and if a hole or defect should develop in the cladding of a fuel element, the hot oxide core could be exposed to steam.

Aronson's calculations, reported by Eichenberg,[12] indicate that the core of such an element, operating near the melting point, could oxidize to a composition from $UO_{2.18}$ to $UO_{2.25}$. Some direct evidence was obtained by Lustman[13] to show that stoichiometric UO_2, irradiated in a defected sheath, may in fact increase in O:U ratio. A sample of oxide from a defected irradiated rod, initially stoichiometric, was analyzed and found to have a post-irradiation average composition of $UO_{2.06}$. Recent Chalk River tests have confirmed that oxidation can occur in defected irradiation-test specimens. For example, a sample of oxide from the outer, cooler region of a swaged, purposely defected rod changed in composition from $UO_{2.00}$ to $UO_{2.21}$ during irradiation in a pressurized-water loop. As will be indicated later, an increase in O:U ratio may have a deleterious effect on the irradiation behavior of uranium dioxide fuel.

Some work on the chemical stability of UO_2 in other possible coolants has been reported. The rate of oxidation of UO_2 in CO_2 has been measured by Antill *et al.*[14] at temperatures from 500 to 900°C. They found that UO_2 was much less reactive than U metal. At 700°C, the weight gain of sintered UO_2 pellets of density 9.6 g/cm^3 was 0.008 mg/cm^2-hr compared to 400 to 560 mg/cm^2-hr for U metal. Carbon dioxide is often used as a protective gas over cold-pressed UO_2 pellets when they are heated in a presintering step to remove the organic binder and die lubricant. Thus, there should be little worry about the compatibility of UO_2 with CO_2, unless there is an appreciable increase in the reaction rate in an irradiation field. Judging from thermodynamic data, UO_2 should also be stable in the presence of liquid sodium. According to Nichols,[15] there is some evidence that high-density stoichiometric material is compatible with Na or NaK at 600°C.

Sintered UO_2 pellets are compatible with many sheathing materials. No appreciable reaction occurs between zirconium and UO_2 until a temperature of 700°C is reached.[16] Little reaction occurs between UO_2 and aluminum at temperatures up to 500°C.[17] According to Murray *et al.*,[11] no reaction in the solid state has been found between solid UO_2 specimens and beryllium or stainless steel at 600 to 700°C. Recent work by Pidgeon and Toguri[18] has demonstrated that sintered UO_2 pellets, in contact with graphite plates, do not react appreciably after a 10-hr heating in argon, up to 1500°C.

Melting Point. Several values for the melting point of UO_2 have been published as indicated in Table 13-1. From a survey of these papers, it would appear reasonable to favor a value near 2800°C as the true melting point.

Change in Volume on Melting. The limitation on central core temperature in a uranium dioxide fuel element has not yet been established. Many designers have set the melting-point temperature as a limit, intuitively, until such time as irradiation experience may justify the use of elements with molten cores. It would be useful to know even for present de-

TABLE 13-1. PUBLISHED VALUES FOR THE MELTING POINT OF UO_2

Reference	Date	Atmosphere	Melting Point (°C)
Ruff and Goecke[19]	1911	H_2 , N_2	2176
Friederich and Sittig[20]	1925	N_2	2500–2600
Lambertson and Mueller[21]	1953	Vacuum, He	2878 ± 22
Ackermann[22]	1955	Vacuum	2405 ± 22
Wisnyi and Pijanowski[23]	1956	Vacuum, H_2 , He, Ar	2760 ± 30
Ehlert and Margrave[24]	1958	Vacuum	2860 ± 45

signs, however, if uranium dioxide expands appreciably on melting, in order to determine what void space should be provided in highly rated fuel where the melting point might be exceeded under abnormal operating conditions. Two measurements are under way at present, one at Stanford Research Institute and the other at the University of Toronto. In the Stanford investigation, the UO_2 will be melted in a solar furnace,[25] whereas at Toronto a carbon-electrode arc-furnace with a water-cooled copper hearth will be used.[26] In both experiments, high-speed motion-picture cameras will be used to record the change that occurs when a molten drop of UO_2 solidifies.

Thermal Conductivity. Unfortunately, uranium dioxide has such a low thermal conductivity that the advantage of its high melting point is largely offset. There have been many thermal-conductivity measurements made on sintered UO_2 in recent years, as Figure 13-3 illustrates. The data plotted have all been corrected to theoretical density assuming a linear dependence of thermal conductivity with porosity. It will be noted that values differing by more than a factor of two have been obtained on un-irradiated UO_2 at temperatures below 200°C. At higher temperatures there is better agreement, the difference being only 30 per cent in the range applicable to operating fuel elements; i.e., above 400°C. A 30 per cent uncertainty in the thermal conductivity results in a much larger uncertainty in calculated fuel-core temperatures, however, as will be evident from a later graph (Figure 13-11).

Recently, Eichenberg[32] measured the center temperature of an assembly of UO_2 pellets clad in stainless steel during irradiation in the Materials Testing Reactor. The pellets had been prepared from thermally decomposed uranyl nitrate by cold-pressing and sintering in hydrogen, thus paralleling the process used for the manufacture of the oxide fuel elements of the Pressurized Water Reactor. Values of the effective thermal conductivity required to produce an observed UO_2 central temperature ranging from 150 to 600°C were calculated and are shown in Figure 13-3. It will be noted

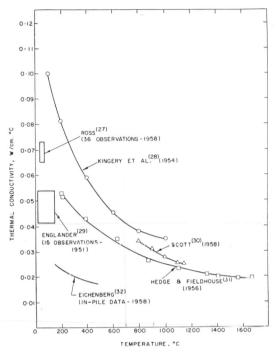

Figure 13-3. Several published values for the thermal conductivity of UO$_2$, corrected to the theoretical density.

that the calculated results are about a factor of 3 lower than the corrected Kingery data.

Ross[27] has measured the thermal conductivity of stoichiometric UO$_2$ pellets at 60°C after irradiations up to an integrated thermal neutron flux of 2×10^{19} n/cm^2. The pellets were prepared by cold-pressing and sintering UO$_2$ powder prepared by the hydrogen reduction of ammonium diuranate. The maximum central temperature in the pellets during the irradiation did not exceed 500°C. The measurements were made on a divided-bar-type, comparative-heat-flow apparatus, using Zircaloy-2 probes, and are plotted in Figure 13-4. Only a small decrease in thermal conductivity, about 25 per cent, was observed after an irradiation of 9×10^{17} n/cm^2. Longer irradiations produced no further significant change. Additional measurements by Ross on samples irradiated for shorter periods are under way at present to determine the irradiation level at which the decrease occurs.

There appears to be a marked disagreement between Eichenberg's results and those of Ross. It is possible that the thermal conductivity of UO$_2$ in

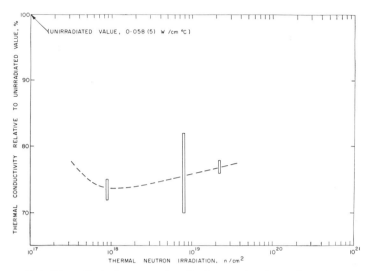

Figure 13-4. The effect of neutron irradiation on the thermal conductivity of UO at 60°C.[27]

a neutron flux could be appreciably lower than postirradiation measurements would indicate, due to the presence of point defects which might anneal out when the irradiation ended. Fuel element tests described later do not support such a hypothesis, however.

Several laboratories have reported that a threefold decrease in thermal conductivity at 60°C can be produced in uranium oxide pellets by increasing the O:U ratio above stoichiometric by 8 per cent.[3, 15, 27] On the other hand, Thackray's values for hot-pressed $UO_{2.13}$ over the temperature range from 100 to 600°C, as reported by Murray and Livey,[33] were essentially the same as the corrected values of Kingery et al.[28] for stoichiometric UO_2. The measurements by Ross[27] on the variation of conductivity with O:U ratio using two samples, one pure uranium oxide and the other with a 0.1 per cent TiO_2 addition, are reproduced in Figure 13-5. Results on a steam-sintered sample with an O:U ratio of 2.21 are included. The conductivity of 0.017 w/cm-°C determined for the latter sample approaches the theoretical lower limit of 0.015 w/cm-°C for the UO_2 lattice determined by Kingery, and reported by Belle[3] and Eichenberg.[32] It is not yet known whether a comparable decrease in conductivity occurs with increased O:U ratio at higher temperatures.

It is possible that some of the apparent discrepancies in thermal-conductivity measurements are due to a variation in the fabrication technique used in the preparation of specimens. Ross[27] has recently found, for example, that the conductivity of stoichiometric UO_2 pellets, prepared by steam

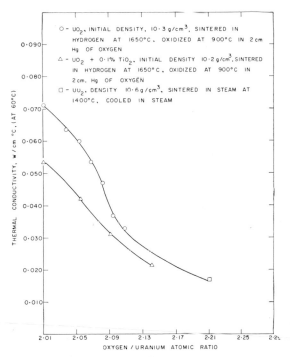

Figure 13-5. The effect of oxygen:uranium ratio on the thermal conductivity of UO₂ at 60°C.[27]

sintering at 1400°C followed by hydrogen cooling, is 25 per cent lower than for those which were also steam-sintered but annealed in hydrogen before cooling (see Table 13-2). Much work remains to be done before the thermal conductivity of uranium oxide fuel elements in operation can be predicted with certainty.

Thermal Expansion. The several published values for the linear thermal-expansion coefficient of uranium dioxide are in reasonable agreement as will be seen from Table 13-3. Murray and Livey[33] reported that the bulk density and O:U ratio had little effect on the thermal expansion coefficient.

Fabrication of UO₂

Cohesive uranium dioxide bodies can be fabricated from a variety of starting powders by conventional ceramic processes such as cold-pressing, extrusion, slip-casting and isostatic pressing. Dense bodies can be produced from the resultant compacts by sintering in hydrogen, steam, nitrogen, vacuum or inert gases such as argon or helium. The required sintering temperature is largely dependent on the nature of the starting powder and

TABLE 13-2. EFFECT OF SINTERING METHOD ON THE THERMAL CONDUCTIVITY
OF URANIUM OXIDES[27]

O:U Ratio	Density (g/cm³)	Method of Fabrication	Thermal Conductivity at 60°C, corrected to theoretical density (w/cm-°C)
2.01 ± 0.01	10.3	Sintered in hydrogen at 1650°C for 2 hr, cooled in hydrogen	0.070 ± 0.005
2.03 ± 0.01	10.45	Sintered in steam at 1400°C for 3 hr, cooled in hydrogen	0.051 ± 0.003
2.01 ± 0.01	10.45	Sintered in steam at 1400°C for 3 hr, annealed in hydrogen at 1400°C for 2 hr, cooled in hydrogen	0.067 ± 0.002
2.21 ± 0.01	10.6	Sintered in steam at 1400°C for 2 hr, cooled in steam	0.017 ± 0.001

TABLE 13-3. THERMAL EXPANSION OF URANIUM DIOXIDE

Temp. Range (°C)	Mean Coefficient of Linear Expansion (10^{-6}/°C)	Reference
20–720	11.5	Thewlis[34]
20–946	10.8	Gronvold[5]
27–400	9.0 ⎫	
400–800	11.0 ⎬	Burdick and Parker[35]
800–1260	13.0 ⎭	
400–900	10	Murray and Livey[33]

may range from 1300 to 2000°C. Other fabrication methods include rotary
swaging and loose compaction of powder in metal sheaths, and hot pressing in metal or graphite dies. Fabrication methods pertinent to the preparation of uranium dioxide fuel elements are reviewed below.

Powder Preparation. Uranium dioxide powder can be prepared by the
hydrogen reduction of several different uranium compounds. These include
UO_3, UO_3 hydrates, U_3O_8, ammonium diuranate, uranium oxalate and
uranium peroxide. UO_2 has also been prepared by steam oxidation of
uranium hydride or uranium metal. Uranium dioxide powders prepared by
different methods show wide variations in physical characteristics such as
surface area, particle density, porosity distribution and crystallite size, as
pointed out by many authors.[2, 36, 37, 38, 39] Such variations have a marked
effect on the sinterability of the powder as illustrated in Table 13-4.

Pellets with densities above 10 g/cm³ can be produced from the least
sinterable powder shown in Table 13-4, however, if high compacting pressures and long sintering times are used. The first oxide charge for the PWR,
for example, was prepared by compacting UO_2 powder obtained from the

TABLE 13-4. VARIATION IN SINTERABILITY OF UO_2 PREPARED FROM DIFFERENT SOURCE MATERIALS[40]*

Source of UO_2	Preparation Route	Sintered Density (g/cm³)
Mallinckrodt Chem. Co.	Pyrolysis of uranyl nitrate hexahydrate (U.N.H.) to UO_3, reduction with H_2	7.8
Shattuck Chem. Co.	Believed similar to Mallinckrodt	8.6
National Lead Co.	Believed similar to Mallinckrodt	9.1
Eldorado Mining and Refining Co.	Pyrolysis of U.N.H. to UO_3, reduction with H_2	9.2
Eldorado Mining and Refining Co.	Pyrolysis of U.N.H. to UO_3, UO_3 hydrated by wet ball-milling, then reduced with H_2	10.3
U.K.A.E.A., Springfields	Precipitation of A.D.U. from U.N.H., reduction with H_2	10.6
Mines Branch, Ottawa	Precipitation of A.D.U. from U.N.H., reduction with H_2	10.1–10.7
A.E.C.L., Chalk River	Precipitation of A.D.U. from U.N.H., reduction with H_2	10.4–10.6

* All Pellets cold-pressed at 2800 kg/cm² (40,000 psi) and sintered for 30 min. at 1700°C in hydrogen.

Mallinckrodt Chemical Works at 17,500 kg/cm² (250,000 psi) and sintering for 8 hr in hydrogen at 1675°C.[41] The pellets obtained varied in density from 10.2 to 10.4 g/cm³.

Powders of low sinterability can be activated by wet ball-milling before hydrogen reduction as shown in Table 13-4. A simpler, more economic method is to grind UO_3 powder to particle sizes less than 1 μ in a fluid jet mill and then to reduce in hydrogen. Pellets with densities up to 10.7 g/cm³ have been produced from such powder after pressing at 2800 kg/cm² (40,000 psi) and sintering for 1 hr at 1625°C.[39] Many laboratories have investigated the effects of chemical additives to promote more rapid sintering of uranium dioxide. Canadian workers have verified the many earlier reports on the effectiveness of a 0.1 per cent TiO_2 addition and have found that 0.4 per cent Nb_2O_5 has an even larger effect.[39, 42] (See Figure 13-6.)

The preparation of uranium dioxide powder via the ammonium diuranate route has been extensively investigated by Watson et al.[10, 39, 43] The production of a reproducible ammonium diuranate (ADU) powder was accomplished by the batch precipitation of ADU from a uranyl nitrate solution with a uranium concentration of 100 g/l at 60°C, by the rapid addition of concentrated, aqueous ammonium hydroxide until a pH of 9 was reached. The ADU was separated by filtration, washed with water and oven-dried in air at 200°C. Deviations from the above procedure in the direction of higher uranium concentration, slower precipitation rate or final pH were

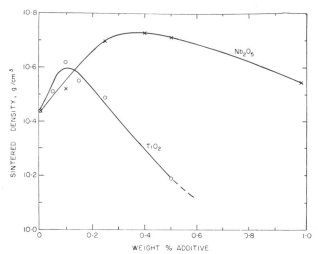

Figure 13-6. The effect of TiO_2 and Nb_2O_5 additives on the sintered density of UO_2 .[39]

found to alter the character of the ADU so that the UO_2 product sintered to a lower density. When the precipitation was carried out by continuously mixing two liquid streams, however, the only variable which affected pellet density appreciably was the pH of the mixed solutions. The best powders were produced when the pH was between 7 and 8. The recommended conditions for conversion to UO_2 were to load the ADU in trays to a depth not exceeding 2 in. and to reduce in hydrogen for 1 hr at 900°C. The resulting pyrophoric powder was cooled to room temperature in hydrogen and stored in a protective atmosphere of carbon dioxide for 1 to 2 hr, after which it could be handled and stored in air. After 30 days' storage in air, the O:U ratio had increased to 2.25 as already mentioned (see Figure 13-2).

Several tons of UO_2 powder have been produced by the Eldorado Mining and Refining Company, Port Hope, Ontario using both batch and continuous precipitation. Sintering tests for 1 hr at 1625°C on many samples pressed at 2800 kg/cm² (40,000 psi) have consistently produced pellets with densities between 10.4 and 10.6 g/cm³.

Although uranium dioxide pellets of the required quality for use in fuel elements can be prepared from "ceramic-grade" powders at relatively low compacting pressures and sintering times, it is still not certain whether these will be less expensive than pellets made from less sinterable powders. For example, the Eldorado Company is marketing "standard-grade" UO_2 , prepared by the hydrogen reduction of $UO_3 \cdot 2H_2O$ in a moving-bed furnace, for $1.15/lb less than ADU-type UO_2 .[44] A careful cost analysis for each specific fuel geometry would be required to indicate whether the cost advantage of such cheaper powder would be offset by the larger capital investment in dies and compacting presses, and a lower furnace output.

It should be noted that ADU-type UO_2 powder, made by the route outlined above, offers some advantage for more economic fuel production, in that it can be satisfactorily cold-pressed without the use of an organic binder. It is necessary to apply a lubricant such as stearic acid to the die walls during the pressing operation to obtain crack-free compacts, which can then be charged directly to the sintering furnace without the presintering treatment normally used for binder removal.

Method of Compaction. The most common method used for the preparation of UO_2 compacts is dry pressing in hardened-steel or tungsten-carbide dies. Usually, an organic binder such as paraffin wax, polyethylene glycol or camphor is added to increase the green strength of the compact during subsequent handling operations. A small amount of stearic acid, 0.2 to 0.4 w/o*, is often added to act as a die lubricant.[39]

Extrusion of uranium dioxide shapes has been carried out in several laboratories.[37, 45] The extrusion process may offer some advantage where a large length-to-diameter ratio is required, or for the fabrication of large-diameter tubes of UO_2, but no fuel element manufacturer has yet chosen the technique in preference to automatic dry pressing. Other possible compaction processes such as slip-casting, isostatic pressing and hot-pressing would appear to have been similarly rejected up to the present.

The compaction of uranium dioxide powders in metal sheaths by rotary swaging has been investigated extensively in the United States[37, 46] and in Canada.[39, 47] In both laboratories it was found that, of the many powders evaluated, arc-fused UO_2 could be compacted at room temperature to the highest density, about 10 g/cm^3, in either Zircaloy-2 or stainless steel sheaths. Much lower densities were obtained when powders with high surface area (such as ADU-type UO_2) were used, as illustrated in Figure 13-7. In the Hanford experiments, higher densities resulted when the oxide was swaged hot, at 600°C.[46]

At first sight, swaging promises a cheaper method of fabrication than the conventional sintered-pellet route. However, the fabrication of fuel elements with a high ratio of diameter-to-sheath thickness may not be economically feasible using a swaging technique. It would seem inevitable that the trend in fuel-element development will be to decrease the sheath thickness to the minimum permitted by fabrication and irradiation experience. As an example, the diameter:sheath-thickness ratio of the UO_2 fuel elements in the PWR is 18:1,[41] whereas the target in the Canadian NPD-2 reactor is 40:1. Recent tests at Chalk River on swaged elements with a ratio near the latter value have shown that small cracks had formed

* w/o = weight per cent

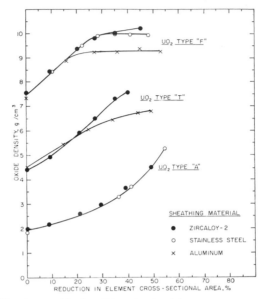

Figure 13-7. Uranium oxide densities obtained by rotary-swaging three different UO_2 powders in three different sheath materials.[39]
Type F: fused UO_2
Type T: UO_3 reduced to UO_2 in H_2 at 1200°C
Type A: ADU reduced to UO_2 in H_2 at 900°C

on the inside surface of the Zircaloy-2 tube during swaging, after a reduction of only 20 per cent in the cross-sectional area of the element. One such element which had been reduced 48 per cent in area at 400°C to 0.8-in. OD and 0.025-in. sheath thickness, was irradiated in a pressurized-water loop in the NRX reactor, and split open immediately when the reactor was started. One of the ends of the swaged specimen, which had been cut off and preserved as an archive sample, was metallographically examined, revealing cracks on the inside Zircaloy-2 surface up to 0.002 in. deep as illustrated in Figure 13-8. As a result of such experience, swaged UO_2 has been rejected as a possible first charge for the NPD-2 reactor. An experimental program is continuing, however, to determine if an economic process incorporating intermediate annealing steps can be evolved to produce crack-free sheaths.

The loose compacting of UO_2 powder in a fuel sheath is simple in concept but, thus far, no method has been found to exceed a packed density of 8 to 9 g/cm^3.

Sintering Method. Ceramic-grade uranium dioxide can be sintered to densities above 10 g/cm^3 in neutral or oxidizing atmospheres at temperatures 300 to 400°C lower than in reducing atmospheres. In Thackray and

Figure 13-8. Typical crack on the inner surface of a Zircaloy-2 sheath containing swaged UO_2, after the element had been reduced 48 per cent in cross-sectional area at 400°C.

Murray's early work,[48] for example, it was found that, with an ADU-type oxide of composition $UO_{2.13}$, after pressing at 1400 kg/cm² (20 000 psi), a density of 10 g/cm³ was reached after 30 min. in argon at 1400°C. Belle and Lustman[2, 3] have concluded from their studies on self-diffusion kinetics that densification in an oxidizing atmosphere occurs by the diffusion of the more mobile, excess oxygen ions, whereas in a reducing atmosphere a plastic or viscous flow model is probable. The effect of excess oxygen on the sinterability of uranium oxide was well demonstrated in Scott and Williams' work on warm-pressing of UO_2,[49] where it was found that fine, nonstoichiometric powders could be compacted in metal dies to densities above 10 g/cm³ in 10 min. at 800°C under a pressure of 1400 kg/cm² (20 000 psi). When the excess oxygen was removed from the UO_2 lattice by the addition of powders such as iron or uranium, the densification was inhibited.

The steam-sintering of wet-ball-milled uranium dioxide has been studied by Arenberg and Jahn.[50] To achieve high densities, they found it necessary to heat the compacts in H_2 to 1400°C before introducing a steam atmosphere. Chalder[40] on the other hand has reported that, with ADU-type oxide, the complete cycle of heating, sintering at 1300 to 1400°C and cooling can be carried out in steam. The resulting pellets of 10.5 to 10.6 g/cm³ density usually are near $UO_{2.15}$ in composition.

The major difficulty with low-temperature sintering is that the product is nonstoichiometric, unless a hydrogen cooling step is introduced. Stoichiometric oxide is preferred as a reactor fuel for reasons which will be discussed in the later section on irradiation behavior. If hydrogen cooling is a process requirement, it is not clear that there is any economic advantage over sintering in a continuously stoked furnace in a hydrogen atmosphere at 1600 to 1700°C.

Although it may be fortuitous, most manufacturers have chosen to prepare UO_2 pellets from a "ceramic-grade" powder of high surface area in continuous rather than batch-type furnaces and in an atmosphere of dry hydrogen or cracked ammonia. Runfors et al.[51, 52] have reported, however, that the sintering temperature can be lowered about 100°C if the hydrogen is first saturated with moisture at room temperature. The effect of the moist atmosphere on furnace life has not as yet been established.

Sheathing, Assembly and Inspection

The important requirements for a fuel-element sheath are a low neutron-capture cross section, good mechanical properties at working temperatures, high corrosion resistance in the hot coolant and compatibility with the core.

For economical water-cooled reactors fueled with uranium dioxide, a zirconium alloy would appear to be the most suitable material. Stainless steel would be acceptable but for its high neutron-capture cross section. Aluminum-nickel alloys are not likely to compete with zirconium, not only because of their lower strength, but also because of lower neutron economy, as indicated by Lewis.[53] For sodium-cooled systems, also, zirconium alloys may prove to be the best choice. In organic liquids, however, zirconium alloys are attacked by the hydrogen which is liberated when the coolant is irradiated. The most suitable material immediately available for service in organics at temperatures near 400°C is stainless steel. Elements clad in stainless steel are likely to be used, also, in several CO_2-cooled reactors now being designed, at least until beryllium fabrication technology has been further developed.

The most common design of uranium dioxide fuel element is that typified by the first loading for the Pressurized Water Reactor.[41] The fuel assemblies consist of a bundle of small round rods, each rod enclosing a stack of right-cylindrical sintered pellets. The diametral clearance between the pellets and the sheath is so specified that the pellets can be loaded easily into the tubes during assembly but will expand into near contact with the sheath when heated in the reactor. Other geometries being developed include a nested tubular-type for use in the Plutonium Recycle Test Reactor[37] and a plate-type for the second loading of the PWR.[41] A rod-type element was chosen for the first loading of the Canadian NPD-2 reactor because of the satisfactory results that had been obtained in several establishments from irradiation tests on such a geometry, and because of the inherent stability of a cylindrical sheath when subjected to an internal pressure.

The effect of external pressure on sheath stability is of major concern, particularly in water-cooled reactors operating at coolant pressures from

70 to 140 kg/cm² (1000 to 2000 psi) where the fuel has a diameter:sheath-thickness ratio greater than 30:1. In the NPD-2 reactor, for example, where the pressure is to be 77 kg/cm² (1100 psi), the proposed 1-in. diameter, 0.025-in. thick Zircaloy-2 sheath will deform plastically at the maximum operating surface temperature of 300°C, forming ridges and dimples, if the fuel-sheath clearance is greater than 0.006 in. in diameter or 0.15 in. axially. To insure accurate control of the diametral clearance, the UO_2 pellets will be centerless-ground to ±0.0005 in. before loading into carefully dimensioned sheaths. In addition, it is probable that an axial clearance of 0.2 in. will be distributed along the 18-in. fuel length by fabricating pellets with concave ends.

The usual method employed to attach end caps to uranium dioxide fuel elements is by fusion-arc welding in an inert atmosphere such as helium or argon. Resistance seam-welding combined with a heliarc fusion weld is being developed to provide a double closure for large-diameter, thin-walled tubes, as outlined by Evans.[37] Electron-beam welding has also been studied as an end-closure method.[54, 55] Since the latter process is carried out in vacuum, however, the resulting fuel element could have poorer heat-transfer properties if the oxide does not expand to contact the sheath when irradiated.

If the fuel elements are short, such as those used in PWR,[41] the only spacers required in the assembled bundle are at the ends. For longer assemblies, intermediate spacers are normally incorporated. These may be wires wound in a spiral around the rod, ribs integral with the sheath, short lugs attached by methods such as fusion-arc or high-frequency resistance welding, or metal grids similar to the type described by Ambartsumyan et al.[56]

There are many methods available for the non-destructive testing of uranium dioxide fuel elements. The sheathing is usually given an internal-pressure burst test by the manufacturer at the mill. Eddy current and ultrasonic tests are often applied to detect the presence of inclusions, voids and internal cracks. After assembly, the fuel rod may be subjected to x-radiographic examination, helium leak testing, and immersion under a liquid such as ethylene glycol in an evacuated container to check the integrity of the welded closures. A further useful test for leak tightness is autoclaving in high-temperature water or steam. A small weight increase is indicative of a cladding defect.

Irradiation Behavior

An extensive report outlining irradiation tests on prototype PWR elements clad in Zircaloy-2 was issued in 1957 by Eichenberg et al.[57] More recently, Robertson et al.[58] have reported on many uranium dioxide fuel tests in the Canadian NRX reactor. Thus, within the past 2 years, a much clearer understanding has been obtained of the irradiation behavior of UO_2. A brief summary of irradiation experience, including several pertinent results from tests just completed at Chalk River, is presented below.

Effect of Heat Rating on Stoichiometric UO_2. Lewis[59] has pointed out the economic advantages of developing a UO_2 fuel that has a high value of the integral

$$\int_{\text{Surface temperature}}^{\text{Maximum fuel temperature}} k(\theta) \cdot d\theta$$

where $k(\theta)$ is the thermal conductivity and is a function of the temperature θ. The latter expression is a most valuable one for use in fuel design, as Robertson *et al.*[58] have shown, since it can be applied without a precise knowledge of either the thermal conductivity or axial temperatures in the fuel. The parameter can be used to compare the irradiation behavior of specimens of differing diameter, enrichment, density, heat rating and fabrication history.

The integral can be obtained as a product of two terms, one determined by the heat-transfer rate measured experimentally, and the other a calculated function of the specimen's properties, e.g.:

$$\int_{T_s}^{T_r} k(\theta) \cdot d\theta = \frac{HR}{2} \cdot fn(\kappa a, r)$$

$$= \frac{q}{4\pi} \cdot fn(\kappa a, r)$$

where

$$fn(\kappa a, r) = 2 \frac{I_0(\kappa a) - I_0(\kappa r)}{\kappa a \cdot I_1(\kappa a)}$$

which has the value unity at $r = 0$ for negligible flux depression, hence uniform heat generation.

$k(\theta)$ = thermal conductivity of uranium oxide at temperature θ
T_r = temperature at radius r
T_s = temperature at uranium oxide surface
H = sheath-coolant surface heat flux
R = radius of outside of sheath
a = radius of uranium oxide
q = heat production per unit length of fuel
I_0 = modified Bessel function of zero order
I_1 = modified Bessel function of first order
κ = reciprocal of effective diffusion length in uranium oxide.

Morison[60] has expressed the dependence of $fn(\kappa a, r)$ at $r = 0$ on uranium

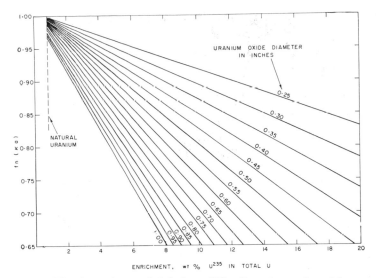

Figure 13-9. The dependence of $fn(\kappa a)$ on UO_2 diameter and enrichment for 95 per cent dense, solid oxide cylinders.[60]

oxide diameter and enrichment for 95 per cent dense, solid oxide cylinders, in the convenient form shown in Figure 13-9. Thus, the computation of the integral has been much simplified.

The published results of Robertson *et al.*,[58] considered along with more recent unpublished results from tests on sintered ADU-type UO_2, show that cylindrical stoichiometric specimens, whose oxide surface temperature was about 400°C during irradiation, have exhibited discernible grain growth when

$$\int_{surface}^{center} k(\theta) \cdot d\theta$$

exceeded 29 ± 3 w/cm. Rod-shaped elements irradiated in pressurized-water loops at Chalk River have exhibited completely satisfactory performance at ratings as high as 50 w/cm. A cross section of such a rod from a 7-element bundle irradiated to 7000 Mwd/tonne U with

$$\int_{400°C}^{center} k(\theta) \cdot d\theta$$

equal to 50 w/cm is shown in Figure 13-10. Central melting would be expected at an integral value of 55 w/cm.

As indicated earlier, by using the above method, physical changes in the cores of uranium oxide fuel elements with similar surface temperatures

Figure 13-10. Cross section of a Zircaloy-2 clad UO_2 rod (0.56 in. dia.) from the CR-V-c test, after an irradiation of 7000 Mwd/tonne U.

can be predicted without information on thermal conductivity and its variation with temperature and irradiation, the temperatures at which grain growth and melting occur, or the type of sheathing used. It was considered useful, however, to plot several irradiation results in such a way that values of the integral producing grain growth and melting could be predicted for solid stoichiometric cylinders with different surface temperatures. This has been done by plotting

$$\int_{0°C}^{T} k(\theta) \cdot d\theta$$

vs. T, a particular temperature in the fuel (see Figure 13-11). For any given irradiation, the value of

$$\int_{T_s}^{T} k(\theta) \cdot d\theta$$

is the difference in ordinates for two points defined by the temperature limits, T_s and T. Several published measurements of the thermal conductivity of UO_2, corrected to 95 per cent density, have been included on Figure 13-11 as a matter of interest, to indicate the "effective" thermal conductivity of irradiated UO_2.

The point on the graph for Pellet Rod III was determined by measuring the central temperature with a thermocouple and by calculating the in-

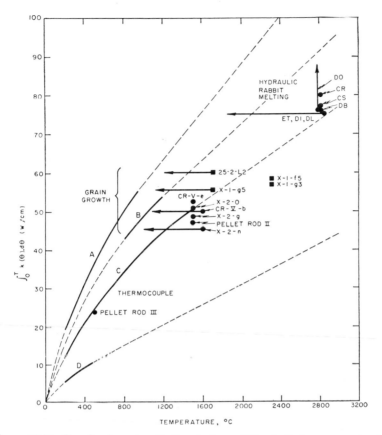

Figure 13-11. Results from irradiation tests on UO₂ plotted on a graph of

$$\int_{0°C}^{T} k(\theta) \cdot d\theta$$

versus T, a particular temperature in the fuel:

● Chalk River data   ■ WAPD data[57]

Several published values for the thermal conductivity of UO₂, corrected to 95 per cent density have been included (solid lines) and extrapolated to 2800°C (dashed lines):

A. Kingery *et al.*[28]   C. Hedge and Fieldhouse[31]
B. Scott[30]   D. Eichenberg[32]

tegral from a knowledge of the neutron flux, hence the heat output from the rod. In plotting the points for the Canadian specimens showing grain growth, CR-V-e, X-2-o, X-2-g and Pellet Rod II, values for the integral from the oxide surface to the observed radius of grain growth were determined by a method similar to that detailed in the following paragraph and illustrated by Figure 13-14. It was assumed that discernible grain growth would be produced in the ADU-type UO_2 at a temperature of 1500°C, for the reasons outlined by Robertson *et al.*[58] When no discernible grain growth was present in the center of an element for comparison with the undisturbed outer area, a minor change in appearance was difficult to detect under the microscope used. Hence, the center temperature of specimens from CR-V-b and X-2-n, where no grain growth was observed, may have been as high as 1600°C. The WAPD specimens 25-2-L2 and X-1-g5, which also showed no grain growth, were made from the less reactive PWR-grade UO_2. Thus, a somewhat higher temperature limit, 1700°C, has been assumed. Specimens X-1-f5 and X-1-g3 showed grain growth corresponding to 2300°C at the maximum-flux positions according to Eichenberg *et al.*[57] The heat outputs from specimens irradiated in the CR-V and X-2 loops were measured calorimetrically, and some were checked by mass-spectrometric analyses to determine burn-up. Published heat fluxes for the WAPD tests,[57] corrected for flux gradient in the case of the X-1 specimens, were used in calculating the integrals.

Unambiguous melting has been observed in uranium oxide specimens irradiated in a water-cooled facility in the NRX reactor known as the "Hydraulic Rabbit," where irradiations of short duration can be carried out. A cross section of a sintered UO_2 specimen, DB, clad in Zircaloy-2 and

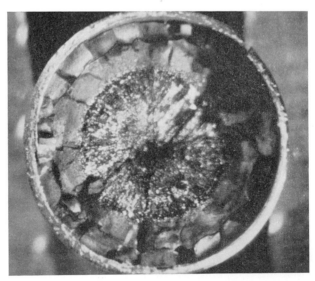

Figure 13-12. Cross section of Zircaloy-2 clad UO_2 rod, DB (0.72 in. diam.) irradiated for 60 sec in the "Hydraulic Rabbit," showing a central area which had been molten.

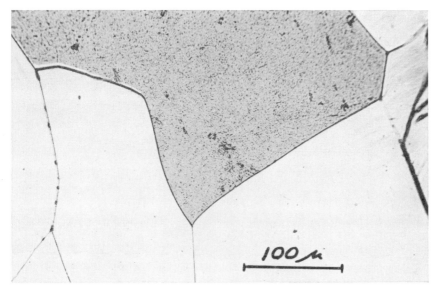

Figure 13-13. Polished section of UO_2 taken from the inner region of element DB (shown in Figure 13-12) that had been molten.

irradiated for 60 sec (Figure 13-12), indicates clearly the extent of melting. A polished section from the inner region that had been molten (Figure 13-13) shows that little visible porosity remained after solidification. The method used to apply the observed radius of melting obtained from a photograph such as Figure 13-12 to the graph shown in Figure 13-11 is illustrated by reference to Figure 13-14 where

$$\int_{\text{surface}}^{r} k(\theta) \cdot d\theta$$

is plotted against the fuel radius r. The curve shown applies specifically to specimens CR and DB, which were similar in diameter and enrichment. The oxide surface temperature of both was calculated to be 250°C. Hence,

$$\int_{250°C}^{T_m} k(\theta) \cdot d\theta \quad \begin{aligned} &= 66 \text{ w/cm for CR} \\ &\text{and} = 62 \text{ w/cm for DB, at the melting temperature } T_m. \end{aligned}$$

Specimen CR was irradiated for only 30 seconds. Later experience indicated that an irradiation time of 60 sec was required to insure that virtual thermal equilibrium had been reached. Thus, the integral for melting in specimen CR is probably somewhat high. Specimen DO had a larger fuel-sheath diametral clearance than the other rabbit samples. Hence, the integral might have been higher if the clearance had been comparable, as

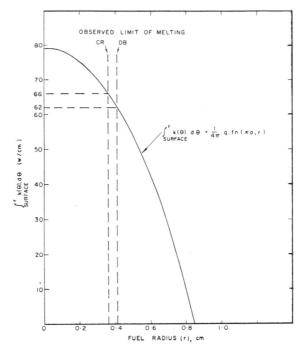

Figure 13-14. The variation of

$$\int_{\text{surface}}^{r} k(\theta) \cdot d\theta$$

with radius r, for "Hydraulic Rabbit" specimens of 0.72 in. diameter and enrichment 4.82 w/o U^{235} in total U.

indicated by the vertical arrow on the graph. Since specimens ET, DI and DL did not melt, the ordinate of Figure 13-11 could be specified, but only an upper limit given to the abscissa.

Small differences in the surface temperature of the oxide can be corrected for, without introducing serious errors, by using an assumed value of conductivity in the difference term alone. In order to plot points on Figure 13-11 for specimens CR and DB, a value of 14 w/cm was assumed for

$$\int_{0°C}^{250°C} k(\theta) \cdot d\theta.$$

With the exception of sample DO, the fuel-sheath diametral clearances of all the specimens shown in Figure 13-11 were small enough so that the oxide should have expanded to contact the sheath while the fuel was being irradiated. It is interesting to note that the "effective" thermal conductivity for such fuel appears approximately the same as the Hedge and Fieldhouse values,[31] corrected for density.

Effect of Fuel-Sheath Clearance. A simple model was proposed by Robertson *et al.*[58] to predict temperatures in fuel elements with large fuel-sheath diametral clearances. The UO_2 cylinder was pictured as remaining centrally located and intact under irradiation, and expanding as if it were at a uniform temperature equal to its mean temperature. The interfacial temperature drop could then be calculated from the thermal conductivity of the gas in the surrounding annulus. It had been appreciated that the model was not physically correct, since it was unlikely that the oxide pellets would remain central in the sheath, and it was known that the pellets would crack from the thermal stresses produced during the irradiation. Evans had reported,[37] for example, that cracking effectively relocated part of the original annular gap to the hotter interior of the fuel. It is only recently, however, that the inadequacy of the model was clearly demonstrated from tests in the EEC loop[61] and Hydraulic Rabbit[62] at Chalk River. The latter tests, on oxide pellets 0.67-in. diameter heated near the melting point in the center, indicated that the oxide surface temperature of specimens with a starting fuel-sheath diametral clearance of 0.017-in. was not more than 100°C higher than those with a 0.005-in. clearance.

These results have led Robertson to suggest a more realistic model[63] in which cracked segments of oxide shift radially outward to contact the sheath, so that the interfacial temperature drop becomes mainly dependent on the interfacial pressure and the properties of the contacting surfaces. The few irradiation data that are available support the choice of the newest model. If the approach is valid, a consequence would be that large differences in assembled diametral clearance could be tolerated in fuel elements where the sheath collapse problem mentioned earlier was of no concern, since such differences would have a relatively small effect on the fuel temperature during irradiation.

Effect of Oxygen-Uranium Ratio. Several tests described by Robertson *et al.*[58, 64] have demonstrated that nonstoichiometric uranium dioxide exhibits much more grain growth and liberates more fission gas than near-stoichiometric pellets irradiated under comparable conditions. The most unambiguous comparison was obtained from the X-2-n loop test where specimens, identical except for their oxygen:uranium ratio, were irradiated in adjacent positions for the same period. After irradiation, two samples of steam-sintered and hydrogen-cooled $UO_{2.00}$ were radially cracked with no apparent grain growth, whereas two samples of steam-sintered $UO_{2.15}$ exhibited cracking and extensive grain growth, as illustrated in Figure 13-15. The amount of fission gas released was 100 to 200 times higher from the nonstoichiometric oxide, as is evident from Table 13-5.

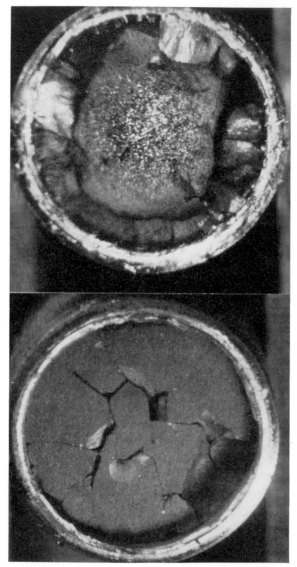

Figure 13-15. Cross sections of Zircaloy-2 clad uranium oxide specimens (0.41 in. diam) of composition $UO_{2.00}$ (left) and $UO_{2.15}$ (right) after an irradiation of ~4500 Mwd/tonne U in the X-2-n test.

The X-2-n experiment clearly indicated that the value of $\int k(\theta)\cdot d\theta$ producing grain growth is markedly lowered if extra oxygen is added to the UO_2 lattice. There are several explanations that might account for such a phenomenon. The oxygen self-diffusion rate is higher in UO_{2+x} than in $UO_{2.0}$;[3] thus grain growth should proceed at lower temperatures in non-stoichiometric oxides. In addition, the thermal conductivity of UO_{2+x} is known to be lower at 60°C, and hence is suspected to be lower at elevated temperatures. The liberation of gaseous UO_3 by the disproportionation of UO_{2+x} might also produce physical changes in the oxide core.

The available irradiation results indicate that stoichiometric oxide should be chosen for optimum performance. If an element were to become defected in service, however, the core could be oxidized by coolants such as water or carbon dioxide. Thus, it is desirable to obtain irradiation experience on purposely defected test specimens, particularly at high heat ratings. Tests under way at Chalk River indicate that defected Zircaloy-2-clad UO_2 can be operated safely in pressurized-water coolant at values of

$$\int_{400°C}^{center} k(\theta)\cdot d\theta$$

as high as 50 w/cm.

Fission-Gas Release. The release of fission gases from irradiated uranium oxide has been studied extensively by Lustman et al.[57, 65] and Booth et al.[58, 66, 67] However, the factors influencing gas release and the actual escape mechanism are still not clearly understood. Booth[66] found that markedly different amounts of gas were evolved from samples of similar density prepared by different fabrication methods. Even for specimens prepared by virtually the same fabrication technique in the same laboratory and receiving similar irradiations, the fission-gas release has varied appreciably.

TABLE 13-5. EFFECT OF OXYGEN: URANIUM RATIO ON FISSION GAS RELEASE FROM URANIUM OXIDE ELEMENTS CLAD IN ZIRCALOY-2 AND IRRADIATED IN LOOP TEST X-2-N[58, 64]

Specimen Identity	Oxide Preparation Method	O:U Ratio	Average Density (g/cm³)	Burn-up (Mwd/tonne U)	$\int_{400°C}^{Center} k(\theta)\cdot d\theta$ (w/cm)	Fission Product Xenon Release (%)
AG	Steam-sintered for 4 hr at 1325°C, then hydro-	2.002	10.41	4600	27.1	0.05
AK	gen sintered for 1 hr at 1325°C	2.002	10.45	4500	26.8	0.13
AA	Steam sintered for 4 hr at	2.15	10.47	4300	25.4	20.0
AS	1325°C	2.15	10.48	4300	25.4	18.5

Where grain growth has been observed, the amount of gas released in long irradiations has always been substantial; e.g., 35 per cent of the fission-product xenon was released from rod 12 of the CR-V-e test in which ~45 per cent of the oxide exhibited grain growth during an irradiation of 7000 Mwd/tonne U.

Lustman[65] has shown that, even with the most pessimistic assumptions, fission-gas release would not limit the performance of the present uranium oxide core in the Shippingport PWR. In reactors operating under lower pressures using elements with larger ratios of diameter-to-sheath thickness, however, the buildup of internal gas pressure might prove to be a severe limitation. On the other hand, Davies[68] has calculated that the fission-gas pressure within a typical fuel element may reach a limiting value at less than 100 atm due to a "knock-on" process where free gas atoms are kinetically excited by fission fragments and re-enter the oxide lattice. An experimental program is under way at Chalk River to determine the validity of the theory.

Conclusion

All the available evidence indicates that sintered, stoichiometric uranium dioxide will be a most satisfactory fuel for many types of power reactors. Its several advantages include:
1. A high melting point.
2. Chemical stability with most reactor coolants.
3. Compatibility with a wide variety of sheathing materials.
4. Ease of fabrication to high densities.
5. An isotropic structure stable under irradiation at core temperatures approaching the melting point.

A disadvantage is its low thermal conductivity. Fortunately, however, the thermal conductivity in operating fuel elements appears to be little reduced even after long irradiation. The release of fission gas may impose a limitation on future fuel element designs but there are not sufficient experimental data available to say this with any certainty at present.

ACKNOWLEDGMENT

The author is indebted to A. S. Bain, G. H. Chalder, W. Evans, R. G. Hart, J. A. L. Robertson, A. M. Ross and M. B. Watson for supplying information in advance of publication. He is particularly grateful to J. A. L. Robertson for many valuable discussions and for Figures 13-11 and 13-14.

References

1. Katz, J. J. and Rabinowitch, E., "The Chemistry of Uranium," National Nuclear Energy Series, VIII-5, New York, McGraw-Hill Book Co., Inc., 1951.
2. Belle, J. and Lustman, B., USAEC Report WAPD-184 (Sept. 1957); also issued in USAEC Report TID-7546, p. 442 (Mar. 1958).

3. Belle, J., Second United Nations International Conference on the Peaceful Uses of Atomic Energy (Sept. 1958) P/2404.
4. Blackburn, P. E., Westinghouse Research Laboratories Report 100FF942-P1 (Jan. 1957).
5. Gronvold, F., *J. Inorg. and Nuclear Chem.,* **1**, 357 (1955).
6. Aronson, S. and Belle, J., USAEC Report WAPD-T-573 (Sept. 1957).
7. Roberts, L. E. J., Adwick, A. G., Rand, M. H., Russell, L. E. and Walter, A. J., Second United Nations International Conference on the Peaceful Uses of Atomic Energy (Sept. 1958) P/26.
8. Perio, P., *Bull. Soc. Chem.,* **20**, 256 (1953).
9. Anderson, J. S., Roberts, L. E. J. and Harper, E. A., **1955** *J. Chem. Soc.,* 3946.
10. Watson, L. C., AECL Report CRL-45 (Nov. 1957); also issued in USAEC Report TID-7546, p. 384 (Mar. 1958).
11. Murray, P., Pugh, S. F. and Williams, J., USAEC Report TID-7546, p. 432 (Mar. 1958).
12. Eichenberg, J. D., USAEC Report WAPD-167 (Mar. 1957).
13. Lustman, B., Westinghouse Atomic Power Division, private communication (Dec. 21, 1957).
14. Antill, J. E., Peakall, K. A., Crick, N. and Smart, E., AERE Report M/M 168 (1957).
15. Nichols, R. W., *Nuclear Eng.,* **3**, 327 (1958).
16. Mallett, M. W., Gerds, A. F., Lemmon, A. W. and Chase, D. L., USAEC Report BMI-1028 (Aug. 1955).
17. Eiss, A. L., USAEC Report SCNC-257 (Feb. 1958).
18. Pidgeon, L. M. and Toguri, J. M., University of Toronto, unpublished work (Sept. 1958).
19. Ruff, O. and Goecke, D., *Z. angew. Chem.,* **24**, 1459 (1911).
20. Friederich, E. and Sittig, L., *Z. anorg. u. allgem. Chem.,* **145**, 127 (1925).
21. Lambertson, W. A. and Mueller, M. H., *J. Am. Ceram. Soc.,* **36**, 329 (1953).
22. Ackermann, R. J., USAEC Report ANL 5482 (Sept. 1955).
23. Wisnyi, L. G. and Pijanowski, S., USAEC Report KAPL-1702 (Nov. 1957).
24. Ehlert, T. C. and Margrave, J. L., *J. Am. Ceram. Soc.,* **41**, 330 (1958).
25. Halden, F. A., Stanford Research Institute, private communication (Oct. 23, 1958).
26. Pidgeon, L. M., University of Toronto, private communication (Nov. 21, 1958).
27. Ross, A. M., AECL Report CRFD-817, to be published.
28. Kingery, W. D., Francl, L., Coble, R. L. and Vasilos, T., *J. Am. Ceram. Soc.,* **37**, 107 (1954).
29. Englander, M., French Report CEA-79 (June 1951).
30. Scott, R. W., AERE Report M/R 2526 (Mar. 1958).
31. Hedge, J. C. and Fieldhouse, I. B., Armour Research Foundation Report G022 D3 (Sept. 1956).
32. Eichenberg, J. D., USAEC Report WAPD-200 (Sept. 1958).
33. Murray, P. and Livey, D. T., Prog. Nuc. Eng. V-1, p. 448, Pergamon Press, 1956.
34. Thewlis, J., *Acta Cryst.,* **5**, 790 (1952).
35. Burdick, M. D. and Parker, H. S., *J. Am. Ceram. Soc.,* **39**, 181 (1956).
36. Anderson, J. S., Harper, E. A., Moorbath, S. and Roberts, L. E. J., AERE Report C/R 886 (Nov. 1954).
37. Evans, E. A., USAEC Report HW-52729 (Sept. 1957); also issued in USAEC Report TID-7546, p. 414 (Mar. 1958).
38. Harrington, C. D., USAEC Report TID-7546, p. 369 (Mar. 1958).

39. Chalder, G. H., Bright, N. F. H., Paterson, D. L. and Watson, L. C., Second United Nations International Conference on the Peaceful Uses of Atomic Energy (Sept. 1958) P/192.
40. Chalder, G. H., AECL Report UK/C6/115 (Sept. 1957).
41. Glatter, J., Losco, E. F., Harford, W. J., Theilacker, J. S., Fischer, R. L., Saunders, W. T. and Wolfe, R. A., Second United Nations International Conference on the Peaceful Uses of Atomic Energy (Sept. 1958) P/2380.
42. Webster, A. H. and Bright, N. F. H., Dept. of Mines and Technical Surveys Report MD-223, Ottawa (Nov. 1957).
43. Watson, L. C., Bancroft, A. R., Bourns, W. T. and Yatabe, E., AECL Report CRCE-716, Parts I, II and III (1958).
44. Eldorado Mining and Refining Co. Ltd., Port Hope, Ontario—Catalogue of Canadian Uranium Products (Aug. 1958).
45. Allison, A. and Duckworth, W. H., USAEC Report BMI-1009 (June 1955).
46. Stenquist, D. R. and Anicetti, R. J., *Nuclear Metallurgy*, V, A.I.M.E. (Oct. 1958).
47. Paterson, D. L. and Chalder, G. H., AECL Report CRFD-759, to be published.
48. Thackray, R. W. and Murray, P., AERE Report M/R 614 (Nov. 1950).
49. Scott, R. and Williams, J., *Trans. Brit. Ceram. Soc.*, **57**, 199 (1958).
50. Arenberg, C. A. and Jahn, C., *J. Am. Ceram. Soc.*, **41**, 179 (1958).
51. Runfors, U., Schonberg, N. and Kiessling, R., Second United Nations International Conference on the Peaceful Uses of Atomic Energy (Sept. 1958) P/142.
52. Schonberg, N., Runfors, U. and Kiessling, R., Second United Nations International Conference on the Peaceful Uses of Atomic Energy (Sept. 1958) P/182.
53. Lewis, W. B., AECL Report DL-33 (Apr. 1958).
54. Briola, J., Second United Nations International Conference on the Peaceful Uses of Atomic Energy (Sept. 1958) P/1161.
55. Wyman, W. L. and Steinkamp, W. I., USAEC Report HW-55667 (Apr. 1958).
56. Ambartsumyan, R. S., Glukhov, A. M., Goncharov, V. V., Kovalev, A. I. and Skvortsov, S. A., Second United Nations International Conference on the Peaceful Uses of Atomic Energy (Sept. 1958) P/2196.
57. Eichenberg, J. D., Frank, P. W., Kisiel, T. J., Lustman, B. and Vogel, K. H., USAEC Report WAPD-183 (Oct. 1957); also issued in USAEC Report TID-7546, p. 616 (Mar. 1958).
58. Robertson, J. A. L., Bain, A. S., Booth, A. H., Howieson, J., Morison, W. G. and Robertson, R. F. S., Second United Nations International Conference on the Peaceful Uses of Atomic Energy (Sept. 1958) P/193.
59. Lewis, W. B., AECL Report DM-44 (Apr. 1957).
60. Morison, W. G., Atomic Energy of Canada Ltd., unpublished work (1958).
61. Bain, A. S. AECL Report UKE-CR-1006 (Dec. 1958).
62. Robertson, J. A. L. and Bain A. S., Atomic Energy of Canada Ltd., unpublished work (Jan. 1959).
63. Robertson, J. A. L., Atomic Energy of Canada Ltd., private communication (Dec. 29, 1958).
64. Bain, A. S. and Robertson, J. A. L., Letter to the Editor, submitted to *J. Atomic Materials* (Jan. 1959).
65. Lustman, B., USAEC Report WAPD-173 (Mar. 1957).
66. Booth, A. H. and Rymer, G. T., AECL Report CRDC-720 (Aug. 1958).
67. Booth, A. H., AECL Report CRDC-721 (Sept. 1957).
68. Davies, J. A., Atomic Energy of Canada Ltd., private communication (Mar. 24, 1958).

14. DEVELOPMENT OF CERAMIC FUELS IN FRANCE

A. ACCARY and R. CAILLAT

Commissariat à l'Énergie Atomique, Centre d'Etudes Nucléaires
Saclay, France

The cost of the energy produced from nuclear fuels makes this energy source hardly competitive with fossil fuels as yet. The main problem is therefore to decrease this cost. This can be achieved in several different ways. One is to increase the temperature of the fluid used in the thermal part of the installation. This means that the fuel elements must withstand a higher surface temperature. In the case of pure uranium the $\alpha - \beta$ transformation restricts the hottest point of the fuel at temperature under 660°C. With alloyed uranium the utilization limit is somewhat higher, but no really refractory uranium alloy is now available as fuel. The best solution of this temperature problem is, thus, the use of ceramics such as UO_2, UC, UN, with melting points (or decomposition point for UN) well above 2000°C without any phase transformation for the solid.

Another way of decreasing the cost of the energy is to reach higher burn-ups. The poisoning of the fuel by fission products cannot be avoided and will always limit the life of a fuel element, but other limitations such as radiation growth, or swelling, which are associated with physical or mechanical properties of fuels, can be alleviated by the proper choice of the fuel material. In this respect ceramics exhibit very desirable properties. They belong to the cubic system, which means they are highly isotropic and therefore will present no radiation growth. Moreover, being harder than uranium and uranium alloys, especially at high temperatures, they will more easily retain the fission gases without swelling.

Ceramics are thus very attractive nuclear fuels and, therefore, have been studied at the Commissariat à l'Énergie Atomique for some time. Efforts have been concentrated on UO_2, which is now sintered in a pilot plant. At the same time, work is under way toward decreased cost of the UO_2 pellets, chiefly by substitution of low-temperature sintering for the high-temperature method currently used.

At a more fundamental stage uranium monocarbide is being studied, chiefly in regard to its thermal properties and its evolution under heat treatment or irradiation.

Uranium Dioxide

The pilot plant with a monthly capacity of 2 to 3 tons is operated by the Compagnie Industrielle des Céramiques Electroniques (C.I.C.E.), using a process developed by a Commissariat à l'Énergie Atomique (C.E.A.) team.*

The starting materials is a UO_2 powder produced for future transformation into UF_4. This powder cannot be utilized as such for sintering and has first to be ground to a finer particle size, which is done under ethyl alcohol in a barrel grinder. This time-consuming operation (48 hr) is also expensive because of the energy which is used, and has the added disadvantage of not yielding a perfect UO_2 powder for sintering. This stage, therefore, is the weakest of the process. The UO_2 is then dried in a flow of hot air.

The next stage is the mixing of a binder necessary for successful cold-pressing. The binder used at C.E.A. is generally 1 per cent camphor dissolved in alcohol; the amount of binder may be as high as 3 per cent depending on the nature of the treated UO_2. It sometimes proves helpful to add some stearic acid (0.5 per cent).

The UO_2 is then granulated in order to better and more uniformly fill the cold press die. The granulated UO_2 is then cold pressed either in a hydraulic press for large pellets or in a mechanical one for the smaller sizes. After cold-pressing, the binder is removed by a 2-hr heating at 150°C under a pressure of 1 mm Hg.

The pellets are then ready for sintering which is performed in a molybdenum resistor furnace in an atmosphere of cracked ammonia at a temperature of 1600°C. The temperature is slowly raised to 1600°C within a period of 40 hr, then is maintained at this level for 6 hr and finally decreased to room temperature within 72 hours. The firing cycle takes 126 hr (which is an excessively long time). This could be improved either by using a continuous furnace which is currently under development or by using a lower firing temperature. The latter solution would conserve energy not only in the lower temperature itself but also by the resultant shorter firing time. Nevertheless, the major saving would be achieved by bringing the sintering temperature down to 1300°C where conventional furnaces could be substituted for costly and fragile molybdenum furnaces. A 1300°C firing is, thus, one of the chief goals.

The last step of the pellet fabrication is a machining to the exact required dimensions with a clearance of $\pm$ 0.02 mm. The apparent density of the pellets is about 10 g/cm³.

* B. Bouillon, R. Delmas, B. François, C. Lugan and J. Roger.

To summarize, the drawbacks of this sintering method are:

1. The high-temperature firing.
2. The necessary grinding.
3. The low density of the pellets, which is considered as being too low for a power reactor.

Bel and Carteret have developed a method for overcoming these drawbacks.[1] As a first step, Carteret investigated the factors governing the size of the UO_2 particles obtained by calcination of UO_4 into UO_3 and subsequent reduction by hydrogen of UO_3 into UO_2. This study showed that, for temperatures lower than 400°C, UO_4 decomposes into a very fine UO_3 and that, above this temperature, U_3O_8 forms. The latter undergoes a grain coarsening by crystallization. This reaction is encouraged by the presence of moisture, as shown in Table 14-1. Thus, the particle size of UO_3 or U_3O_8 can be controlled by the calcination temperature and its duration.

The next step, reduction of UO_3 or U_3O_8 into UO_2, yields a UO_2 powder without any significant change in particle size, provided the reaction is carried out at a temperature at which the UO_3 or U_3O_8 particle size is stable, i.e., under 400°C. The grain size of the UO_2 obtained in this way is then stable under hydrogen up to temperatures as high as 780°C. Under argon or vacuum, UO_2—stoichiometric or not—undergoes a rather fast grain coarsening.

To sum up the results of Carteret's investigation, we may say that by controlling the temperature and time of calcination of UO_4 into UO_3 or

TABLE 14-1. EFFECT OF CALCINATION TEMPERATURE AND SUBSEQUENT REDUCTION TREATMENT ON PARTICLE SIZE AND COMPOSITION

Calcination Temp. (°C)	Dry Air				Moist Air			
	Powder Surface		Composition		Powder Surface		Composition	
	m²/g Powder	m²/g Uranium	% U		m²/g Powder	m²/g Uranium	% U	
100	7	10.5	68.45					
310	6	7.5	80.28	$UO_{3.50}$ 0.10 H_2O	6.5	8.5	77.25	$UO_{3.35}$ 0.85 H_2O
360	7	9	81.17	$UO_{3.35}$ 0.07 H_2O	7.5	9	80.4	$UO_{3.45}$ 0.15 H_2O
410	15	18.5	82.56	$UO_{3.05}$ 0.08 H_2O	18.5	22	81.33	$UO_{3.15}$ 0.04 H_2O
470	17	20	82.35	$UO_{3.10}$ 0.06 H_2O	10	13	83.22	$UO_{2.95}$ 0.03 H_2O
500	13	15.5	83.16	$UO_{2.90}$ 0.10 H_2O	9	10.5	83.02	$UO_{2.85}$ 0.20 H_2O
560	10	11.5	83.49	$UO_{2.85}$ 0.10 H_2O	6	7	84.4	$UO_{2.70}$ 0.04 H_2O
600	5	5.5	84.10	$UO_{2.75}$ 0.07 H_2O	4.5	5	84.64	U_3O_8 0.03 H_2O
640	2	2	84.78	U_3O_8 0.02 H_2O	3.5	4	84.73	U_3O_8 0.01 H_2O
670	1.5	2	84.8	U_3O_8	2	2.5	84.8	U_3O_8
750	1	1.2	84.8	U_3O_8				

Table 14-2. Correlation between Powder Particle Size and the O/U Ratio in Nonstoichiometric Uranium Dioxide

Specific surface m²/g	1.2	3	7	10.5	11.5	12.5	17	19
Ratio O/U..................	2.00	2.06	2.13	2.21	2.22	2.21	2.25	2.29

U_3O_8 and the subsequent reduction of UO_3 or U_3O_8 into UO_2, it is possible to produce a UO_2 powder with a predetermined grain size (the available grain sizes being measured by the specific surface of the powder ranging from 25 m²/g to 1 m²/g). A study to be published shortly describes the application of these findings to the pilot scale production of UO_2 powder of chosen specific surface.[2]

The sintering ability of these different UO_2 powders has also been investigated by Bel. After hydrogen reduction, the UO_2 powder exposed to air at room temperature slowly picks up oxygen without change in the crystallographic system, and the "equilibrium" O:U ratio increases with the powder specific surface as shown by Table 14-2. Sintering of UO_2 of different specific surfaces shows that the final apparent density increases with the specific surface. The question is, then, to distinguish whether powder surface or composition is the controlling factor for the final density.

Bel varied independently these two factors. His most important results are collected in Table 14-3 which shows that (1) under hydrogen atmos-

Table 14-3. Effect of O/U Ratio on the Density of Uranium Dioxide, Sintered at Various Temperatures

No.	Starting Material	Reduction Temp. (°C)	Specific Surface (m²/g)	O/U	Sintering Temp. (°C)	Apparent Density (g/cm³)	Open Density
1	UO_3 (15 m²/g)	1450	1	2.0	1,400	7.7	29%
2				2.0	1,600	8.6	20%
3	UO_3 (15 m²/g)	1200	3	2.02	1,500	10.2	0
4				2 02	1,600	10.3	0
5	UO_3 (15 m²/g)	1000	4	2.05	1,400	10.2	0
6				2.05	1,600	10.4	0
7	UO_3 (15 m²/g)	1000	5	2.05	1,500	10.35	0
8				2.05	1,600	10.4	0
9	UO_3-U_3O_8 (13 m²/g)	850	8–9	2.09	1,400	10.5	0
10				2.15	1,400	10.7	0
11	UO_3-U_3O_8 (13 m²/g)	650	11	2.06	1,400	10.5	0
12				2.10	1,400	10.5	0
13				2.17	1,400	10.55	0
14	UO_3-U_3O_8 (13 m²/g)	650	13	2.06	1,200	10.6	0
15	UO_3 (15 m²/g)	650	15	2.10	1,400	10.55	0
16				2.10	1,600	10.0	3%
17	UO_3 (15 m²/g)	650	17.5	2.20	1,500	10.05	1%
18				2.20	1,600	10.0	1%

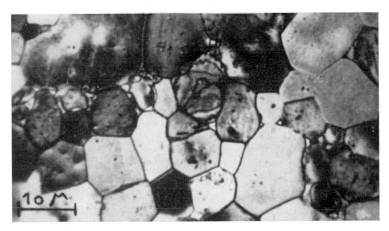

Figure 14-1. Microstructure of uranium monocarbide.

phere, the final density for different compositions of the starting UO_2 is not significantly different; (2) the densities obtained by sintering in argon and in hydrogen are about the same; and (3) sintering in hydrogen at temperatures ranging from 1200 to 1400°C can lead to stoichiometric UO_2 pellets with an apparent density of 95 per cent or more of the theoretical value. To achieve this, the only necessary condition is the use of UO_2 powder with a specific surface of about 10 m²/g as the starting material.

These basic results have been enlarged and applied to the pilot plant scale by Delmas and François.* Their investigation showed that (1) the apparent density of the final product increases with the cold compacting pressure between 1.75 t/cm² and 5 t/cm²; (2) for a given sintering time, the final density of the sintered material fabricated from UO_2 powders of different specific surface (larger than 5 m²/g) depends on the firing temperature, and for each specific surface there is an optimum firing temperature; and (3) the higher the specific surface of the oxide, the lower the temperature of this density maximum.

In conclusion, we should like to stress the importance of the possibility of a 1200 to 1400°C sintering, using a UO_2 powder prepared under strictly controlled conditions and its consequences in decreasing drastically the cost of sintering.

Uranium Carbide

The results reported in this paper on uranium monocarbide concern mainly its thermal properties (structure evolution under heat treatment, thermal conductivity, diffusion with cladding material). The specimens on which the determination were made were prepared by hot-pressing as de-

* Comm. à l'Énergie Atomique.

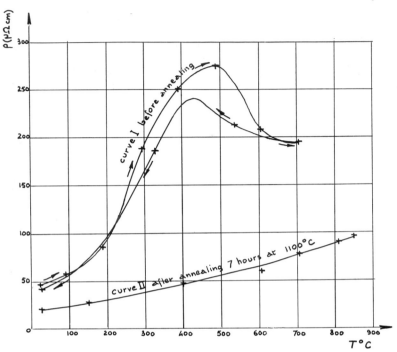

Figure 14-2. Electrical conductivity of UC before and after annealing at 1100°C for 7 hr.

scribed by Dubuisson *et al.*[3] This method was chosen because of the high apparent density reached, which is more than 98 per cent of the theoretical value.

Evolution Under Heat Treatment. The hot-pressing being performed at 1000°C, the monocarbide obtained is of a nonequilibrium structure with very small (average size 1/100 mm), irregularly shaped crystals (Figure 14-1).*

The evolution under heat treatment can be followed by electrical resistivity (Figure 14-2)† as a function of temperature for a specimen just sintered. The nonequilibrium state is revealed by the existence of two different curves, one on heating, the other on cooling. Moreover, the maximum exhibited by the curves leads us to think that uranium carbide behaves as a semiconductor, being an electronic conductor at low temperatures (with a positive resistivity temperature coefficient) and turning into an ionic conductor at higher temperatures (with a negative resistivity temperature coefficient). Curve 2 shows the variation of the electrical resistivity

* Micrographic study by R. Lucas (to be published).
† Resistivity and dilatometric study by J. Dubuisson.

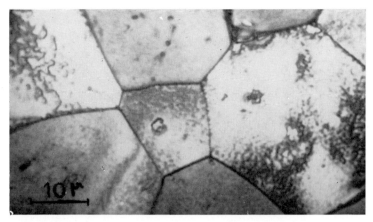

Figure 14-3. Microstructure of uranium monocarbide after annealing at 950°C for 100 hr.

after a relatively short heat treatment (7 hr at 1100°C). This curve is essentially different from curve 1 and suggests a very important evolution. The state, however, does not seem to be very different from an equilibrium one, since the values determined on heating or on cooling fall on the same line; moreover, the evolution has been toward an electronic conductor, since the temperature coefficient of the resistivity is constantly positive.

The evolution under heat treatment is also revealed by micrography. The photomicrograph (Figure 14-3) represents UC after a 100-hr annealing at 950°C. Comparison with Figure 14-1 (just after sintering) shows a large grain growth and, to a certain extent, a straightening of the grain boundaries, suggesting an evolution toward a more stable structure.

Another 100-hr annealing does not change the size or aspect of the grains. This state is, therefore, a stable one for the temperature under consideration.

Figure 14-4 is a photomicrograph of a uranium carbide, heat treated for 7 hr at 1500°C. The grain size is about 10 times larger than for the original carbide and twice as large as for that with the 950°C heat treatment. Thus the final state (not necessarily a true equilibrium state but one in which the evolution is negligibly slow) seems to depend on the temperature.

This heat treatment evolution could cause dimensional changes. To investigate this possibility the stability of UC has been studied under thermal cycling. Figure 14-5 shows a dilatometric cycle involving heating from room temperature to 1140°C at a rate of 100°C per hour and cooling back to room temperature at the same rate. The heating and cooling curves' coinciding perfectly for low temperatures proves that the grain evolution is not accompanied by any change in volume or dimension.

Figure 14-4. Microstructure of uranium monocarbide after heat treatment a 1500°C for 7 hr.

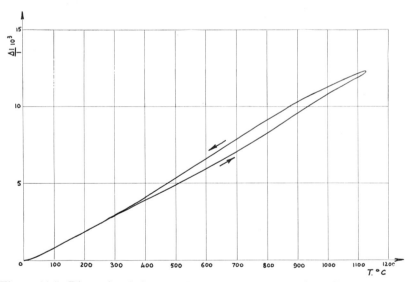

Figure 14-5. Dimensional changes of UC during dilatometric cycle up to 1140°C.

To summarize the heat treatment study, one can say that hot-pressed UC undergoes a fundamental evolution tending toward a more metallic state with a grain growth but without any dimensional change.

Thermal Conductivity. The thermal conductivity of UC has been

TABLE 14-4. THERMAL CONDUCTIVITY OF URANIUM MONOCARBIDE

Temp. (°C)	Thermal Conductivity K (Cal sec^{-1} cm^{-1} °C^{-1})
119	0.046 ± 0.003
181	0.047 ± 0.003
226	0.043 ± 0.003
236	0.044 ± 0.003

measured and the values found are reported in Table 14-4.* These values agree with the ones determined at Harwell,† which were established using sintered UC. They are somewhat different from other values determined on melted and cast UC.[4] The values for cast UC are about 0.06 cal cm^{-1} sec^{-1} °C^{-1}. The reason for this variation lies possibly in the difference of purity between sintered and cast carbide.

The sintered carbide being prepared at low temperature is certainly free of UC$_2$, but could possibly contain other impurities such as oxygen or residual graphite. On the other hand, cast UC is very probably free of oxygen or inclusions, but might contain some UC$_2$.

Nevertheless, the thermal conductivity of sintered UC stands about halfway between that of uranium (0.06 cal cm^{-1} sec^{-1} °C) and that of the oxide (0.02 cal cm^{-1} sec^{-1} °C). Moreover, the conductivities do not decrease perceptibly within the investigated temperature range, which is quite an interesting feature as far as use of the carbide as fuel is concerned.

Diffusion With Cladding Material. The study of this problem should cover the very limited number of high-temperature cladding materials such as graphite, silicon carbide, beryllium, and zirconium. One would expect that the diffusion velocity of UC in graphite, which is not known, would depend strongly on the nature of the graphite employed. The only information presently available is that there seems to be no possibility of formation of UC$_2$ at temperatures lower than 1600°C.

Silicon carbide should be quite stable in the presence of UC. Beryllium and zirconium are limited as cladding material by their mechanical properties as well as by their diffusion properties. In the case of zirconium at 1000°C there is an important creep and a diffusion of carbon from the uranium carbide to the zirconium region where it forms zirconium carbide and probably also causes diffusion of zirconium in the free uranium left by the decomposition of the uranium carbide. These results suggest that zirconium—and probably beryllium—cladding should be restricted to temperatures well under 1000°C.

* C. Gewiss (to be published)
† Private communication

For the present, the problem of cladding remains the major obstacle to a practical exploitation of the full potential of UC as a high-temperature fuel material.

References

1. Bel, A., and Carteret, Y., Second United Nations International Conference on the Peaceful Uses of Atomic Energy, Geneva (1958) P/1165.
2. To be published.
3. Duibuisson, J., Houyvet, A., Le Boulbin, E., Lucas, R., Moranville, C., Second United Nations International Conference on the Peaceful Uses of Atomic Energy, Geneva (1958) P/1162.
4. Secrest, A. C. Jr., *et al.*, "Preparation and Properties of UC Castings," BMI-1309 (1959).

15. FUEL ELEMENTS FOR GAS-COOLED HIGH-TEMPERATURE REACTORS

A. BOETTCHER

Degussa, Frankfurt/M, Germany

In the present stage of reactor development, the question of economy in power reactors is of foremost importance, despite the multitude of unsolved technical problems. The reason is that the economic question largely determines how and when the numerous problems can be solved and thus governs the extent to which technical experience will be gathered. With most reactors this economic factor is strongly influenced by the maximum attainable fuel element temperatures. This is true in particular of gas-cooled power reactors.

The British Atomic Energy Authority is doing a considerable amount of research and development work in this respect in order to promote the Calder Hall-type reactor. The main problems of this development are the creation of suitable fuels on the one hand and the production of temperature-resistant can material on the other.

In order to achieve temperatures of 500 to 600°C at the surface of the fuel elements it appears necessary to reject the use of natural uranium metal as fuel. The underlying reasons are familiar; they originate largely in the unfavorable properties of the alpha phase of uranium and its allotropic transition to the considerably different beta phase, respectively. This phase transition takes place in a temperature region which seems hardly avoidable in the temperatures to be expected within the fuel. In this case there is also nothing to be gained by changing over to uranium alloys with a stabilized gamma phase, because in very many canning materials solid-state reactions and diffusion phenomena profoundly encumber the use of metallic fuels. In addition, the danger of corrosion to the element in a region of high temperature is also considerably increased in the case of damaged cans.

For this reason Great Britain has decided in favor of using uranium dioxide in high-temperature reactors because this largely avoids the difficulties mentioned above. With regard to its behavior within the reactor, the extent to which this material is known raises justified hope that there will

267

be no fundamental difficulties. However, at least a slight degree of enrichment of the oxide will be necessary. The use of uranium monocarbide, a material that has rapidly attracted interest in the course of the last few years, is being hampered by its poor corrosion behavior toward CO_2, compared to that of UO_2. Moreover, only insufficient data have as yet been accumulated as to its behavior in reactor operation. On the other hand, it does not seem improbable that this material, too, will have to be seriously considered—at some future date—for purposes such as where an effective protection against corrosion seems to be possible by applying proper surface treatment. Considerations of this kind are further rendered promising by the studies of cermets on the basis of uranium carbide, presented at the 1958 Geneva Conference.[1,2,3]

Accordingly, whereas the use of uranium dioxide most probably means a sufficient solution of the fuel problem, the questions regarding a suitable canning material seem to be unsolved to a much larger extent. In Great Britain the interest is focused on the use of beryllium metal instead of magnox. The behavior of the former under reactor conditions, its stability and resistance against corrosion, as well as its very low capture cross section for thermal neutrons, make it a likely prospect in every way. As far as can be seen today, the central problem rests with the unfavorable processing properties of this metal and with the resulting high cost of producing beryllium tubes of adequate dimensions. Reliable information as to these prices is still impossible to give today because there has been no sizable production up to now although the technical aspects of the manufacturing process have been solved in essence. But it may already now be estimated that prices of these beryllium tubes will be around \$250 to \$300/lb for quite some time. This amounts to many times the cost of magnox tubes; even when the very advantageous low specific weight is considered, it is still considerably higher than the price of Zircaloy tubes. Of course, it can be assumed that these prices will drop with rising production experience and growing capacities in the corresponding facilities. However, it does seem dubious whether these reduction in costs will suffice to make the use of beryllium metal really economical, i.e., to give a clear advantage to a gas-cooled high-temperature reactor designed on this basis as against reactors of the present type.

For this reason it seems interesting to envisage and scrutinize other possibilities which are being discussed now. A suggestion of this kind is the use of plated zirconium tubes instead of beryllium ones. Pure zirconium with its satisfactory neutron and processing properties has the disadvantage of not being resistant to corrosion by CO_2 in the very temperature region that would be of interest. Therefore, outside plating becomes necessary, using, e.g., pure iron or other suitable steels. The relatively high capture cross section of these materials would have to be balanced by correspondingly reduced wall strengths. In principle, such plating seems technically possible without major difficulties when the proper type of solder is used. This is illustrated by the fabrication of titanium-plated steel grades on production scale, where the problems are at least alike.

Most certainly, the production of this type of fuel element will bring about a host of additional problems, especially so if fins of a more complicated design should be necessary for the elements. In these cases conventional plating techniques would hardly be applicable. However, it should be possible to manufacture a fuel element of the type in question first with a canning of pure zirconium, and then with a finishing coat of soldering metals on its surface. On this preshaped element is shrunk a tube of iron or steel with a very low wall thickness. The tube is then closed on both ends, and, in a pressurized autoclave, a firm metallic bonding is produced at the working temperatures of the solder. In spite of the complicated fabrication, tubes of this type should be considerably less expensive then beryllium tubes. By using a solder which in itself is sufficiently corrosion resistant toward CO_2, one can reduce to a tolerable level the dangers always existing in the form of defects in plated materials.

Another method which has been under discussion in Great Britain for a long time is the use of metal oxides for can materials; i.e., aluminum oxide, zirconium oxide, beryllium oxide, magnesium oxide, or mixed oxides. As these oxides are particularly heat resistant, this method seems especially promising. On the other hand, it presupposes clarification of a large number of questions. True, the fabrication of suitably dimensioned ceramic tubes which are vacuum-tight up to about 1000°C is technically possible today. But, after the fuel has been filled in, their vacuum-tight seal will necessitate a considerable amount of testing under reactor conditions, so that a sufficiently reliable canning method may be selected. A very fundamental difficulty is the low stability against temperature changes incurred in all oxide-ceramic materials. This drawback will lose its importance as soon as it is possible to operate these elements at surface temperatures of at least 900°C, because, in this temperature region, the majority of interesting oxides show a relatively good stability under temperature changes. In order to charge and discharge such elements, preheating or cooling of the element might thus be necessary.

The relatively poor heat conductivity is another disadvantage of these oxides. However, it might not be so decisive after all, because the conductivity of uranium oxide is similar and thus the temperature gradients within the can itself will, in all probability, be tolerable. Considerations of this kind are encouraged by the fact that in a chemical production process outside the reactor sphere—a process for which we have gathered considerable experience—aluminum oxide tubes of similar dimensions and relatively large lengths behaved unexpectedly well under continuous operation. In these tubes there is a radial heat flow of some 30 w per sq cm (0.155 sq in.) in a temperature range of 1100 to 1200°C, with an additional large temperature gradient along the length of the tubes. In this case, the large amount of recyrstallization existing after prolonged continuous operation did not cause any damage to the tubes; above all, it did not decrease the tightness of the fit. Most probably there will be difficulties primarily in the production of these tubes with close tolerances with regard to diameter and other geometric dimensions. However, general experience in the field of oxide ceramics gives rise to the hope that these difficulties will not prove prohibitive to the use of oxides as canning materials.

It should be mentioned that, in principle, the use of carbide-type can material cannot be excluded, especially not in the case that uranium monocarbide or a cermet is used as fuel. But it may be assumed that, here, an economically sound solution is met by no lesser difficulties than in the case when oxide materials are used. In the case of oxide- as well as of carbide-type can material, a series of additional problems will be encountered with regard to the interface between fuel and can material compared with the use of purely metallic cans. If carbides are used, for instance, a deformation of the can through the pressure of the cooling gas will practically be eliminated; in the case of oxide cans, this happens only very slowly and to a minor extent so that the creation of temporarily poor heat transfer conditions from fuel to can must certainly be taken into account. Because of the relatively low specific heat flux in fuel elements of gas-cooled reactors, and, with regard to the lattices of fuels under consideration which are stable also toward high temperatures, it is most likely that this problem will not assume major proportions. Maybe it will achieve importance indirectly through the possibility that, in the neighborhood of hot spots, solid-state reactions might take place between can and fuel. Therefore, it will have to be an essential part of a comprehensive study to carefully investigate character and speed of the solid-state reactions taking place in the temperature interval of interest, as these reactions most probably will play an important part in the production of this type of fuel element.

In summarizing the observations up to this point, it could be said that it seems possible that the multitude of studies to be undertaken in order to explore the use of oxide-type or carbide-type can materials exclude their use in the immediate future, as would also be the case with beryllium, even though the results of these studied should be positive. Thus, the use of these types of canning materials will most likely be deferred—if they should be used at all—to a somewhat later phase of development of fuel element materials.

Parallel to the continued development of gas-cooled reactors of the British type, the essentially new approach that is being tried today by Great Britain and Germany arouses special interest. The following discussion is restricted to an approach suggested by R. Schulten, and pursued in Germany by Brown, Boveri and Co. and Krupp. In the U.S.A., the reactor is called "potato-heap reactor"; the fuel elements have been developed in the Degussa laboratories. As was stated at the Second Geneva Conference,[2] the fuel elements consist of graphite balls, 2 to 2.3 in. (5 to 6 cm) in diameter. The fuel is inserted into a bore hole, the opening then sealed with a graphite plug as shown in Figure 15-1. For elements of this type, the question of radiation damage seems of secondary importance, if the type of graphite used is sufficiently stable under irradiation conditions. This seems most likely in this case, because the type of graphite used was most carefully selected, and results obtained have borne this out.

The behavior of the fuel filling, which consists of a mixture of uranium carbides and graphite, is of minor importance because even a deterioration of its thermal conductivity or mechanical stability will be unable to influence the functioning of the fuel elements to any essential degree. The reason for this is that, in a case of poor thermal contact between fuel insert and graphite cladding, sufficient heat flow is guaranteed by radiation. The fuel itself will have to fulfill no mechanical requirements at all. With regard to damage by radiation, however, the behavior of the "cement" used for fastening and sealing the plug is important. There are not sufficient data as yet as to its stability under the influence of irradiation, but, because of its composition, it may safely be assumed that it will prove sufficiently stable. This stability is further strengthened by the design of the seal which has been made in such a way that it will not be placed under

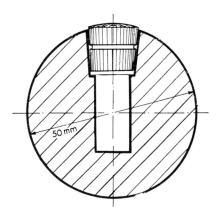

50 mm

Figure 15-1. Fuel element consisting of graphite sphere with fuel inserted in bore hole.

any larger mechanical stress. Without irradiation, the stability of the cement is greater than that of the graphite.

A considerable amount of research work was necessary to develop a suitable seal of the kind just described. The solution of this problem seems to be not only technically sufficient, but also thoroughly satisfactory from an economic point of view. Another task of importance was the creation of a fitting shape for the fuel to be inserted. It appeared obvious to insert a mixture of uranium oxide and graphite and transfer this mixture into stable carbides by means of a suitable temperature treatment inside the graphite ball. This solution proved somewhat unfavorable from an economic point of view, however. For this reason, Degussa is now fabricating cylindrical bodies closely fitting the bore hole of the graphite ball. They consist of a mixture of uranium carbides and carbon. Without the influence of irradiation, they have a thermal conductivity one-third of that found in graphite and a relatively high mechanical strength which makes their transport and insertion possible without difficulties. Owing to the close tolerances, there is a relatively good heat transfer from the fuel insert to the graphite.

Shaped materials of this fuel type may be regarded as cermets of carbon and uranium carbides. Even at temperatures considerably higher than the melting points of all known uranium carbides, there is no macroscopically recognizable liquid phase or decomposition. Thus, the properties of heat transfer will not change greatly during reactor operation even with relatively poor thermal contact. The comparatively high carbon content enables bonding of a large part of the fission products as carbides within the fuel insert, which largely suppresses their diffusion to the surface of the graphite ball. Since, on the one hand, the temperature of this fuel insert will most probably be considerably higher than that of the graphite—perhaps in the region of 1500°C or higher—and, on the other hand, the percentage of carbon is high, it may be assumed that there will be a quick self-healing of possible radiation damage, which would guarantee sufficiently constant operating properties.

It is thought that this type of fuel element has the advantage of higher operating safety, as compared with the quasi-homogeneous solution which had also been studied at Degussa. The homogeneous solution, i.e., the fabrication of balls with a content of uniformly distributed uranium carbide, seemed much more attractive from the economic point of view on first sight than the heterogeneous solution which is now preferred. But it includes a host of additional technical difficulties which it was desired to avoid, at least in the first charge. Difficulties of this kind comprise, among others for example, the question of radiation stability of the homogeneous elements fabricated under these circumstances. The techniques used so far in the production of reactor graphite cannot be applied here, as they include a high-temperature treatment which is not applicable in this case. It would cause a major part of the uranium brought into the graphite to evaporate. Thus, other methods of fabrication have to be discovered which have not yet been proved to lead to a similarly radiation-resistant graphite. Furthermore, the fuel will be found on the surface of the elements if it is distributed homogeneously throughout the graphite, which would unavoidably lead to a considerably higher contamination of the primary cooling circuit with radioactive fission products. For these reasons, it seemed necessary to encase such a homogeneous mixture again in a fuel-free graphite cladding. This process is possible, no doubt, but it would, in all probability, destroy possible economic advantages of the homogeneous solution. Finally, the reprocessing of these homogeneous elements might show disadvantages as against those of heterogeneous ones. Despite all the deliberations, there cannot yet be a final decision as to which of the types described will ultimately be preferred. It may be hoped that the first testing reactor, which is now in its planning stage, will offer the possibility of testing the properties of the various types in the sense of a materials test reactor, and thus render the operation data necessary for the construction of a power reactor.

At the present time it is still impossible to weigh the chances of a conventional gas-cooled high-temperature reactor against those of the "potato-heap" reactor. In the former, the development of fuel elements is the technically decisive problem which is, no doubt, connected with a multitude of open questions. As far as can be judged today, the Brown, Boveri-Krupp reactor will not contain any insurmountable technical difficulties with regard to fuel elements. In the case of the "potato-heap" reactor, it is a question of the technical design, safety problems, etc., which will be likely to decide the future prospects of this project. Both types have in common that their intensive pursuit is reasonable and urgent in view of the identical aim: to produce nuclear energy more economically.

References

1. Boettcher, A., Schneider, G., "Some Properties of Uranium Monocarbide," Second United Nations International Conference on the Peaceful Uses of Atomic Energy, Geneva (1958) P/964.
2. Boettcher, A., Schulten, R. and Wirths, G., "Fuel Elements for a High-Temperature Reactor," *ibid.*, P/1005.
3. Murray, P. and Williams, J., "Ceramic and Cermet Fuels," *ibid.*, P/318.

16. HIGH-TEMPERATURE CREEP OF URANIUM-LOADED GRAPHITES

LEON GREEN, JR.*

*Head, Applied Mechanics
Corporate Research Operation, Aerojet-General Corporation
Azusa, California*

Introductory Investigation

The obvious attractiveness of graphite as a material for high-temperature fuel elements has prompted a growing interest in the physical and mechanical properties of grades containing uranium. As distinguished from the various *ad hoc* measurements of strength and creep properties performed during the last decade, the first systematic investigation of the effect of uranium content on high-temperature mechanical behavior of graphite was initiated by the Los Alamos Scientific Laboratory as part of a nuclear rocket propulsion program.[1, 2] The graphites employed were manufactured by basically conventional procedures, except that normal UO_2 was added to the filler flour at the start of the process to yield grades of graphitized stock identified as follows:

Stock Identification	Volume Concentration of Uranium (g/cc)	Representative Carbon Density (g/cc)†
CK	0	1.71
LDH	0.125	1.73
LDC	0.250	1.66
LDP	0.350	1.63

† Weight of uranium subtracted

Single specimens of each grade at each of two nominal temperature levels were subjected to tensile creep under varying stress levels increased incrementally to produce eventual rupture. The results (including data on

* Now Senior Staff Member, Aeronutronic, A Division of Ford Motor Company, Space Technology Operation, Newport Beach, Calif.

some pure commercial grades) reported by Wagner, Driesner, and Kmetko[3] at the 1958 Geneva Conference were correlated in the form

$$\epsilon = \frac{d\epsilon}{dt} = f(U) \left(\frac{\sigma}{\sigma_b}\right)^n \exp\left(-\Delta H/RT\right) \tag{1}$$

where ϵ = creep strain, σ = stress (psi), σ_b = breaking stress, U = uranium content (g/cc), n = empirical constant, ΔH = activation energy (cal/mole), R = gas constant (cal/mole°K), T = absolute temperature (°K). The adjustable parameters were evaluated from measurements of the slopes of the segments of strain-time curve during 10-min. intervals of creep under each of the different stress levels. This procedure yielded values of $f(U) = 4 + 8U - 125 U^2$, $n = 3.8$, and $\Delta H = 69$ kcal/mole. Comparison of the observed steady-state slopes with those calculated from Eq. (1) showed agreement within ±30 per cent for 51 per cent of the cases, which included 14 tests of specimens fabricated from pure commercial grades. The extreme deviations reported were instances in which the calculated slope was high by a factor of 3.9 and low by a factor of 7.4.

Continued Investigation

To supplement this brief investigation, the LASL sponsored a comprehensive program of various high-temperature property measurements by Aerojet-General on selected grades of graphite. Included in the program were continued tensile creep measurements on the stocks described above. The experimental technique and complete creep data obtained have been reported elsewhere,[4, 5] and for the purposes of the present discussion it is sufficient to summarize the test conditions. Three temperature levels (2000, 2200, and 2400°C) and three stress levels were employed. Each test was of a 60-min. duration under a single stress level, following which the level was increased in rapid 80-psi increments to produce failure. Duplicate tests under each condition of material, stress, and temperature were performed, thus using a total of 66 specimens, not including those which failed on application of the creep load. Typical examples of the creep curves obtained are shown in Figure 16-1.

Correlation of Results

Whereas Wagner *et al.* correlated their results by fitting an Arrhenius rate approximation $\dot{\epsilon} = A \exp\left(-\Delta H/RT\right)$ to the regions of "steady-state" or "secondary" creep of pseudoconstant slope, this procedure was not considered applicable to the present results because (among other reasons) the data indicated a creep rate decreasing in magnitude throughout the duration of the test. One alternative approach is provided by the suggestion

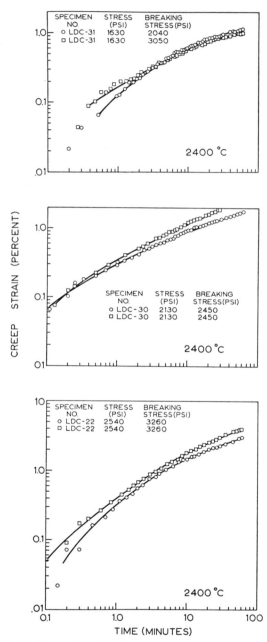

Figure 16-1. Typical examples of high-temperature tensile creep curves and ranges (Grade LDC stock at 2400°C).

of Dorn[6] that the structure developed during the course of creep depends upon a temperature-compensated time $\theta = t \exp(-\Delta H/RT)$ and that $\epsilon = \epsilon (\theta)$. Thus, identical values of θ are achieved during time t_1 and t_2 for creep to a given strain under equal stresses but different temperatures T_1 and T_2, and, assuming that ΔH does not vary strongly with temperature,

$$\Delta H = \frac{R \ln (t_1/t_2)}{\dfrac{1}{T_1} - \dfrac{1}{T_2}} \tag{2}$$

Using average values of time required to effect a creep strain of 0.1 per cent, this approach (which lumps effects of stress, temperature, and structure into the activation energy) has been employed to derive apparent activation energies for creep of graphites described above,[4, 5] and the reported results exhibited a wide range of values manifesting a considerable variation in structure between nominally identical specimens. Such a piece-to-piece variation is, of course, common to all grades of graphite manufactured according to conventional quality control standards. In the correlation of Eq. (1), compensation for this scatter is provided by use of the stress value which produced failure of each individual specimen to form a normalized stress ratio, but such a correlation is of little value for design purposes since at present only a nominal estimate of σ_b can be provided without breaking the particular piece of graphite concerned. The degree of scatter involved is shown by the results of tensile strength measurements on the four stocks concerned,[4, 7] data which are summarized in Figure 16-2.

By Dorn's method, values of the apparent activation energy can be quickly derived for analysis of the creep mechanism. However, no information concerning the pre-exponential or frequency factor of the Arrhenius rate relation is provided, and such information is desirable not only for engineering predictions of short-time creep, but also to facilitate extrapolation of the short-time, high-temperature creep data to those conditions of longer life at lower temperature which are of interest for applications more mundane than a nuclear rocket engine. For this purpose it may be assumed that the time to effect a given reference creep strain can be approximated as

$$1/t = A \exp(-\Delta H/RT),$$

or $\qquad\qquad\qquad\qquad\qquad\qquad\qquad\qquad\qquad\qquad\qquad$ (3)

$$\ln (1/t) = \ln A - \Delta H/RT$$

and a plot of $\ln (1/t)$ vs. $1/T$ thus yields a slope and intercept defining ΔH and $\ln A$, respectively. Writing $T(\ln A + \ln t) = \Delta H/R$, this conventional approach was employed by Larson and Miller[8] in a manner

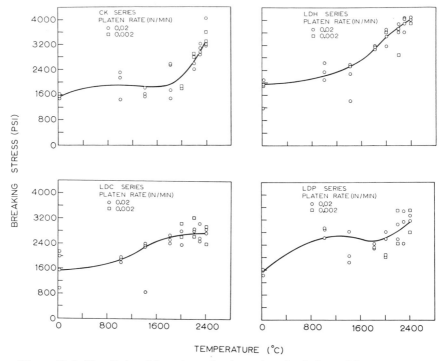

Figure 16-2. Tensile breaking strength of uranium-loaded graphites *vs.* temperature.

simplified by arbitrarily considering the correlating lines to converge at a single value C of the $\ln A$ intercept (a value which was considered as a "universal" constant independent of material and environment) and then using the group $T(C + \ln t)$ as an extrapolation parameter. As has recently been demonstrated,[9, 10] such an approximation obviously can lead to significant errors in prediction of creep or rupture times.

It was judged that neither a temperature-compensated time derived from activation-energy data nor a Larson-Miller group embodying only frequency-factor data constituted a reliable correlation parameter. Accordingly, the graphite creep data from the present investigation were fitted to Eq. (3) by the method of least squares, and the derived rate parameters are collected in Table 16-1. As anticipated, the values of ΔH so derived agree well with the average (for a given stress level) of those calculated by Eq. (2) as previously reported.[4, 5] An unexpected result, however, was the close proportionality found between the values of ΔH and of $\ln A$. The ratios $\Delta H / \ln A$ presented in Table 16-1 decrease with increasing stress, as shown in Figure 16-3, but appear to be insensitive to uranium content.

TABLE 16-1. SUMMARY OF TENSILE CREEP DATA FOR
URANIUM-LOADED GRAPHITES

Temp. (°C)	Stress (psi)	$t_{0.1}$* (min.)	ΔH (kcal/mole)	$\ln A$	$\Delta H/\ln A$	ΔH_{av} (kcal/mole)	Calc. $t_{0.1}$ (min.)	
							From ΔH	From ΔH_{av}
Grade CK Stock								
2000	1630	20.6					9.17	9.03
2200	1630	3.85	76.2	13.9	5.46		2.35	2.32
2400	1630	1.68				76	0.74	0.73
2000	2130	4.75					4.16	4.14
2200	2130	1.08	76.4	15.1	5.04		1.06	1.06
2400	2130	0.36					0.33	0.33
Grade LDH Stock								
2000	1630	72.0†					50.7	10.8
2200	1630	1.90	135	25.8	5.23		4.54	2.51
2400	1630	0.90					0.58	0.73
2000	2130	6.70					5.07	4.57
2200	2130	1.60	87.0	17.3	5.04	82	1.07	1.06
2400	2130	0.37					0.29	0.31
2000	2540	1.25					1.25	2.13
2200	2540	0.90	24.0	5.07	4.74		0.83	0.50
2400	2540	0.56					0.56	0.14
Grade LDC Stock								
2000	1630	11.5					13.2	8.67
2200	1630	1.13	88.7	17.4	5.11		2.70	2.32
2400	1630	0.63					0.70	0.75
2000	2130	1.73					3.38	3.97
2200	2130	1.70	65.2	13.5	4.83	74	1.05	1.06
2400	2130	0.19					0.39	0.35
2000	2540	1.30					1.88	1.97
2200	2540	0.67	68.0	14.6	4.66		0.56	0.53
2400	2540	0.13					0.20	0.17

TABLE 16.1—Continued

Temp. (°C)	Stress (psi)	$t_{0.1}$* (min.)	ΔH (kcal/mole)	In A	ΔH/in A	ΔH_{av} (kcal/ mole)	Calc. $t_{0.1}$ (min.)	
							From ΔH	From ΔH_{av}
Grade LDP Stock								
2000	1630	5.90					6.34	8.85
2200	1630	0.81	63.5	12.5	5.07		2.04	2.32
2400	1630	0.75					0.78	0.74
2000	2130	2.33					3.88	4.05
2200	2130	1.30	72.6	15.0	4.84	75	1.06	1.06
2400	2130	0.20					0.35	0.34
2000	2540	3.00					2.31	2.01
2200	2540	0.70	90.0	18.8	4.80		0.46	0.53
2400	2540	0.15					0.12	0.17

* Average of values from duplicate tests.
† Value from one test, extrapolated to 0.1% strain. Other specimen did not approach reference creep strain.

This fortuitous correlation, expressed by the least-squares line shown in Figure 16-3, permits the frequency factor (with the dimensions of min^{-1}) to be written

$$A = \exp\left[\Delta H / (6.1 \times 10^3 - 0.53\sigma)\right]$$

and thus the time in minutes required for creep to the specified degree to be estimated from the empirical equation

$$t_{0.1} = \exp\left[\frac{\Delta H}{RT} - \frac{\Delta H}{6.1 \times 10^3 - 0.53\sigma}\right] \tag{4}$$

where ΔH is given as a function of stress and composition by Table 16-1 or Figure 16-4. In order to check the accuracy of such an estimate, values of $t_{0.1}$ were computed from Eq. (4) using the individual values of ΔH obtained, and are presented in Table 16-1 for comparison with the experimental values. Comparison shows that agreement within ±30 per cent was obtained in 49 per cent of the cases, and that the extreme deviations corresponded to instances in which the calculated time was high by a factor of 2.4 and low by a factor of 2.3. It is thus seen that the proposed correlation exhibits the same order of accuracy as that of Eq. (1) without requiring knowledge of the individual specimen breaking strength.

Extrapolation to Lower Temperatures

As indicated earlier, a means of extrapolating the present high-temperature, short-time creep data to lower temperature is desirable not only for

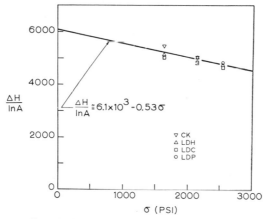

Figure 16-3. Correlation of high-temperature creep rate parameters.

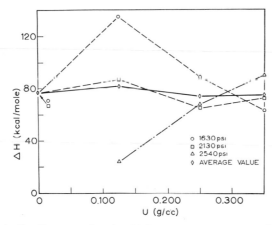

Figure 16-4. Activation energies for high-temperature creep of uranium-loaded graphites.

order-of-magnitude engineering estimates, but for delineation of the temperature regime to which further research should be directed. Within certain obvious limits, Eq. (4) also provides a basis for such an extrapolation. One question involved in this process concerns the possible decrease in the apparent activation energy with decreasing temperature (as suggested by the results of Dorn) in the range $T/T_m \leq 0.45$, and the establishment of an average value appropriate for extrapolation purposes. As a first step it was of interest to evaluate the sensitivity of the creep-time estimate to changes in ΔH, and for this purpose average values of the activation energy, shown in Table 16-1 and Figure 16-4 as ΔH_{av}, were employed. These values indicate that, on the average, the LDH stock showed the greatest resistance

TABLE 16-2. ACTIVATION ENERGIES FOR DIFFUSION OF UC_2
AND CARBON IN GRAPHITE

Diffusion Couple	Temp. Range (°C)	Activation Energy (kcal/mole)
UC_2-Impregnated Graphite and Graphite[11]	2150–2600	53
UC_2 and Graphite[12]	1650–2400	82 ± 20
C^{14} and Graphite[13]	1835–2370	90* (163)
		75.4† (112)†
C^{14} and Natural Graphite[14]	1840–2195	163 ± 12

* Theoretical calculation of ΔH_v by Dienes.
† Derived value of ΔH_b.

to creep, and it should be noted that this same grade also exhibits the greatest tensile strength at high temperatures,[3, 4, 7] a trend possibly correlative with the relative carbon density. The averages are seen to be only slightly greater than the constant value of 69 kcal/mole, independent of uranium content or environment, by which Wagner *et al.* fitted Eq. (1).

The results obtained by Dorn[6] and his co-workers using various pure metals indicate that at high temperatures (i.e., $T/T_m \geq 0.45$) the activation energy for creep is approximately equal to that for volume self-diffusion. For purpose of a similar comparison for the case of the graphite stocks concerned, the activation energies for diffusion of carbon and UC_2 in graphite are collected in Table 16-2. The investigation by Loftness[11] employed polycrystalline graphite, solution-impregnated with UC_2 as the active member of the diffusion couple, whereas the subsequent study by Loch, Gambino, and Duckworth[12] employed sintered UC_2, and that of Feldman, Goeddel, Dienes, and Gossen[13] employed C^{14} in the form of amorphous carbon. All of these studies used polycrystalline, manufactured graphite as the passive element of the couple. In comparison with the value $\Delta H_v = 163 \pm 12$ kcal/mole obtained by Kanter[14] using single crystals of natural graphite, it would appear that the experimental activation energies derived by the earlier investigators corresponded to grain-boundary diffusion. A similar evaluation of the average apparent activation energies for creep of graphite presented in Table 16-1 and Figure 16-4 suggests that, while the creep rate may be diffusion-controlled, the controlling mechanisms may involve atom movements at grain boundaries.

The creep times $t_{0.1}$ computed from Eq. (4) using the ΔH_{av} values are also collected in Table 16-1, which shows that the precision of the estimate was thereby reduced to the point that agreement with the measured values within ±30 per cent is realized in only 36 per cent of the cases, with the extreme deviations being high by a factor of 2.5 and low by a factor of 6.7. Although predictions of such limited precision are useful only for engineering estimates of a preliminary design nature where order-of-mag-

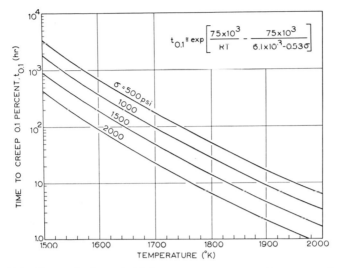

Figure 16-5. Extrapolation of high-temperature creep-time approximation to lower temperatures.

nitude accuracy is welcome, such precision is sufficient for purpose of extrapolation to delineate areas requiring further research.

The most obvious limitation of Eq. (4) is that it cannot be extrapolated to very low stress levels, since the linear approximation of Figure 16-3 would indicate a finite frequency factor (or creep rate) at zero stress. On the other hand, the data of Figure 16-2 indicate that the design stress for a structure of the graphites under discussion will be limited (by considerations of failure at room temperature) to a level of the order of 1000 psi. For purposes of the present extrapolation, a stress range from 500 to 2000 psi was considered to include most practical values. An average value of $\Delta H = 75$ kcal/mole was selected as appropriate for this extrapolation, and the times (converted to hours) estimated for creep to 0.1 per cent strain at temperatures in the range 1500 to 2000°K are shown in Figure 16-5. Acceptable creep limits for conventional power-package components are of the order of 1 per cent in 10^4 hours, and Figure 16-5 indicates that the maximum temperature at which such creep life might be expected for lightly stressed graphite structures will be of the order of 1500 to 1600°K. Confirmation of this highly extrapolated estimate by creep tests of 10 to 100-hr duration at temperatures from 1500 to 2000°K is recommended.

Effect of Irradiation

Experimental investigations of the effect of irradiation or particle bombardment on creep appear to have been limited to metals at intermediate temperature levels at which the observed effects were not great, consisting of either a slight increase at the higher temperatures or a slight decrease due to hardening effects at the lower temperatures.[15] Investigations of radiation effects on mechanical properties of nonmetals appear to consist of measurements of hardness changes in ionic solids as a function of the integrated dose of various types of radiation.[16] The only information concerning radiation effects on the creep of nonmetallic solids presently known to the author is the theoretical estimate of the influence of a fast neutron flux on the creep of graphite by Schoeck,[17] who considered the rate of the thermally-activated creep to be (volume) diffusion-controlled by climbing of dislocations, and the bombardment effect to lie in the creation of Frenkel defects. The estimate was presented in terms of the ratio of the (steady) creep rate under irradiation, $\dot{\epsilon}_i$, to that without radiation $\dot{\epsilon}_o$:

$$\frac{\dot{\epsilon}_i}{\dot{\epsilon}_o} = 1 + \frac{a^2 \alpha f}{D\rho} \tag{5}$$

where a = lattice parameter (cm), α = measure of neutron free path length and number of Frenkel defects produced per primary knock-on, f = fast neutron flux (n/cm^{2}sec), D = coefficient of thermally activated diffusion (cm^2/sec), ρ = atomic fraction of places where defects can anneal out.

A graphical presentation of this estimate is shown in Figure 16-6, which indicates the values of a, α, and ρ selected by Schoeck from various sources. Taking $D = 10^{-19}$ cm^2/sec as corresponding to a temperature $T_m/2$, it was estimated that a fast flux of 10^{13} n/cm^{2}sec would approximately double the creep rate. If the lattice self-diffusion coefficient is expressed as $D = 4.5$

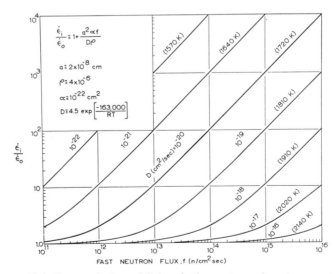

Figure 16-6. Extrapolation of Schoeck theory to various temperatures.

exp $(-163,000/RT)$ according to the results of Kanter,[14] a temperature $T_m/2$ (about 1890°K for graphite if T_m represents the sublimation temperature) might effect a somewhat greater value of D, with the effect of irradiation thus reduced accordingly. Schoeck emphasized that his analysis was simplified and was intended only for order-of-magnitude estimates. In view of this limitation, together with the earlier observation that creep might be controlled by boundary rather than lattice diffusion, it was considered permissible for the presentation of Figure 16-6 to include estimates of the effect for a range of diffusion coefficients or temperatures, even though recognizing that, at the lower temperatures, nondiffusional creep mechanisms might become rate controlling. The fact that the estimates shown in Figure 16-6 are thus only semiquantitative should not invalidate a slight modification of Schoeck's conclusion so as to state that any observable effect of radiation on creep of pure graphite might best be observed when $0.4 \leq T/T_m \leq 0.5$ and $f > 10^{12}$ n/cm²sec. Reference to Figure 16-5, however, reveals that this intermediate temperature range is the one of most interest for applications involving conventional lifetimes, and the need for confirmatory in-pile creep measurements in this temperature range would appear evident.

Conclusion

Extrapolation of an empirical equation correlating short-time, high-temperature tensile creep data indicated that structures of certain pure and uranium-loaded graphites might enjoy conventional creep lives at temperatures of the order of 1500 to 1600°K under conditions of light stress (the order of 1000 psi) and no irradiation. However, review of a theoretical estimate of the effect of irradiation on creep indicated that in and slightly above this temperature range a significant increase in creep rate of pure graphite might be effected by fast-neutron fluxes of 10^{12} n/cm² sec or greater. No estimate of the effect of combined neutron and fission-fragment bombardment upon the creep of materials containing a finely dispersed fissionable phase is known to the writer. The above observations serve to emphasize the desirability of continued investigation of the creep behavior of graphites extended to include tests of high-strength stocks permitting a wider range of applied stresses, tests of increased duration in the range 1500 to 2000°K, and in-pile tests of both pure and fuel-loaded stocks in the same temperature range.

References

1. Schreiber, R. E., "Nuclear Rocket Propulsion Program at Los Alamos," American Rocket Society Preprint 689–58, New York, Nov. 1958.
2. Schreiber, R. E., "Nuclear Rocket Propulsion Development at Los Alamos," *Trans. Am. Nuclear Soc.*, **1**, No. 2, 41 (Dec. 1958).

3. Wagner, P., Driesner, A. R., and Kmetko, E. A., "Some Mechanical Properties of Graphite in the Temperature Range 20 to 3000 C," Second United Nations International Conference on the Peaceful Uses of Atomic Energy, Geneva (Sept. 1958) P/702.

4. Green, L., Jr., Stehsel, M. L., and Waller, C. E., "Mechanical Property Measurements on Pure and Uranium-Loaded Graphites at Elevated Temperatures," Aerojet-General Report No. 1537, 23 Dec. 1958.

5. Green, L., Jr., Stehsel, M. L., and Waller, C. E., "Tensile Creep of Pure and Uranium-Loaded Graphites," submitted for presentation at the 1959 Nuclear Congress, March 5–10, 1959, Cleveland, Ohio.

6. Dorn, J. E., "The Spectrum of Activation Energies for Creep," pp. 199–226 in "Creep and Recovery," Cleveland, American Society for Metals, 1957.

7. Green, L., Jr., Stehsel, M. L., and Waller, C. E., "Tensile Stress-Strain Properties of Pure and Uranium-Loaded Graphites," *Trans. Am. Nuclear Soc.*, **1**, No. 2, 160, (Dec. 1958).

8. Larson, F. R., and Miller, J., "A Time-Temperature Relationship for Rupture and Creep Stress," *Trans. ASME*, **74**, 765 (1952).

9. Conrad, H., "Correlation of High Temperature Creep and Rupture Data," ASME Paper No. 58-A-96, New York, Dec. 1958.

10. Goldhoff, R. M., "Comparison of Parameter Methods for Extrapolating High-Temperature Data," ASME Paper No. 58-A-121, New York, Dec. 1958.

11. Loftness, R. L., "The Diffusion of Uranium Carbide in Graphite," NAA-SR-64, Aug. 2, 1950.

12. Loch, L. D., Gambino, J. R., and Duckworth, W. H., "Diffusion of Uranium Through Graphite," AIChE Preprint No. 125, Nuclear Engineering and Science Congress, Cleveland, Ohio, Dec. 12–16, 1955.

13. Feldman, M. H., Goeddel, W. V., Dienes, G. J., and Gossen, W., "Studies of Self-Diffusion in Graphite Using C-14 Tracer," *J. Appl. Phys.*, **23**, 1200–1206, (1952).

14. Kanter, M. A., "Diffusion of Carbon Atoms in Natural Graphite Crystals," PhD Thesis, Illinois Institute of Technology, June 1955. Also, "Self-Diffusion in Natural Graphite Crystals," *Phys. Rev.*, **98**, 1563, (1955).

15. Vineyard, G. H., "Radiation Damage in Metals and Alloys," pp. 704–720 in "Metallurgy and Fuels," (Ed., Finniston and Howe) Progress in Nuclear Energy Series No. V, New York, McGraw-Hill Book Co., Inc., 1956.

16. Varley, J. H. O., "Radiation Damage in Covalent and Ionic Solids," *ibid.*, pp. 672–703.

17. Schoeck, G., "Influence of Irradiation on Creep," *J. Appl. Phys.*, **29**, 112, (1958).

17. FUEL ELEMENT FABRICATION AND FUEL ELEMENT PROBLEMS IN THE U.K.

H. K. HARDY

Chief Metallurgist, Research and Development Branch
United Kingdom Atomic Energy Authority, Industrial Group
Risley, Warrington, Lancashire, Great Britain

The United Kingdom has undertaken the largest nuclear power program of any country. The target put forward in 1955 was for 2000 Mwe by 1965.[1] The target was later raised to 5000 to 6000 Mwe by 1966.[2, 3]

The reactors now being built for this program are improved versions of the Calder Hall design. They are graphite-moderated, CO_2-cooled; the fuel is natural uranium metal canned in magnesium alloy. In order to get at the through-put of fuel elements it is guessed that the first 3500 Mwe of the British program will be supplied by this type of reactor. The four stations now under construction—Bradwell, Berkeley, Hunterston and Hinkley Point—have an installed capacity of about 1400 Mwe. Four or five additional stations will be needed to furnish the rest of the 3500 Mwe, leading to a total of 8 or 9 different fuel elements. In order to calculate the size of the fuel element business for these reactors it is necessary to know that (1) the life of the fuel elements is 3000 Mwd/metric ton average; (2) the thermal efficiency is 30 per cent; and (3) the load factor is 80 per cent.

In about 5 years time, the output of fuel elements for the British program will be about 1100 metric tons per year. At present prices this would be in excess of £20M per year but the price is expected to fall. If each fuel element contains 10 kg of uranium on the average, about 100,000 fuel elements will be made per year.

A new factory has been built at Springfields to manufacture these fuel elements. The uranium concentrates come in at one end, the cans come in halfway along the line and the finished fuel elements go out at the other end, 500 yards away.

NOTE: The presentation of this paper at the International Symposium on Nuclear Fuel Elements was made by Dr. G. B. Greenough, Deputy Head of Laboratories, Windscale, U.K.A.E.A.

Figure 17-1. Calder Hall fuel element.

Figure 17-2. Bradwell fuel element.

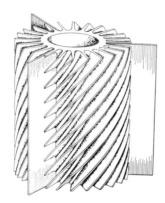

Figure 17-3. Fuel element with helical fins and splitters.

Calder Hall and Newer Fuel Elements

At this point it may be well to consider the Calder Hall and the first four civil fuel elements. Figure 17-1 illustrates the Calder Hall fuel element. It has circumferential fins just over 2 in. in diameter and is stacked in a channel about 4 in. in diameter. As the coolant gas passes up the channel, the circumferential fins produce intense vortexes in between the fins resulting in high heat transfer coefficients. The Bradwell fuel element in Figure 17-2 is also a stacked fuel element. The heat-transfer surface consists of helical fins and there are four splitters or vanes which extend nearly to the channel walls. This is shown more clearly in Figure 17-3.[4] As the coolant gas passes over the helical fins, vortexes are again formed which move along the helix. This draws cooler gas from the outer region of the channel down one side of the splitter while heated gas is pushed outward when it meets the splitter at the other end of the helical fin. The Berkeley fuel element, Figure 17-4, has a similar type of heat-transfer surface, is shorter, and is independently supported from graphite struts which slide

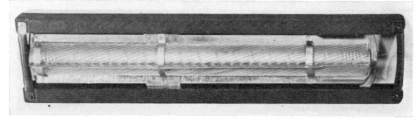

Figure 17-4. Berkeley fuel element.

Figure 17-5. Hunterston fuel element.

Figure 17-6. Hinkley Point fuel element.

in keyways in the moderator. Figure 17-5 shows the Hunterston fuel element,[5] which is independently supported in a graphite sleeve. In this case the heat-transfer surface has longitudinal fins and the vanes are helical. The Hinkley Point fuel element, Figure 17-6, is stacked and again has helical fins and longitudinal splitters.

Design Considerations

It is recognized that fuel elements are never just an incidental item in the reactor design. Successful and competitive power reactors are designed around the fuel elements; the fuel elements influence nearly every part of the reactor design; successful fuel elements are (1) thermodynamically efficient, (2) capable of achieving the required irradiation life, and (3) suitable for large-scale manufacture.

The difficulties of removing heat from the fuel element arise because (1) nuclear considerations lead to a highly concentrated fuel of low surface area; (2) the coolant gas has a low conductivity and low thermal capacity; (3) metallurgical considerations—or in other words metallurgical ignorance —at present place an upper limit on the uranium temperature at the alpha-beta transformation; and (4) a high gas-exit temperature is needed to produce good steam conditions. In order to meet these conditions efficiently the temperature drop from can to coolant must be as low as possible. On the credit side, of significant help are the high thermal conductivity and low neutron absorption of magnesium canning alloys which give the freedom to provide a good heat-transfer surface. The answers which the fuel element designers have given to the heat-transfer problem have been illustrated in the foregoing illustrations. The new fuel elements have better heat-transfer characteristics than the Calder Hall design. This has allowed the first British stations to achieve greater heat release per unit core volume than was obtained in Calder Hall.

In the Calder Hall fuel elements with circumferential fins, the heat-transfer characteristics are very sensitive to the shape of the fin tip profile. With the fins at an angle to the direction of gas flow and splitters, the heat-transfer characteristics are much less affected by minor geometrical changes. The Stanton numbers and friction factors of the new fuel elements have standard deviations only one-third those of the Calder Hall fuel element. Consequently, the new fuel elements will show much less scatter about the mean operating temperature. The lower can-to-can temperature variation eases the problem of designing the fuel elements to operate successfully under the extreme conditions encountered in the reactor.

Calder Hall Fuel Element Experience

The operational experience with the Calder Hall fuel element has been very satisfactory. There have been 6 failures and 16 suspected failures out of the first 50,000 fuel elements. The failures have usually occurred at fairly low levels of irradiation. Postirradiation examination has not always given a conclusive answer but most of the failures have been attributed to small manufacturing defects, possibly in the end welds, or to occasional malhandling on loading. Most of the suspect failures have been identified in the bottom fuel elements which operate with an average can-surface temperature of about 200°C. Very small and very slowly rising signals were observed on the channel detection gear indicating that small slowly developing leaks had occurred. Postirradiation examination showed no defects except for slight intergranular cavitation in the can wall. It is believed this has provided a leak path across the can wall allowing the slow permeation of coolant to the uranium. Grain boundary cavitation is a normal feature of slow plastic deformation in many metals and alloys and intensive laboratory studies have been made of its occurrence in magnesium alloys. The Calder Hall cans have a mean grain size of 0.030 in. against a wall thickness of 0.060 inch. There are some regions in which a single grain occupies the whole wall thickness. In the civil fuel elements, this trouble will be overcome in two ways. There is a new process which leads to a very much smaller grain size, smaller by a factor of 5, and this gives a very much higher ductility. In addition a design feature of the Calder Hall fuel elements which caused strain concentration in the can wall has been removed.

The fuel has proved to be very stable dimensionally under irradiation. No evidence of wrinkling, excessive growth or swelling has been found in the Calder Hall fuel elements. The thermal and irradiation creep rates have been close to the predicted values. The bowing of the fuel elements due to these effects has been kept within acceptable limits by longitudinal braces which support the elements against the channel wall.

An unexpected phenomenon was encountered which proved to be a false alarm. Small bulges were found on the radiographs of a number of irradiated fuel elements. The bulges were about 2 to 3 mm high and 1 or 2 cm in diameter; sometimes they ran around the bar. They occurred preferentially about one-third the distance from the end of the bar. When the can was removed the bulge was found to be due to a powder. X-ray diffraction identified beta-uranium hydride and uranium oxide. It was thought at first that the hydride had come from the hydrogen in the uranium bar. The possible formation of uranium hydride had not been seriously considered in the original analysis of the behavior of the fuel element. Little bumps of uranium hydride on the surface of the uranium bars in the reactor would have been a nuisance because they would react rapidly with hot carbon dioxide if the can were punctured. If the uranium hydride had formed in the reactor, all the hydrogen would have had to be extracted from the bars before canning. In fact, it was discovered that the hydride bulges were being formed by corrosion in the cooling pond where the elements are stored under 20 ft of water. The anaerobic corrosion of uranium leads to a mixture of beta-uranium hydride and uranium oxide. It was found that the number and size of bulges were related to the storage time in the pond. No bulges were found on dry-stored elements. The investigation of the hydride bulges comprised much work but the conclusion that the bulges had formed by corrosion after discharge from the reactor was completely proved.

To summarize, for the irradiation levels attained, the Calder Hall experience has proved the fuel element design, and has shown that very high standards can be maintained for the manufacturing and inspection techniques on tens of thousands of fuel elements. It has been found that the ductility of the magnox can has been inadequate at the lowest operating temperatures. The ductility can be increased by reducing the grain size. The ductility required from the can can be reduced by refining the design.

Civil Reactor Fuel Element Considerations

The fuel elements for the Electricity Authority reactors are intended to have a longer life, 3000 Mwd/metric ton average, at somewhat higher operating temperatures than the Calder Hall fuel elements. Full-scale statistical life-testing of the fuel elements is not usually possible before operation of the first reactor of a new design. Such a method as the sole technique of fuel element development and proving would in any case be the wrong approach. It is considered that the stresses and strains imposed on the fuel elements by their operating conditions can be analyzed, starting from the basic properties of the materials and their behavior under irradiation. The analysis permits a reasonable estimate of the fuel element behavior and lines. In one of the Geneva papers[6] it was shown how the analysis was applied to the Calder Hall fuel elements and confirmed by the irradiation results. This type of study is regarded as a most important part of the fuel element development. Fuel element analysis, as it is termed, is studied continuously by a special group at the Springfields Laboratories of the U. K. Atomic Energy Authority.

The irradiation results, combined with the fuel element analysis, have allowed definition of the phenomena which may limit the life of the civil reactor fuel elements. The chief sources of strains are (a) irradiation effects, (b) temperature and temperature gradient effects (c) support and charging stresses and (d) coolant forces. It has already been mentioned that the low-temperature ductility of magnox had proved to be lower than wished, and that the fine grain size and different design details will provide sufficient factor of safety against the strains likely to be imposed at low irradiation temperatures.

The most important problem in the life of the civil fuel elements is the swelling of uranium due to the release of the fission product gases at high irradiation temperatures. The present data, based on small specimens irradiated at Harwell to burn-ups in excess of 4000 Mwd/metric ton, indicate a maximum swelling of up to 15 per cent by volume at the highest irradiations. In practice a design is being made to accommodate a 20 per cent volume change. This value seems large at first sight, but there is ample reason to believe a mean linear dimensional change of 7 per cent can easily be accommodated. There are adequate clearances around the fuel elements. The swelling occurs only at the highest temperatures where the magnox has excellent creep ductility. Swelling to this extent might affect the heat-transfer properties of the Calder Hall fuel elements with circumferential fins. Tests have shown that the heat-transfer properties of the new civil fuel elements are unaffected by the dimensional changes. There is on hand an extensive irradiation program to define more closely the extent of swelling over a wide range of conditions and also to study methods of controlling it by alloying and other metallurgical techniques. One will then be able to refine the design of the fuel elements to take advantage of the more precise information.

There are good reasons for believing that the 3000 Mwd/metric ton average will be achieved. The terms of the "buy-back" price for the fuel elements from the Electricity Authorities has given the U.K.A.E.A. a big incentive to achieve the maximum irradiation.

Research and Development

The contract between the Electricity Generating Boards in Great Britain and the Consortia* is for the supply of a nuclear power station and for the design of a fuel element. The U.K.A.E.A. advises the Generating Boards, guides the Consortia and manufactures the fuel elements designed by the Consortia. Research and development on the fuel elements is carried out both by the Authority and the Consortia with the following broad division of major interests. The Consortia do most of the work on the out-of-pile proving of the fuel elements, the Authority is responsible for most of the work to establish the manufacturing route. These fields of work interact and overlap; each party does some work outside its main field.

Basic work on fuels, canning alloys, fuel elements, graphite and steel is carried out under a joint collaborative program between all the Consortia and the U.K.A.E.A. The cost of the work contributed by the Consortia is in excess of £400,000 a year. The Research and Development Branch effort is on more than twice this scale, and is supplemented by irradiation studies which are wholly the responsibility of the U.K.A.E.A. About two-thirds of all the research and development effort toward the design of the civil stations is devoted to the fuel, canning alloys and fuel elements.

Research and development work on fuel elements within the Authority is carried out at the following locations: The Metallurgy Division of the Research Group at Harwell does basic work on fuel-canning alloys and conducts irradiation studies in two materials testing reactors. The Research and Development Branch of the Industrial Group has a theoretical and advisory group at Risley, laboratories at Culcheth where basic studies are made of fuels and canning materials, laboratories at Springfields where the manufacturing route is worked out and the fuel elements are tested, and laboratories at Windscale which mount irradiation experiments in Calder Hall reactors and examine the irradiated fuel elements. A large expansion has been started at Windscale of the facilities for the postirradiation examination of fuel elements from the civil reactors. The first stage of this will

* Agency to carry out the design and construction.

cost about £1M. The irradiation program is integrated on an Authority-wide basis and includes the Dounreay materials testing reactor which is used chiefly for work of direct interest to the Industrial Group.

The Research and Development Branch is one of the largest units in Great Britain to be organized on a project basis. Full use is made of modern concepts of management. The organization is by line from the Director to the Heads of Laboratories and by staff from the Chief Scientists who have functional responsibility to the Research Managers at the laboratories. An organization of this type is both strong and flexible. The targets can be clearly defined and the effort adjusted to the importance and difficulties of the problems.

Eight stages are recognized in the research and development work on fuel elements: (1) basic studies of the properties of fuels and canning alloys (2) the accumulation of irradiation data on specimens of fuels and canning alloys (3) design of the heat-transfer surface and of the fuel element (4) development for manufacture and inspection and out-of-pile proving trials, (5) irradiation tests of prototypes, (6) transfer to large scale production, (7) proving and refining of each type of fuel element in the early years of each new reactor combined with (8) the measurement of the actual fuel element operating conditions in the reactor.

Figure 17-7 shows how the research and development work is related to the constructional program. Large reactors are being built and 5 years have been allowed between the decision to construct and the development of full power. The fuel elements are ready for charging into the reactor at the end of the fourth year. Their detailed design and manufacturing route are given at the end of the third year. A fairly full specification of the fuel element design and manufacturing methods is available at the end of the second year. The fuel element and its behavior throughout the whole

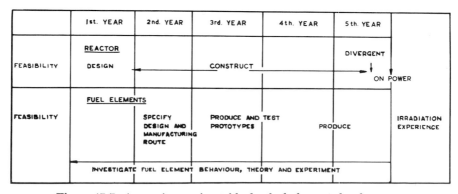

Figure 17-7. Approximate timetable for fuel element development

period is studied. The fuel element research and development, procurement and production are programmed in the same detail as every feature of the design and construction of the complete station.

The fuel element designs change in detail during the development period as new information and new ideas come forward. The requirements that the fuel elements shall be thermodynamically efficient, capable of achieving the required irradiation life and suitable for large-scale manufacture have each to be considered whenever any minor changes are made. Even small changes often have consequences which go beyond the fuel elements. The designers of the manufacturing plant wish to finalize the designs and methods of manufacture as early as possible. Similar views are held by the people who are going to operate the plant. They want to know what they will have to make and how they are going to make it. The longer the research and development period that can be allowed the better the fuel element design will be. The different points of view must be reconciled in the final design. It is at this stage that much of the technical judgment must be exercised. The decisions will be taken much more readily when their need is related to a clearly defined timetable for development and manufacture. The liaison between each Consortia and the different branches of the U.K.A.E.A. has to be very close. As far as the Research and Development Branch is concerned, successful co-ordination is possible because the organization is on a project basis.

It is expected that the later nuclear power stations in Great Britain will possess advanced gas-cooled reactors. Windscale is proceeding with the design and construction of an experimental advanced gas-cooled reactor (the A.G.R. project). The fuel elements are to be uranium oxide clad in beryllium. It is known how to make high-density pellets of UO_2 by the million and the U.K.A.E.A. irradiation program is directed toward confirming the stability of this material which has been reported from the U.S.A. and Canada.

A very intensive effort is being put forth on beryllium. The advantages of beryllium are that it has a melting point of 1280°C and a neutron absorption one-sixth that of magnesium. The disadvantages are: (1) beryllia dust is toxic; (2) the safe limit is 2 $\mu g/m^3$; (3) beryllium is not cheap but the price will come down as the output rises; (4) beryllium easily develops a preferred orientation which means low ductility in certain directions of extruded components; (5) the ductility is low at very slow creep rates; (6) there is an n-alpha reaction under irradiation and the ductility will probably be reduced under irradiation. Why, then, is such a large effort being made on beryllium? The calculated cost of electricity from A.G.R. stations with beryllium fuel elements is cheaper than the cost using stainless steel cans. The successful use of beryllium could save several million pounds sterling per year on the basis of the probable future nuclear power program in Great Britain and the lifetime of the reactors.

In summation, the United Kingdom is engaged on the largest nuclear power program of any country. Successful fuel elements will make a most significant contribution to the success of the program. A large fuel element industry is being built. To solve the technical problems demands first-class scientific effort and first-rate organization. The limited technical effort available in Great Britain has made it necessary to concentrate on a very small number of reactor systems. Most of the effort is devoted to the improved versions of the Calder Hall reactors. The same principle of concentrating effort on targets which are really worthwhile will be applied when the next round of reactors is reached in our expanding nuclear power program.

References

1. "A Programme of Nuclear Power," White Paper, Command 9389 (Feb. 1955).
2. "Capital Investment in the Coal, Gas and Electricity Industries," White Paper, Command 132 (April 1957).
3. "Capital Investment in the Coal, Gas and Electricity Industries," White Paper, Command 415 (April 1958).
4. Ritz, H. L., "The Polyzonal Spiral Fuel Elements," Second United Nations International Conference on the Peaceful Uses of Atomic Energy, Geneva (1958) P/48.
5. Wootton, K. J. and Dennis, W. E., "The Development of the Hunterston Fuel Element," Second United Nations International Conference on the Peaceful Uses of Atomic Energy, Geneva (1958) P/1523.
6. Hardy, H. K. and Lawton, H., "The Assessment and Testing of Fuel Elements," Second United Nations Conference on the Peaceful Uses of Atomic Energy, Geneva (1958) P/306.

18. FUEL ELEMENT FABRICATION AND PROBLEMS FOR THE EL-3 EXPERIMENTAL REACTOR IN FRANCE

B. DE LASTEYRIE

Director, Cie. pour l'Etude et la Realisation de Combustibles Atomiques
Bonneuil-sur-Marne, France

INTRODUCTION

Description of the Reactor

The EL-3 experimental reactor was built at Saclay (France) by the French Atomic Energy Commission (C.E.A.) to study the effect of irradiation on fuel elements and on structural materials.

Reactor data published by the C.E.A. are as follows:

Thermal power	15 Mw
Max. flux of thermal neutrons	10^{14} cm^{-2} sec^{-1}
Fuel	Slightly enriched uranium
Moderator	Heavy water
Reflector	Heavy water and graphite
Main coolant	Primary loop—heavy water
	Secondary loop—ordinary water
Heavy water, mean temp.—inlet	40°C (104°F)
outlet	55°C (131°F)
Velocity of water	7.5 m/sec (22.5 ft/sec)
Reflector and shielding coolant	Atmosphere air

General Characteristics for All Possible Fuel Elements

Slightly enriched uranium is used in all fuel elements, with the fissile content being determined by structural additions. The specific power at maximum load is 40 Mw/ton. The maximum temperature of the can surface (boiling prohibited along the can) is 120°C.

EL-3, 1st and 2nd Loadings

Various possible designs of fuel elements were studied, such as clusters of rods, externally cooled tubes, and externally plus internally cooled tubes. Different canning materials were evaluated: A-5 aluminum, Zircaloy and

297

stainless steel. Both metallic- and ceramic-type fuel materials were evaluated.

For the first and second loadings, various alloys with 1.35 w/o* enriched uranium as fuel material were made. These were as follows: 1.5 w/o uranium with 2, 3 or 10 w/o molybdenum; and 1.5 w/o uranium with 1.5 w/o niobium and 4.5 w/o zirconium.

THE THIRD LOADING OF EL-3

Description of a Cell

In each reactor channel is a fuel element made of an A-5 aluminum tube containing four fuel rods. Each fuel rod is held and centered in position by three fingers located 120° apart around the aluminum tube, as shown in Figure 18-1. Centering the fuel rod provides a coolant channel and room for thermal expansion.

Each fuel rod consists of a 1.6 w/o enriched uranium-10 w/o molybdenum thin-walled tube closed at each end with 3-mm thick natural uranium-10 w/o molybdenum pellets (Figure 18-2).

The natural uranium pellets are welded under vacuum into the ends of the enriched uranium tube to form the hollow uranium rod. The dimensions of the hollow uranium section are as follows:

Length	320 mm (approx. $12\frac{9}{16}$ in.)
OD	29.5 mm (approx. $1\frac{3}{16}$ in.)
ID	22 mm (approx. $\frac{7}{8}$ in.)

The surface of the uranium section is square-threaded, 1.5 mm wide by 0.5 mm deep. The entire section is canned in an impact-extruded A-5 aluminum can 1.05 mm thick and having a heavy section of extrusion billet remaining at one end.

After the uranium has been inserted into the tube, the upper end of the aluminum can is sealed by vacuum welding an aluminum end plug in place. Both ends of the aluminum can are machined to form the end sections, as shown in Figure 18-2. These end sections permit the joining of the fuel cartridges to each other to form the fuel element assembly (Figure 18-1).

Technical Characteristics

Materials. The first purpose was to prepare a very safe fuel, capable of achieving an initial burn-up of no less than 3000 Mwd/ton. The uranium alloy containing 10 w/o of molybdenum was chosen because it retains its γ-phase at room temperature and presents practically no swelling after thermal cycling or irradiation. In order to maintain a sufficient reactivity, the parasitic capture of a greater amount of molybdenum was compensated

* w/o = weight per cent.

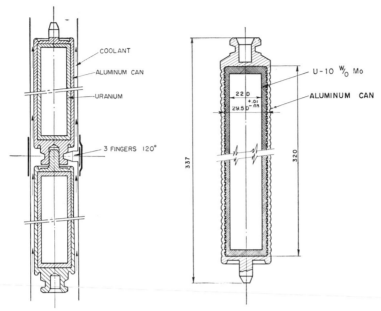

Figure 18-1. EL-3 fuel rod   Figure 18-2. EL-3 fuel rod.
assembly principle.

by the use of a more highly enriched uranium. In fact, 1.6 w/o enriched uranium was used, while, with the former U-1.5w/o Mo alloy, the necessary enrichment was only 1.35 w/o.

As canning material, commercial grade A-5 aluminum presented a more corrosion-resistant material than did a purer metal.

All weldings were done under vacuum, to avoid oxidation and keep surfaces in good condition.

Bonding between Uranium and Can. The Technology Service of the Atomic Energy Commission (C.E.A.) worked extensively on the bonding between the uranium and the aluminum cladding, and ultimately chose a mechanical bonding process. A general outline of these studies follows.

In the case of a threaded rod, with a can drawn tightly on it, there is a stiff longitudinal bonding between can and rod, all along the rod.

When the reactor is in operation, fuel elements undergo thermal cycling, and each material tends to follow its own thermal elongation law. By comparing area cross sections and mechanical strengths of both materials, it is obvious that the can will follow length variations of uranium, and therefore, that strains will appear in it.

Messrs. Bernard and Gauthron of C.E.A. studied these strains and tried to give an analytical expression of the phenomenon. Though it was

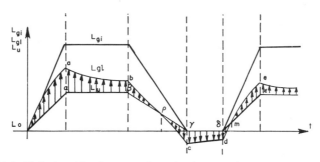

Figure 18-3. Relationship between lengthening strain and temperatures in a bonded can.

very difficult to obtain significant results, a modified relaxation machine was used, which recorded continuously and automatically strains appearing in the can. The fuel element itself, at the same time, was being heated and cooled according to a preset program. The cycle chosen consisted of continuous heating, holding at high temperature, cooling at constant rate, holding at room temperature, and so on.

In Figure 18-3 three curves are plotted. The first one, L_u, gives the length of uranium at an instant t; another, L_{gi}, gives the length of an unbonded can, at the same time; the last one, L_{gl}, gives the length that a bonded can would reach if it were separated from the uranium, just at the time t.

On incipient heating, L_{gl} and L_{gi} are the same L_o; later on this is not so, because plastic and elastic phenomena appear, due, respectively, to too great stresses and too high temperatures.

If there had been no bonding, the can would be longer than the uranium during heating. As plastic deformations appear, the can is, in fact, shorter than it would have been without bonding, so that, on cooling, it has the same length as the uranium before room temperature is reached. The can is then without strain, and, later, new strains of opposite direction will appear. On the second cycle, the phenomenon is the same, but strains are less than at the first time.

Messrs. Bernard and Gauthron have determined the relationship between temperature, length, strain and time which controls the process.

The application of these studies to the production of the EL-3 fuel elements gave very good results: hot canning acts as a first thermal cycling, so that strains are either positive or negative, but always rather small in themselves.

Fabrication

In the following, only the most important steps of the fabrication process are described (Figure 18-4), viz: (1) melting; (2) heat treatment, under

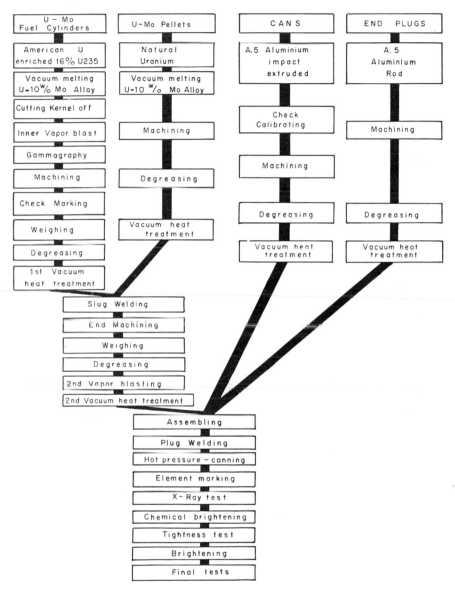

Figure 18-4. EL-3 fuel rod assembly lines.

vacuum, of rods and pellets; (3) vacuum welding by electronic beam of pellets and of plugs of the cans; (4) hot canning; (5) testing. In the Addendum, a method for recovering uranium scraps and turnings is described.

Melting and Casting. The furnaces in use were designed by Mr. Ortel of the C.E.A., and are built under contract by the Compagnie Générale de Radiologie.

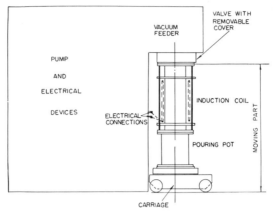

Figure 18-5. Melting furnace as applied to alloy fabrication.

From an operational point of view, these furnaces may be considered as involving two parts (Figure 18-5): (1) A steady or fixed part, including electrical apparatus, rotary and diffusion pumps, and the control board; (2) A set of mobile parts, easy to connect to the electrical generator and the vacuum feeder. For example, the melting vessel has only to be introduced closely under the vacuum feeder, and, after evacuation, the outer atmospheric pressure maintains the vessel tightly in position.

Between the steady and the mobile parts of the furnace is a valve with removable cover. The steady part contains a 100-kva, 4-kHz alternator, which usually supplies 150 amps under 600 v.

Vacuum is obtained by means of a 8000 l/sec diffusion pump, and the rough vacuum is provided by two 200 m³/hr rotary pumps.

Each movable group includes from bottom to top, a hand-driven carriage holding: (a) a vessel containing the molds and a 3 kva preheater; and (b) a silica tube supporting the water-cooled induction coil and the graphite crucibles. All these parts are connected by means of water-cooled flanges.

One point of interest is the valve with the removable cover, designed and developed by Mr. Ortel, which makes it possible to use the furnace continuously. Some minutes after casting, as soon as the metal is solidified, a sealing plate is put under vacuum on the movable group, which is then removed and allowed to cool by itself. The furnace is then available for a new run.

The cooling movable group is now kept under static vacuum, but a device to maintain these groups under dynamic vacuum is being studied.

All the pieces of the melting equipment (Figure 18-6) are machined from graphite. The dual-melt method is used. In the upper crucible are placed the short molybdenum pins, followed by the uranium billet. At the

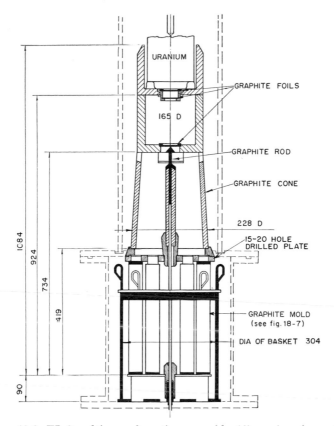

Figure 18-6. EL-3 melting and casting assembly (dimensions in mm).

bottom of that crucible is placed a graphite holder with two thin circular graphite foils. The upper foil is closed and maintains the melt during alloying. Afterward, that foil is broken by means of the thermocouple plunger. The molten metal flows into the lower crucible through a 2-mm hole, and is degassed in the second crucible. Then the foil at the bottom of the lower crucible is broken by a graphite rod driven from the bottom of the casting vessel.

The two crucibles are supported by a graphite cone, placed on a plate with 15 to 21 drilled holes. Under each hole is placed the mold, Figure 18-7, containing the kernel which is centered by a film called a "star" through which uranium flows.

Before being used, all graphite pieces are carefully degassed between 1200 and 1300°C; then they receive a wash of ThO_2 deposited with a brush, or by some modified slip-casting process.

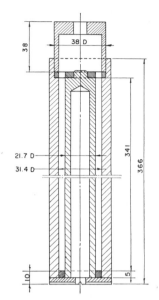

Figure 18-7. EL-3 graphite mold.

The load is heated by thermal radiation emitted by the upper crucible. The uranium melts, and molybdenum is progressively dissolved. Alloying requires approximately one hour; the melt is maintained one hour more in the upper crucible to be degassed, then is poured through the 2-mm hole into the second crucible as a thin stream. The molten metal is then heated to 1540°C for 10 min. and cast in the molds. As stated, the molds are preheated around 450°C at the bottom, by a special preheater, and about 650°C at the top by radiation of the crucible.

The following casting results were obtained:

Uranium	44 kg 784 g
Molybdenum	4 kg 976 g
Alloy	49 kg 760 g

Loss in crucibles	2 kg 250 g
Overload and bulk scraps	7 kg 980 g
15 rods (dead-head included)	39 kg 100 g
Loss	0 kg 430 g
	49 kg 760 g

The melting cycle is given in Figure 18-8.

With the instrument control panels, the following can be checked: (a) vacuum, by usual methods; (b) temperature. At the start, the temperature

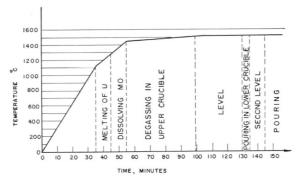

Figure 18 8. Melting cycle, U 10 w/o Mo.

is followed by means of an optical pyrometer; and, later, by insertion into the melt of a pyrometric plunger containing a Pt-Pt-13 % Rh thermocouple.

Some problems had to be solved in order to protect the thermocouples. After some trials, a Pythagoras tube, surrounded with a graphite can, was chosen.

The raw material and alloy analyses, and the γ-tests performed before sending the uranium slugs for machining will be described under "Tests."

Machining. Machining is done on usual lathes, using tungsten carbide tools. The only difference is that the machining is done under a 120 1/hr distilled-water flow, which is not recovered. The cast slug weighs 2 kg 600 g. After machining, the yield was as follows:

Dead-head (directly back to melting)	0 kg 550 g
Chips	0 kg 450 g
One machined slug	1 kg 600 g
	2 kg 600 g

By recovering all that can be directly melted, the theoretical yield is:

Uranium	90 kg
Molybdenum	10 kg
Alloy	100 kg

Alloy in slugs	72 kg
Chips	20 kg 200 g
Alloy retained in the crucible	6 kg 600 g
Loss	1 kg 200 g
	100 kg

Degreasing. As the slug has been machined under water, it is free of surface impurities, and the degreasing treatment is simplified: the material

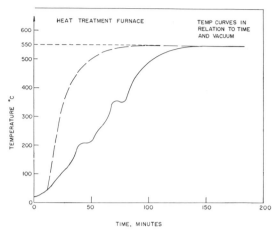

Figure 18-9. Furnace temperature as a function of time and vacuum. *Left curve:* theoretical. *Right curve:* actual conditions for 10^{-4} mm vacuum.

is immersed in a wetter bath, rinsed, treated in a mixture of alcohol $+2$ per cent acetone, and dried in hot air.

Vacuum Heat Treatment of Slugs and Pellets. Furnaces electrically heated and held under high vacuum are used in order to remove gas from slugs after chemical treatment and relax the casting strains.

All inner parts of the furnace are carefully degreased with the 3-component mixture (in per cent: acetone 5, benzene 2, alcohol 2). All workers wear clean white gloves.

During heating, the pressure at a value equal to or better than 10^{-4} mm Hg is maintained. For this purpose a special device was developed in which the current delivered by a Penning gage is amplified and opposed to an adjustable supplier. The resultant signal is applied to an electronic switch which controls the heating of the furnace. Figure 18-9 gives a curve showing the change of furnace temperature with time and vacuum.

A temperature of 550°C is maintained for 2 hours. During furnace cooling, air is admitted when the temperature is less than 40°C. If the slugs are not immediately used in the line, they are stored under a static pressure better than 10^{-3} mm Hg, in movable vessels.

Welding of Pellets and Aluminum Plugs by Electronic Beam, under Vacuum. Mr. Stohr, Chief of the Department of Technology, Metallurgy and Applied Chemistry Division (C.E.A.) discovered this method, and has described it extensively in his paper* presented at the Technical Fuel Element Symposium, held in Paris, November 1957.

With Stohr's technique it is possible to focus an electron beam on as

* U.S. Atomic Energy Comm. Report TID-7546, p. 9–17 (1958).

small a target as desired. The heat released on that spot is very great, and it is possible to melt and weld accurately, without oxidation, all kinds of metals. Results are particularly good with refractory (tungsten, molybdenum, tantalum) or highly oxygen-sensitive materials (zirconium, beryllium, uranium).

With the earlier machine, the vacuum had to be cut off after each weld to remove the piece. A new type machine has been completed that facilitates

Figure 18-10. Vacuum-welding machine.

Figure 18-11. EL-3 element before canning.

16 welds without opening the vessel. All welds for the EL-3 fuel elements are made in this way.

Figure 18-10 is a photograph of the electron beam welding machine, and Figure 18-11, the components before canning.

Hot Bonding. The can, accurately checked from all points of view, receives the slug and the aluminum plug, and is welded, as previously described.

For hot bonding, the sealed slug is introduced into a hot thick-walled vessel, able to withstand temperatures up to 400°C and pressures up to 200 kg/cm² (3000 psi). Once the element has been stabilized at 400°C, the air pressure is applied for 20 minutes. In order to avoid strains, the temperature in the vessel has to be very uniform.

This treatment gives a mechanical, tight bond between uranium and the aluminum can by "strain-acting bonding" without diffusion.

Refining. At the end of the assembly line, fuel elements are brightened in a bath of diluted caustic soda, then in diluted nitric acid, and finally in alcohol. Afterward, the fuel element is enclosed in a polyvinyl sheath with silica-gel.

Tests

1. The uranium and aluminum suppliers check their own supplies and furnish an analysis.

2. The can dimensions and the perpendicularity of the bottom to the axis of the can are checked.

3. The molybdenum content of the alloys is accurately weighed; for this purpose, molybdenum is precipitated with lead acetate as lead molybdate.

4. Micrographic examination is used to observe the uranium carbide

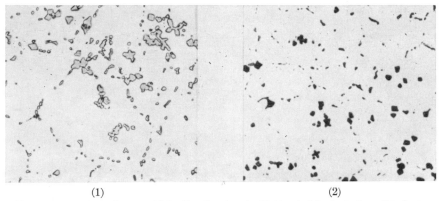

(1)   (2)

Figure 18-12. Uranium carbide distribution in U-10 w/o Mo fuel slug. (1) electro-polished; (2) mechanically polished (Al_2O_3), etchant $H_2O_2 + H_2SO_4$.

distribution. Figure 18-12 shows micrograph No. 1—sample as electro-polished; micrograph No. 2—mechanically polished (Al_2O_3); etchant $H_2O_2 + H_2SO_4$.

5. The soundness of all cast slugs is checked by means of an 11c Co^{60} source. With five 30 × 40, 0.25 mm Pb screened plates, 35 slugs and 7 penetrometers can be recorded. The time of exposure is $1\frac{1}{2}$ hr, and the distance of the source 1.5 meters.

6. Density is checked by hydrostatic measurements. By means of micrography, it is verified that no molybdenum remains in the crucible scraps.

7. The U^{235} enrichment is controlled as follows. A radium-beryllium source, the strength of which is continuously measured, is placed in graphite bulk. A slug is introduced into the graphite channel, and the new neutron flux appearing in a second counter is measured. The device having been previously gaged with slugs of known enrichment, the enrichment of any piece of the same shape can be determined.

8. The welds are not checked, because experience has indicated that this welding method is absolutely safe.

9. The canning is verified by two ways: (a) x-ray record, to determine that the aluminum has been thoroughly inserted in the thread of the uranium slug; (b) a helium desorption test, to verify the tightness of the can. The canned slug is held under helium pressure of 15 kg/cm² for 24 hours (Figures 18-13, 14 and 15). Afterwards, the slug is held for 15 min. under a vacuum of 10^{-2} mm Hg, so that if the helium has penetrated through the very small holes of the can, it is detected by a mass spectrograph. If such a helium signal is noted, the slug is refused, decanned, cleaned again, sealed in a new can, hot-pressure treated, and rechecked.

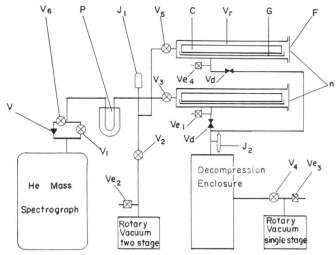

Figure 18-13. Helium desorption test.

C—element
Vr—desorption enclosure
F—fast closing valve
G—basket
Ve$_{1,2,3,4}$—air-admittance valves
V—fine control needle valve

V$_{1,2,3,4,5,6}$—diaphragm valves
Vd—valve
J$_1$—Pirani gage
J$_2$—discharge gage
P—liquid nitrogen condenser
n—number of enclosures following the number of elements

Figure 18-14. Pressure tubes, helium desorption test machine.

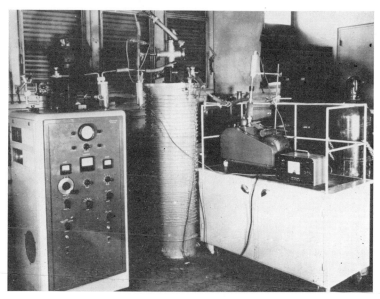

Figure 18-15. Helium desorption test machine.

Figure 18-16. EL-3 element.

Conclusions

The fuel elements (Figure 18-16), obtained from accurate computations and after careful manufacture, have given very satisfactory results.

In order to gain information on their in-pile behavior, some are extracted from time to time from the reactor, for examination, after increasing burn-up. Up to the present time no swelling or canning defects have been observed, although the burn-up is greater than 2000 Mwd/ton.

ADDENDUM. SCRAPS AND CHIPS RECOVERY

Due to losses of uranium by crucible absorption, formation of small pieces in the casting assembly, and chips from machining, these fragments of uranium have to be recovered. Uranium absorbed in graphite can be recovered, with caution, by calcination and chemical treatment. Pieces issued from casting assembly can be metallurgically recovered, by (a) remelting with magnetic stirring of the melt (scraps are very rich in UX and Th^{234}, and very radioactive) and (b) induction melting. New scraps are slightly radioactive and are rejected during pouring.

After strong compacting, chips are obtained either as bulk pieces or as fine particles, according to their brittleness. (For example, molybdenum chips are very brittle.) After degreasing they can be remelted in an induction furnace. The micrographs in Figure 18-17 show metal remelted from highly oxidized turnings. The metal is sound, though the inclusions are rich.

The cost of these recovery methods has to be lower than the price of

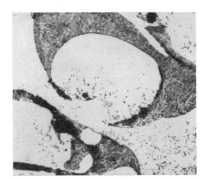 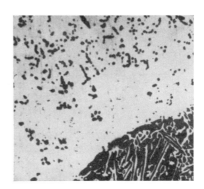

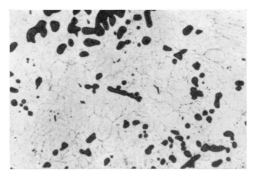

Figure 18-17. Metal remelted from highly oxidized turnings: 3 typical microstructures showing various types of oxide inclusions.

the recovered uranium. According to the U^{235} enrichment, it may have to be recovered or considered as finally lost. This problem is now being studied.

ACKNOWLEDGMENT

The help of the French Atomic Energy Commission (C.E.A.) and the kindness of Messrs. Salesse, Departmental Head of Applied Metallurgy and Chemistry, and Stohr, Head of the Technology Service of D.A.M.C., and of their collaborators, are gratefully acknowledged.

19. PROBLEMS OF FUEL ELEMENT CORROSION IN WATER

J. E. DRALEY

Corrosion Research, Metallurgy Division
Argonne National Laboratory, Lemont, Illinois

It is clearly impossible to describe in one chapter the corrosion problems for all fuel elements. Rather than attempting to give a brief outline mentioning the corrosion problems in all of the most interesting environments, attention will be limited to water as the heat-transfer medium.

There are two basic reasons why it is desirable to clad most nuclear fuels. The elemental fissionable materials (uranium and plutonium) are not resistant to corrosion by water at elevated temperatures. Consequently, contact between water and fuel would result in the corroding away of the fuel and severe contamination of the cooling water. Furthermore, the nature of the corrosion process for uranium is such that it does not simply wear away at the surface, but can be expected to show more violent reactions. Deep local penetrations or cracking can cause swelling, with resultant blocking of the flow of cooling water and jamming of the fuel element in place. Even if the fuel is corrosion resistant, however, it is still quite desirable to have it covered with a material which will block recoil fission fragments from being liberated into the water. In this case the requirement for integrity in the cladding is not nearly so great, however, since a small perforation might result in the discharge of only a small amount of radioactive material to the coolant.

The situation can become quite complex when the fuel element is clad. The basic problems, however, are the same: corroding away of the fuel, contamination of the water, and swelling of the fuel element with its potentially serious consequences. There are two harmful results of corrosion of the cladding. One is possible perforation, allowing the water to reach the fuel. The results are as mentioned for non-corrosion-resistant fuel. Even for nonreactive fuel materials such as UO_2 there are possible complications such as absorption of liquid water with subsequent violent formation of steam by nuclear heat. The other objection to corrosion of the cladding exists because of the requirement to transfer heat from fuel element to water. If there is an accumulation of corrosion product, a large temperature increment will be required across it to maintain the desired heat flux. This results in a higher metal temperature which usually causes higher corrosion rates, and the effect is cumulative.

Sometimes corrosion products, both from fuel element cladding and from other parts of the system, are carried in the water and deposited on the fuel element surface where the temperature is highest and the radiation field is greatest. This deposit is known as "crud." Another effect of too large a deposit of corrosion products on fuel element surfaces can be a reduction in the thickness of a narrow water passage, tending to restrict the flow. This will result in either a reduction in the rate of heat transfer or an increase in the pumping power required to maintain the flow rate. There are other places in reactor systems where "crud" deposits are particularly objectionable. One of these is on the mechanisms that are normally used to position control rods. Another complication is caused by the erosive effect of suspended solids. Components such as pump impellers are sensitive to this. Sometimes low regions, where there is little or no flow rate of the water, can be plugged with crud.

Uranium Corrosion

Uranium reacts with pure water to form the stable oxide UO_2. When the water contains dissolved air at room temperature this corrosion product takes the form of a thin continuous film, providing excellent corrosion protection. The thickness of this film is uniform and interference colors are exhibited as it gradually grows thicker. Eventually the protective film breaks down at local sites on the metal surface, resulting in considerably more rapid corrosion at those positions. These active areas gradually increase in size. The corrosion product in these regions is apparently the same uranium dioxide that forms the thin film, except that it is dark and powdery. Corrosion behavior in aerated distilled water at several temperatures is illustrated in Figure 19-1. The slope of the corrosion curve, or the average corrosion rate for the specimen, is observed to increase toward a limiting value. This is indicative of the kind of behavior just described for corrosion at room temperature. The initial slow reaction is of shorter duration as the temperature is increased. The importance of the temperature itself as a determining factor is not known, since the concentration of dissolved oxygen diminishes as the temperature rises.

In oxygen-free water (achieved in these tests by actively bubbling hydrogen through the water) corrosion is rapid from the beginning of the test and proceeds at a constant rate. Short sections of lines having the same slope as corrosion curves in this type of oxygen-free water are shown on Figure 19-1 for comparison with the curves for aerated water.

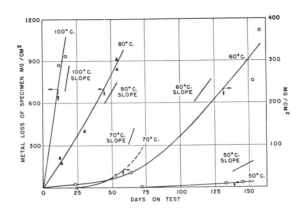

Figure 19-1. Corrosion of uranium in aerated distilled water at various temperatures.[1]

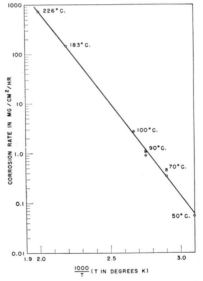

Figure 19-2. Effect of temperature on corrosion rate of uranium in hydrogen-saturated water.[1]

An Arrhenius plot of the constant corrosion rates in hydrogen saturated water is shown in Figure 19-2. Short-time corrosion data at 350°C have been obtained at Hanford. This corrosion rate fits on an extrapolation of the line in Figure 19-1. It appears that the factor which controls the corrosion rate of uranium in water is the same over the temperature range investigated.

It is remembered that the corrosion rate of uranium in boiling distilled water is relatively rapid from the beginning of the exposure (except for a short induction period sometimes encountered). The addition of 5 per cent of zirconium to uranium as an alloying constituent allows the formation of the protective oxide film in actively boiling distilled water. After long exposure, local sites of film breakdown occur as for unalloyed uranium in aerated water at lower temperatures. Apparently there is a requirement for some dissolved oxygen in this boiling water, however, for if purified helium or hydrogen is bubbled through the boiling water the protective film is not formed. The corrosion rate is then only a fewfold smaller than that for unalloyed uranium.

It is possible to stabilize the protective film more effectively by further alloying. The addition of $1\frac{1}{2}$ per cent niobium to the 5 per cent zirconium-uranium alloy provides a protective film at all oxygen concentrations and at all temperatures studied. A binary alloy containing 3 to 6 per cent niobium has about the same structure as uranium and as the uranium-zirconium-niobium ternary alloy, and corrodes much the same as the latter. The addition of more niobium or of 10 per cent or more molybdenum produces binary alloys in which the metallic structure of gamma-uranium is readily retained to room temperature. It is also possible to provide corrosion resistance by formation of the compound U_3Si. The corrosion behavior of these alloys is illustrated in Figure 19-3. Corrosion rates have generally been constant with respect to time, and these rates were used in preparing the figure. Recently, uranium-titanium binary alloys and uranium-titanium-niobium ternaries (about 4 per cent total alloying constituents) have shown good corrosion resistance in water at elevated temperatures.

All of these alloys, with the possible exception of the uranium-silicon compound, are subject to a kind of discontinuous failure after long exposure in distilled water at elevated temperatures. This is apparently the result of accumulation in the metal of some of the hydrogen produced in the

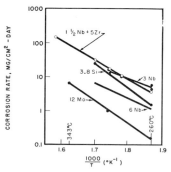

Figure 19-3. Corrosion rate of uranium alloys in distilled water[1].

corrosion reaction. In the gamma-phase alloys, crystals of a new phase have been observed to form internally within corroded specimens. This is believed to be a form of uranium hydride. Since there is an increase in volume due to the formation of this substance, high internal stresses are produced and samples crack or crumble. The same kind of mechanical damage occurs to the zirconium-niobium alloy and the low-niobium binary alloys. In these cases it has not been possible to see uranium hydride as a second phase. However, the hydrogen content of the corrosion samples does increase, as determined by analysis.

In general, the alpha-phase alloys must be quenched from the gamma-phase region for good corrosion resistance. In this condition they are not dimensionally stable under irradiation, and the irradiation largely destroys their corrosion resistance. The alloys having the gamma-uranium structure are not subject to these problems, but seem to be quite stable under irradiation. For U_3Si the situation has not been entirely determined, but indications are that it, too, is stable.

Aluminum Corrosion

The 1100 aluminum alloy has been used in many nuclear reactors. At ordinary temperatures its resistance to corrosion by pure water is quite satisfactory. The reaction is characteristically rapid at the beginning of the exposure period and thereafter diminishes. This behavior is illustrated in Figure 19-4 in which the change in weight of 1100 specimens is shown as a function of time in oxygen-saturated water at 70°C. Points subsequent to the first week seem to indicate a constant corrosion rate in this figure and for other tests lasting not more than a few months However, Figure 19-5 shows an apparent continuous decrease in corrosion rate for a test lasting nearly 1000 days. The line drawn in this figure is for the equation shown. Although it is not at all certain that the reaction kinetics are properly represented by this equation, it is clear that corrosion rates become quite low as the exposure time increases. Estimated rates of metal reaction correspond to average penetration rates as follows: 8.1 μ-in./yr at 100 days, 2.8 μ-in./yr at 300 days, 0.9 μ-in./yr at 900 days.

At 200°C and below, corrosion curves for 1100 aluminum are of quite similar form as indicated in Figure 19-6. Again the test duration is relatively short so that the use of straight lines to represent the corrosion curves is not necessarily justified. It has, nevertheless, seemed profitable to so represent the curves and to use the slopes as the "corrosion rates." The logarithm of this type of corrosion rate is plotted against the reciprocal of the absolute temperature in Figure 19-7. The break in the curve for distilled water is perhaps the result of the change in the bulk corrosion product which occurred in the vicinity of 100°C. At 90°C and below, this product

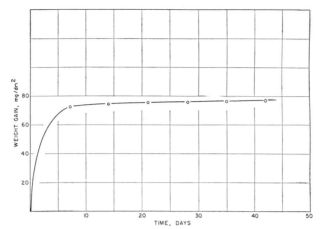

Figure 19-4. Corrosion of 1100 aluminum in oxygen-saturated distilled water at 70°C.*

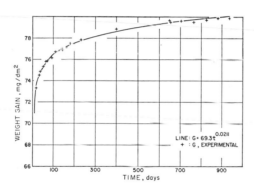

Figure 19-5. Corrosion of 1100 aluminum in oxygen-saturated distilled water at 70°C.*

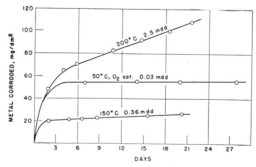

Figure 19-6. Corrosion of 1100 aluminum in distilled water. (Ref. 2, Pt. I)

* Draley, J. E., "Corrosion in the Atomic Energy Industry," Proceedings, Corrosion Control Short Course, Univ. of Oklahoma, April 1–3, 1958; pp. 215–240.

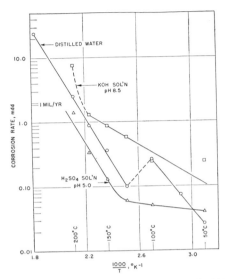

Figure 19-7. Effect of temperature on corrosion rate of 1100 aluminum. (Ref. 2, Pt. I).

was observed to be bayerite $(Al(OH)_3)$; at 125°C and above, it was found to be boehmite $(AlOOH)$.

A test run at 290°C indicated a corrosion rate, for the first week or so, which would fit on an extension of the distilled water curve in Figure 19-7. Subsequent to that time, however, the corrosion rate increased with time and areas of local attack appeared on the surface. Typical of the first stages of this kind of attack is the appearance of the samples shown in Figure 19-8. Note the local swellings along stringers in the metal and around severely disturbed metal as at the drilled supporting holes. At higher temperatures this kind of attack occurs earlier in the corrosion exposure and proceeds very rapidly. Samples are completely disintegrated (converted to oxide) during as little as 4 hours' exposure to water at 315°C.

A theory involving damage by corrosion-product hydrogen predicted not only that externally applied anodic current should be protective, but also that the addition to the water of easily reducible cations of metals having low hydrogen overvoltage should be valuable. If all the hydrogen produced could be formed in a condition (molecular) or at a position unavailable to the aluminum surface, no penetration of its structure should occur. When 1100 aluminum was immersed in a dilute nickel sulfate solution, dendritic nickel formed at spots on its surface, and the local attack did not occur. However, a basic salt precipitated at elevated temperature. Acidification with sulfuric acid prevented this and corrosion behavior at 275°C is as indicated in Figure 19-9.

Figure 19-8. 1100 aluminum samples after 2 weeks in water at 275°C.*

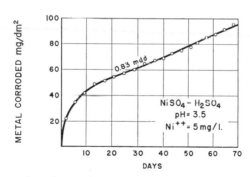

Figure 19-9. Corrosion of 1100 aluminum at 275°C. (Source, see footnote to Figure 19-4.)

The disintegrating attack can also be prevented by alloying. More work has been done with alloy X8001 (made by the addition of 1 per cent nickel to the 1100 alloy) than with any other. Short-time corrosion behavior in water and in a dilute solution of phosphoric acid are given in Figure 19-10. Data are also shown for alloy A198X, containing 1 per cent nickel plus 0.1

---

* Draley, J. E., and Ruther, W. E., "Some Unusual Effects of Hydrogen in Corrosion Reactions," *J. Electrochem Soc.*, **104,** 329–333 (1957).

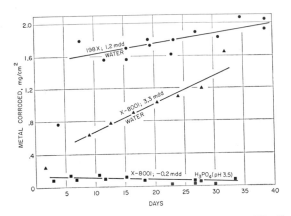

Figure 19-10. Corrosion of various aluminum alloys at 290°C. (Source, see footnote to Figure 19-4.)

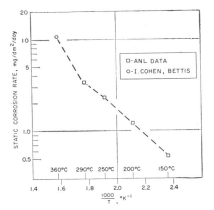

Figure 19-11. Effect of temperature on the corrosion rate of X8001-type aluminum alloys.*

per cent titanium, in a pure aluminum base. In water, alloy A198X appears to have a lower corrosion rate than X8001. The phosphoric acid shows promise as a quite good inhibitor.

The dependence of the slope of the 10- to 60-day portion of the corrosion curve on temperature is shown in Figure 19-11. There have been a number of peculiarities observed in the corrosion of these alloys. Sometimes the corrosion curve breaks upward after a period of testing. Some of the unusual effects are particularly striking at high flow rate (water past

* Draley, J. E., Breden, C. R., Ruther, W. E., and Grant, N. R., "High Temperature Aqueous Corrosion of Aluminum Alloys," Second International Conference on Peaceful Uses of Atomic Energy (Sept. 1958) P/1139.

sample surface). There it has frequently been found that samples added as replacements during a corrosion test have corroded to a considerably greater extent than the samples originally loaded. Also, different laboratories have reported much different results under nominally the same conditions. These anomalies have to some extent been clarified by the observation that corrosion behavior has depended on the ratio of the exposed sample area to the volume of the water in the corrosion test loop. This factor has been presumed to be associated with accidental contamination of the water during the test. The higher surface-to-volume ratios provide best corrosion behavior, so it is presumed that the contamination is beneficial.

The corrosion observed with fairly good surface-to-volume ratios (200 cm² per gallon of water) is given in Figures 19-12 and 13. Even a small

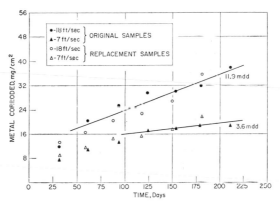

Figure 19-12. Corrosion of aluminum alloy X8001 in water at 260°C. (Source, see footnote to Figure 9-11.)

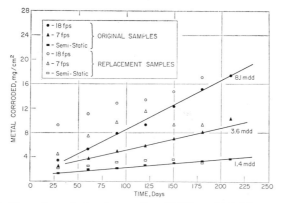

Figure 19-13. Corrosion of aluminum alloy X8001 at 315°C in pH 5.5 phosphoric acid. (Source, see footnote to Figure 9-11.)

concentration of phosphoric acid is indicated to offer significant inhibition, since only about a third as much corrosion occurred in 7 months when it was present (pH 5.5 at room temperature) as when it was absent, at 315°C.

Although some results look very encouraging, there have been a number of cases where severe corrosion resulted, and it is not yet possible to specify conditions which will insure that the best corrosion behavior will be obtained. The use of phosphoric acid is not as straightforward as it may seem, since pitting has occurred at some concentrations. These pits have apparently not exceeded 1 mil in depth, but it would be necessary to be certain that penetration would not occur before it could be specified for use.

Zirconium Corrosion

The aqueous corrosion of zirconium is characterized by a diminishing rate of reaction. Although there has been some conflicting evidence concerning the kinetics of the reaction the corrosion curves are generally drawn as straight lines on a log weight-gain- log time-plot. The curves in Figure 19-14 were reported by Thomas.[4]

After prolonged exposure the dark corrosion product is observed to turn white, with subsequent flaking and more rapid reaction. This kind of behavior is represented by the shaded areas in Figure 19-14. Numbers in parentheses refer to the number of specimens represented. This "breakaway" corrosion behavior has variously been ascribed to the formation of zirconium hydride at the metal oxide interface, and to mechanical rupturing of the growing oxide film. It does not occur in dry oxygen. The phenomenon must be described as incompletely explained.

The corrosion behavior of zirconium is strongly dependent on the concentration of certain impurities. For example, Figure 19-15 shows the effect of nitrogen in zirconium on its corrosion in water at 315°C, and Figure 19-16 shows the effect of carbon. These are two of the most deleterious contami-

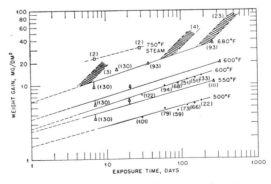

Figure 19-14. Corrosion of crystal bar zirconium in water.[4]

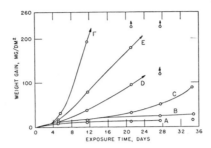

Figure 19-15. Effect of nitrogen content (in ppm) on aqueous corrosion of crystal bar zirconium at 315°C.[4]

NITROGEN CONTENT

	Nominal	Analyzed		Nominal	Analyzed
A	30	30	D	70	40
B	40	30	E	80	90
C	50	30	F	140	130

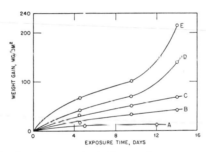

Figure 19–16. Effect of carbon content (in ppm) on aqueous corrosion of crystal bar zirconium at 315°C.[4]

CARBON CONTENT

	Nominal	Analyzed		Nominal	Analyzed
A	300	300	D	1300	900
B	700	400	E	1500	1000
C	1100	600			

nants, from the point of view of corrosion resistance. It has been observed that tin as an alloying constituent in zirconium tends to overcome their harmful effect. Figure 19-17 shows the influence of the addition of tin on the corrosion of sponge-base-zirconium alloys containing 60 ppm nitrogen. Exposure conditions are given for each curve.

With this kind of protection against the harmful effect of nitrogen and carbon and with the known desirability of iron, chromium, and nickel as alloying constituents, Zircaloy-2 was developed. Its composition includes, in per cent, 1.5 Sn, 0.12 Fe, 0.10 Cr, and 0.05 Ni. Its corrosion behavior in water is summarized in Figure 19-18. It is observed that, again, there is an

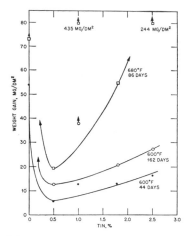

Figure 19-17. Effect of tin content on aqueous corrosion of arc-melted sponge-base zirconium alloys.[4]

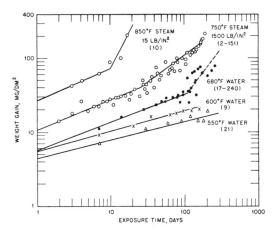

Figure 19-18. Corrosion of Zircaloy-2 in high temperature water and steam.[4] Note: The figures in parentheses are the number of samples tested.

upward break in the corrosion curves. However, the rate of reaction subsequent to the break in the curve is substantially lower than is true for unalloyed zirconium, and this is one of the primary advantages of Zircaloy-2 over zirconium.

Stainless Steel Corrosion

Although stainless steel is a material of considerable interest for construction of reactor components, not many people have felt it suitable for use in constructing fuel elements. This is because, in water-cooled moder-

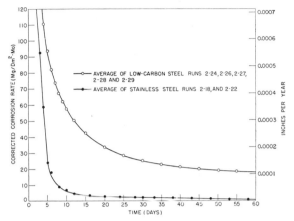

Figure 19-19. Corrosion of low-carbon and stainless steel in pH 10.6 NaOH or NH₄OH.*

ated reactors, neutron absorption by stainless steel is generally considered objectionably high.

A number of investigators have observed the corrosion of stainless steels in water at elevated temperatures. Probably the clearest data have been reported by Bloom, Krulfeld, Fraser and Vlannes.* Corrosion rates reported by these authors are shown in Figure 19-19, together with a representative curve for low-carbon steel. In general, all of the austenitic stainless steels show very similar corrosion behavior. There is little effect of water (solution) pH in the range 7.0 to 10.6 in the absence of oxygen. There is apparently a maximum in the dependence of amount of corrosion on dissolved oxygen concentration.

General References

Uranium

1. Foote, F. G., "Physical Metallurgy of Uranium," *Proc. Int. Conf. on Peaceful Uses of Atomic Energy*, Geneva, **IX**, 60–64 (Aug. 1955).

Aluminum

2. Draley, J. E., and Ruther, W. E., "Aqueous Corrosion of Aluminum," Part 1 "Behavior of 1100 Alloy," *Corrosion*, **12**, 441t (1956); *Ibid.*, Part 2, "Methods of Protection Above 200°C," p. 480t.
3. Dillon, R. L., and Troutner, V. H., "Observations on the Mechanisms and Kinetics of Aqueous Aluminum Corrosion," General Electric Co., Hanford Atomic Products Operation, report HW-51849 (Sept. 30, 1957).

---

* Bloom, M. C., Krulfeld, M., Fraser, W. A., and Vlannes, P. N., "Corrosion Studies in High Temperature Water by a Hydrogen Effusion Method," NRL 4711 (March 9, 1956).

Zirconium

4. Thomas, D. E., "Corrosion of Zirconium and its Alloys," pp. 553–686, Ch. 11 in "Metallurgy of Zirconium," B. Lustman and F. Kerze (Eds.), New York, McGraw-Hill Book Co., Inc., 1955.

Stainless Steel

5. DePaul, D. J. (Ed.), "Corrosion and Wear Handbook for Water Cooled Reactors," USAEC TID-7006, March 1957.

20. FUEL ELEMENT BEHAVIOR UNDER IRRADIATION

LEONARD W. KATES

Director of Engineering, Sylvania-Corning Nuclear Corporation
Bayside, New York

A great deal has been said and written concerning the factors affecting the economics of nuclear power (see Chapters 1, 2 and 3). It is generally agreed that there are three major factors which influence it greatly: namely, capital costs, fuel cycle costs, and thermal efficiency of the plant. In regard to fuel cycle costs, it is possible to reduce these by decreasing the cost of fuel element fabrication, by a reduction of the separations, recovery, and waste disposal costs and by increasing fuel element life as long as there is no sacrifice of operating temperature, specific power, neutron economy, and the like, which would result in a net operating cost increase.

There are several important factors that markedly affect fuel element life and may be limiting, including corrosion of the cladding, poisoning of the core by high cross section fission products and radiation damage.[1, 2, 3] The first two factors are relatively predictable on the basis of out-of-pile corrosion experiments and with the data and analytical techniques available to the nuclear physicist. Radiation damage is much less predictable and usually requires for its evaluation a series of in-pile, static capsule tests and ultimately dynamic or in-pile loop tests of the final fuel element design. There has been a great deal of this type of testing done, particularly capsule testing, over the past several years which has led to a considerable amount of data being evolved. These data are aimed primarily at evaluating specific materials for specific applications under particular conditions of temperature, flux and burn-up, so that it is often difficult to generalize on it. What is more, control of test variables is a major problem and post-irradiation inspection is complicated. In spite of all this, certain significant factors become apparent. Some of the most outstanding are:

1. The nature and properties of the fueled core of the elements.
2. The temperature of irradiation.
3. The burn-up.

4. Metallurgical factors, such as preferred orientation.

5. The strength of the cladding material under the test conditions.

The damage observed is the result of interaction among these factors; for example, the temperature determines the strength properties of a particular fuel element, so that for a given amount of fission gas produced, swelling may or may not occur depending on the test temperature. For high burn-ups, however, swelling may occur even at lower temperatures because of increased gas pressure. Some of these effects may be illustrated in the following.

Effects of Irradiation on Fuel Materials

It has been known for some time that metallurgical treatment has a profound effect on the dimensional stability of unalloyed uranium under irradiation.[4, 7, 8] Figure 20-1 shows the elongation of uranium as a function of burn-up for samples rolled at 300°C, at 600°C, and rolled at 300°C and water-quenched after 30 min. at 735°C and recrystallized at 575°C for 2 hours. Uranium rolled at 300°C has a higher degree of preferred orientation than uranium rolled at 600°C. Beta quenching reduces to a very low figure the preferred orientation resulting from prior rolling so that the growth is considerably less even at much higher burn-ups. The recrystallization treatment, which gave the material an equiaxed grain structure, had no marked effect on the growth under irradiation. The beta-treated specimens had a rougher surface than the rolled ones after irradiation. This is associated with the coarser grain size resulting from the beta quench. The temperature of irradiation was in the range from 50 to 220°C.

The effect of irradiation on the mechanical properties of uranium[5, 9]

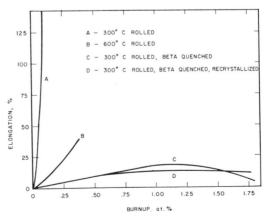

Figure 20-1. Effect of different fabrication treatments on the lengthwise growth of uranium under irradiation.[4]

is shown in Figure 20-2. The embrittling effects of the radiation are quite marked, the elongation decreasing from about 18 per cent to less than 1 per cent and the yield strength increasing from 38,000 to about 70,000 psi after 0.10 per cent burn-up. It is also interesting to note that the damage has been done to the room temperature mechanical properties in the first 0.02 per cent of burn-up.

Figure 20-3 shows the effect of postirradiation annealing on the room-temperature ductility of uranium specimens for various burn-ups to 0.10

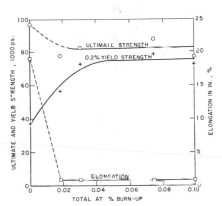

Figure 20-2. Effect of burn-up on the room-temperature mechanical properties of irradiated uranium.

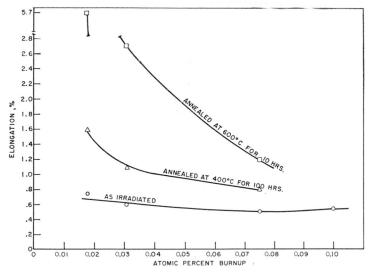

Figure 20-3. Effect of postirradiation annealing on the room-temperature ductility of uranium.

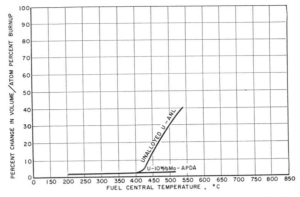

Figure 20-4. Effect of irradiation temperature on fuel volume.[10]

per cent at about 150°C.[6] It can be seen that there is a marked increase in ductility as the annealing temperature is increased, but that the effectiveness of the annealing is more marked at the lower burn-ups than at the higher one. The yield strength also exhibits a recovery upon annealing, from the high values shown by the as-irradiated material to values approaching unirradiated uranium. This improvement in mechanical properties is associated with the annealing-out of radiation-induced defects in the metal lattice. The greater the burn-up, however, the more permanent is the effect of the radiation and in no case does the recovery of elongation approach that of the unirradiated material (19 per cent in this case).

The information presented, so far, has been on unalloyed uranium irradiated at low temperatures. Because the economics of power reactors is so intimately tied up with thermal efficiency, it is desirable to be able to operate the fuel elements at as high a temperature as possible. The effect of irradiation temperatures on the behavior of various fuel materials is shown in Figure 20-4.[10] For unalloyed uranium, swelling starts at about 400°C and increases almost linearly. What might be done about this by alloying is also indicated in the figure. The Atomic Power Development data on U-10 % Mo alloy show no swelling to over 500°C and more complete data on this alloy, presented in a slightly different way, are shown in Figure 20-5.[11] The density decrease is limited to below 4 per cent for burn-ups up to about 2 a/o* and to an irradiation temperature of about 600°C. Beyond that, there is a substantial increase in swelling at the higher burn-ups although the 0.6 per cent burn-up samples have not decreased in density at a temperature as high as 700°C. It should be noted that these data represent several different metallurgical heat treatments, two fabrication methods, and different cladding thicknesses on the clad specimens.

* a/o = atomic per cent, w/o = weight per cent.

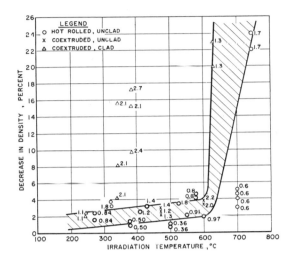

Figure 20-5. Per cent change in density of fuel elements as a function of irradiation temperature and burn-up.[11]

It can be generalized, however, that, for all burn-ups below 2 a/o, temperature must be kept below about 600°C to prevent severe distortion.

There have been a great many data taken on the irradiation of uranium metal and high uranium alloys in addition to those just presented, most of them showing similar trends. As to the mechanism of swelling, unalloyed uranium does not swell appreciably at temperatures below 350 to 400°C because the fission gas atoms diffuse too slowly to form molecular gas bubbles. They are apparently retained in the metal lattice. At the higher temperatures, diffusion and agglomeration are possible, however, and bubbles filled with gas are formed.[12, 13, 14] The effect of the alloying element is probably due largely to increasing the high-temperature strength so that greater gas pressures can be tolerated, although other factors such as phase stabilization and reduced diffusion rates are undoubtedly of importance.

One class of metallic fuel materials that is of unusual interest is that in which the core alloy contains plutonium or thorium. This is the ultimate type of reactor fuel where the fertile material, the fissionable isotopes produced by breeding, or both, are incorporated into the fuel element. The results of some capsule tests on Th-U alloys, irradiated at the Materials Testing Reactor by Atomics International, are shown in Figure 20-6.[10] The volume increases shown are relatively minor even at high irradiation temperatures, indicating a high degree of stability for this material.

Results of low-temperature (200°C maximum center temperature) tests at Argonne National Laboratory on Th-U alloys, varying from 0.13 to

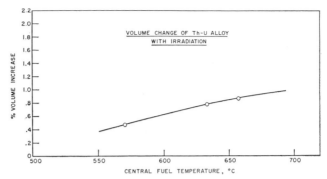

Figure 20-6. Irradiation of thorium-10 w/o uranium; 0.3 per cent burn-up of all atoms.[10]

5.53 w/o U and with burn-up as high as 4.4 a/o, also show only small dimensional changes.[6] These and other similar data lead to the conclusions that thorium, containing small amounts of uranium, is a fuel material of considerable promise. The reason for the stability of this system is associated with the fact that uranium is relatively insoluble in thorium so that much of the uranium is present as a dispersed phase. The thorium matrix is quite resistant to radiation damage so that the alloy is really a dispersion-type core material with most of the fuel isolated in discrete particles throughout the matrix.

Plutonium-uranium alloys have come under scrutiny from the radiation damage standpoint because of their application to fast breeder reactors.[3, 5, 6, 15-18] The results of some irradiation tests at Argonne on cast U-Pu base alloys are shown in Table 20-1. The maximum test temperature shown is

TABLE 20-1. DATA ON URANIUM-PLUTONIUM BASE ALLOYS

Composition (w/o)	Approx. Calc. Max. Temp. (°C)	Calc. Burn-up of All Atoms (%)	Volume Increase (%)	Density Decrease (%)
U-20 Pu-5 Mo	340	0.27	0.74	0.74
U-20 Pu-5 Mo	280	0.43	1.80	1.45
U-20 Pu-5 Mo	270	0.20	1.76	0.68
U-20 Pu-5 Mo	260	0.38	2.07	0.62
U-20 Pu-5 Mo	190	0.28	1.80	1.08
U-20 Pu-5 Mo	270	0.40	3.00	1.59
U-20 Pu-5 Mo	220	0.15	0.40	0.23
U-20 Pu-10.8 Fs*	310	0.92	2.63	1.29
U-20 Pu-10.8 Fs*	280	0.81	1.69	0.18
U-20 Pu-5.4 Fs*	520	0.40	2.37	0.91
U-20 Pu-5.4 Fs*	450	0.33	0.78	0.28

* Fission alloy.

520°C and the maximum burn-up is 0.92 per cent. It can be seen that dimensional changes are generally low with the maximum volume increase being 3 per cent. In addition to the small volume and density changes, it was reported that the surface finish of the specimens was good. Other cast alloys, containing up to 15 per cent Pu, were irradiated to higher burn-ups (1.7 per cent maximum for the 15 per cent plutonium alloy) and showed severe surface roughening. The best irradiation stability was found with the U-20w/oPu-5w/oFs alloy. The nominal composition of fissium is 4.6 w/o Zr, 25.9 w/o Mo, 39.8 w/o Ru, 6.5 w/o Rh, 23.2 w/o Pd.

Other plutonium alloys have been tested to some extent, notably Pu-Al and Pu-Al-Si. The metallurgy of the Pu-Al system is quite similar to that of the U-Al system where there is considerable background information available. Irradiation information on these materials indicates the following general results. There is an increase in hardness of core alloys containing 1.65 w/o Pu and 1.65 w/o Pu-12 w/o Si in aluminum, after burn-ups at two levels—25 and 50 per cent of the plutonium atoms. Visual examination showed no dimensional changes. These samples were clad in Zircaloy-2. Additional work on this system has led to the conclusion that fuel elements, with plutonium contents of 5 and 10 w/o, irradiated to essentially 100 per cent burn-up of the plutonium atoms, would not be significantly damaged by radiation. A loading of Al-Pu fuel elements has been fabricated at Hanford and irradiated in the MTR. The behavior of these elements will be discussed subsequently.

From the foregoing examples, plus a great deal of other information, it is clear that there are severe radiation damage limitations on uranium metal and uranium base alloys as regards such important operating factors as temperature and burn-up, which may result in swelling, distortion and loss of mechanical properties. For this reason, uranium oxide and other ceramic fuels have been carefully investigated over the past several years and have proved to be very advantageous from the standpoint of radiation stability. It should be noted, however, that the advantages inherent in oxide fuels are offset, to some extent, by certain intrinsic disadvantages, particularly the poor thermal conductivity of the ceramic and its relatively low uranium atom density as compared to metal. From the standpoint of economical power, it is not always clear which is the best approach to fuel element core material designations, but it depends on the reactor type and a host of detailed design characteristics. That is to say, there is no *best* material, at least not at this time, any more than there is any *best* reactor.

Very much, indeed, has been written and said about the radiation-damage resistance of UO_2 fuels, and the story is well known.[2, 3, 5, 6, 19-24, 31, 32] Extensive test programs have been carried out by Westinghouse Atomic Power Division and by Atomic Energy of Canada, Ltd., data from them

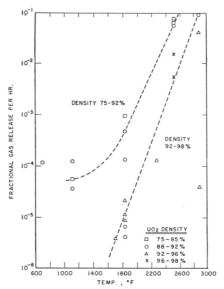

Figure 20-7. Fission-gas release from natural UO_2. (Data from Westinghouse Bettis plant, compiled by the Naval Reactors Branch.)

being reported elsewhere in this volume. For comparative purposes, with information on metals and alloys, however, some summary data are included here. Uranium dioxide is structurally isotopic, so that there is no evidence of the growth that is observed in uranium metal under irradiation. The major problems with using UO_2 as a fuel are associated with the effect of various fabrication and use factors on the release of fission gas from the matrix of the oxide.

The effect of the UO_2 density and the temperature on fission gas release from UO_2 is shown in Figure 20-7. The gas release increases with increasing temperature and it is greater at a given temperature for low-density oxide than for high-density material. This suggests that the gas is released by a solid state diffusion mechanism. At densities lower than about 92 per cent, the porosity is interconnected so that the rate of diffusion would be increased. The open lattice structure of the UO_2 would be expected to accommodate large quantities of fission products without appreciable distortion.

It is estimated that 1 to 10 per cent of the fission gases produced is released during irradiation, depending on density and temperature. If central melting occurs, 15 to 20 per cent of the gas is released. In a large number of radiation tests, with burn-ups ranging up to 6000 Mwd/ton and central temperatures beyond the melting point of UO_2 in a few cases, no significant dimensional changes were observed. Data from Bettis for some

TABLE 20-2. DATA ON HIGH BURN-UP ZIRCALOY-2-CLAD UO_2
FUEL ELEMENTS

Burn-up (Mwd/ton)	Calc. central Temp. (°C)	Dimensional Changes (in.)		Molten Zone, Diam. (in.)	Fission Gas Release, % Kr^{85}
		Diam.	Length		
14,000	2400	0	0	Not melted	
22,000	2750	+0.012	0	0.200	
25,000	2750	+0.015	0	0.230	
12,000	2200	0	0	Not melted	
6,430	1400	0	0	Not melted	0.25
12,400	2750	+0.009	+0.009	0.250	13.6
12,100	2750	+0.008	+0.015	0.275	15.3
6,100	2200	0	0	Not melted	
6,700	2400	0		Not melted	
14,400	2750	+0.002		0.290	
15,500	2750	+0.018		0.325	35.6
7,930	2400	0		Not melted	1.2

higher burn-ups are shown in Table 20-2. These data show the increase in fission gas release due to central melting. The dimensional changes that do occur appear to be a result of swelling due to the increased fission gas in the melted samples. There are many other factors to be considered in using UO_2 as a fuel. The effect of excess oxygen in the UO_2, for example, leads to a mass transfer effect within the cladding tubes and an unduly large release of fission gas. Cracking of the UO_2 invariably occurs, although this appears to be a thermal effect rather than one due to radiation. This results in a further decrease in conductivity, however, which may lead to melting and increased gas release. Grain growth near the center of the pellets may lead to substantially increased gas release, and sintering of the oxide at the center may result in circumferential cracks with a resultant further decrease of thermal conductivity. Many of these effects have been observed and many excellent references on them are available.[31, 32]

Other oxide core materials have been investigated, but to a much lesser extent than UO_2. Urania-thoria and urania-plutonia are of interest in the various breeder programs. Experiments on these have been conducted at several locations under a variety of test conditions and with samples of different compositions.[2, 3, 6, 15, 16, 19] This makes it difficult to generalize on the results, but it is safe to say that after irradiations up to 1.25 per cent of total metal atoms—in the case of ThO_2-UO_2 (up to 10 w/o UO_2)—although cracking of the pellets was observed, cladding distortion was slight at central temperatures below 2000°C. Data on UO_2-PuO_2 are even sparser, but a few radiations have been made with Pu depletions up to 35 per cent and temperatures as high as 600°C. Sintering effects and central void formation have been observed in the ceramic, but no cladding distortion or failure has manifested itself.

Uranium carbide and uranium-thorium carbide mixtures are materials that are being investigated because of their better thermal conductivity as compared to the oxides. Some samples have been irradiated and the preliminary data are of interest. Recent results obtained at Battelle Memorial Institute indicate that the fission gas release from uranium carbide is slightly less than that expected from recoil alone, about 0.1 per cent in this case.[25] This is for irradiations of about 2000 Mwd/ton burn-up and temperatures of about 770°C. The carbide test specimens are in the form of arc melted rods, 0.100 in. in diameter, cast to shape. Some slight growth, perhaps 1 or 2 per cent, was observed, but there is a question as to whether this occurred during irradiation or after, because of moisture pickup. Uranium carbide is hydrolyzable and tends to pick up moisture from the atmosphere, even without any radiation. After irradiation, the material cannot be handled in air and may even fall apart in a moist atmosphere. This increased sensitivity to moisture may be due to the formation of microcracks during irradiation, which exposes more surface area for hydrolysis. Uranium carbide powder is known to behave in this manner. Very little gross cracking or breaking up of the carbide was observed, much less than is normally seen in uranium oxide. The small amount of fission gas released and the small amount of cracking observed are encouraging signs for the use of this material. Unless a method is found to stabilize the compound against hydrolysis, however, its use would appear to be limited to liquid-metal or gas-cooled reactors.

With the exception of some brief comments in connection with the thorium-uranium alloys, nothing has been said about the radiation behavior of dispersion-type fuel elements. Inasmuch as these materials have been discussed extensively in Chapters 9 and 10, nothing further will be said on the subject except that, in general, fuel element core materials of this type are extremely resistant to the damaging effects of radiation.

Effects of Irradiation on Cladding

Turning our attention now from fuel element core materials to cladding materials, the major concern is with the effects of radiation on the mechanical properties and on the corrosion behavior. Fuel element life may be limited as much by either of these effects as it is by deterioration or dimensional instability of the core material. Irradiation generally has a hardening effect on most metals and alloys:[26] that is, the yield strength often increases markedly, accompanied by a reduction in the ductility. The ultimate strength also increases, but usually not to the same extent as the yield.

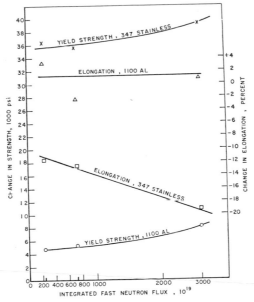

Figure 20-8. Effect of neutron irradiation on tensile properties of aluminum and stainless steel.

These radiation effects are not unlike the effects of cold-working on metals and they are due to essentially the same cause, namely, defects in the metal lattice. In the case of cold-working, the defects arise from fragmentation and lattice distortion while, under neutron irradiation, vacancies and interstitial atoms are generated by the action of the bombarding particles on the lattice. The effect of irradiation on some cladding materials is shown in Figure 20-8.[2, 20]

As expected, the yield strengths of both 1100 aluminum and 347 stainless steel are increased by exposure to radiation. The unirradiated strength values for these materials are 18,400 and 61,600 psi, respectively. Regarding elongation, the unirradiated value of 63 per cent for 347 stainless steel is reduced to about 43 per cent at the longest exposure. The 1100 aluminum, however, does not change significantly in this regard. The maximum radiation damage shown, 2600×10^{19} nvt, represents a substantial exposure. It is fortunate that the changes observed between 240 and 2600×10^{19} nvt are not marked.

The effects of irradiation on the tensile properties of some magnesium alloys have been investigated. After 10^{20} nvt at 40 to 50°C, no changes in the tensile properties were observed. Any radiation damage that occurred was apparently annealed-out at temperatures below 40°C. The recovery from radiation damage in Zircaloy-2 is shown in Figure 20-9.[5] This is

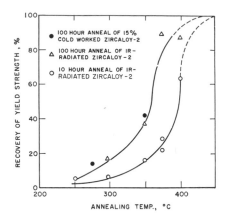

Figure 20-9. Yield strength recovery of irradiated Zircaloy 2. (Data from G. E. Hanford Works.)

comparable to the recovery from cold-working, the points lying along the same curve. As would be expected, the amount of recovery after 10 hr of annealing is somewhat less than that after 100 hr at any given temperature. Additional work on Zircaloy-2 has shown that the recovery from radiation hardening effects occurs at lower temperatures than recovery from strain hardening effects.

Long burn-up in a fuel element could be seriously limited if the corrosion resistance of a normally satisfactory cladding material were adversely affected by radiation. Some work has been conducted along this line over the years, not only on cladding metals and alloys but also on structural materials which might be in contact with the coolant under intense irradiation fields for long periods of time. A review of the recent literature is somewhat disappointing insofar as conclusive information is concerned.[2, 5, 6, 15-20] It appears that, in general, radiation does not have severe effects on the corrosion resistance of the common cladding materials to the usual coolants.

For example, it has been reported that, on the aluminum alloy M-388 (1 per cent Ni in 1100 Al), tested under dynamic corrosion conditions both in-pile and out-of-pile, there was essentially no difference in the corrosion rate.[19] That the corrosion rates obtained were high, as compared to static tests on the same material, is significant regarding the use of the material in a reactor, but the effects of in-pile exposure, as such, are not deleterious. Other data have shown that the corrosion rate of 1100 aluminum in hot water is enhanced by reactor irradiation.

The effect, however, is dependent upon the oxidizing power of the water rather than upon radiation effects in the material, and depends upon the purity of the water. Factors such as water purity, heat flux and water-flow rate are controlling, rather than changes in the metal structure. The corrosion of "Inconel" by fused fluoride fuel mixtures has been studied at Oak Ridge National Laboratory. Here again, the effects of radiation did not cause enhancement of the corrosion rates, results on in-pile and out-of-pile samples being essentially identical. As indicated above, any corrosion effects associated with irradiation of cladding materials appear to be secondary effects—changes in the coolant chemistry; hot spots in certain areas of the fuel element structure leading to excessive local temperatures and, hence, increased corrosion rates; erosion effects due to the rapidly moving coolant; and the like. This is fortunate in the sense that extensive corrosion testing can be carried on under out-of-pile conditions and the results translated to in-pile applications with a high degree of certainty.

In general, radiation damage to cladding metals does not limit the life of the fuel element, the damage to the core material being much more significant in this regard. On the basis of the work done over the past few years, pile exposure effects on cladding metals may be summarized as follows:

1. The yield and tensile strengths increase quite markedly and do so to a greater extent for annealed material than if the metal is cold worked. The yield-strength increase is usually greater than the tensile-strength increase.

2. The ductility is usually decreased, the change being greater for annealed material. The hardness usually increases.

3. The elastic constants are not appreciably affected.

4. The impact properties are affected in such a way that metals are often more brittle after irradiation. The ductile-brittle transition temperature may be raised by as much as 100°C in certain steels.

5. The creep rate and the fatigue strength are not affected very much but there are only limited data on these.

6. Changes in corrosion resistance are usually minor as indicated previously.

7. Minor changes have also been reported on diffusion coefficients, electrical resistivity, thermal conductivity, density, and damping capacity, but these would not be expected to limit fuel element performance or irradiation time in the reactor.

Effects of Irradiation on the Bond

The heat-transfer bond between fueled core and protective cladding is a vital consideration in the use of the fuel element. Radiation damage to the bond could conceivably result in bond failure, a decrease in thermal conductivity of the bond and subsequent overheating of the core material at the affected spot. Failure of the bond also leads to spaces where fission gases, normally retained in the core lattice, would precipitate out and cause blisters or even rupture of the cladding.

In metallic fuel elements, the bond may be of several types. If the core alloy and cladding are sufficiently similar with respect to thermal expansion properties and are compatible with respect to interdiffusion, a diffusion bond is satisfactory. This type of interface is found in fuel elements which are roll-bonded aluminum-clad with an aluminum-uranium alloy core or stainless steel-clad with a stainless-UO_2 core, as well as in many other systems. When diffusion bonds do not result in strong, stable interfaces, a braze layer or diffusion bonding layer may be used. The cladding of uranium with aluminum, using an AiSi layer or a thin layer of nickel at the interface, is an example of this type. When the core and cladding cannot be made into an integrated whole, such as in the case of stainless steel-clad uranium alloy, a sodium or NaK liquid-metal layer is used. In the latter case, a space is left above the liquid metal level so that fission gases coming off the core material do not form bubbles in the bonding layer which would be trapped between the core and cladding and impair the transfer of heat locally, causing hot spots.

When one considers what might happen under irradiation to bonds of the types described, several conclusions can be drawn. In the case of diffusion bonds and in those containing an intermediate layer, one would expect embrittling effects similar to what is experienced in the cladding material itself. The effects would be more pronounced, however, because the bond is in close proximity to the fuel material so that recoil of fission fragments, as well as neutron bombardment effects, would prevail. The deterioration of mechanical properties, coupled with the high thermal stresses due to large temperature gradients between core and surface and dynamic stresses due to cycling, could lead to bond failure. That is to say, a bond which behaves satisfactorily when tested by extremes of thermal cycling in an out-of-pile test may break because of a loss in ductility from neutron and fission fragment damage when irradiated.

Another possible effect at the interface is that of growth of a brittle interfacial layer. Increases of diffusion rates in metals have been noted under irradiation, as previously mentioned, and this could lead to the growth of intermetallic layers above and beyond that to be expected by temperature effects alone. The strength of an interfacial bond is known to be affected by its thickness. If increased diffusion rates result in the formation of thicker intermetallic layers, premature failure is a possibility, particularly under cyclic conditions. In the case of a liquid metal bond, contamination of the bonding layer by fission fragments might result in corrosion effects on either the cladding or fuel alloy, or both. Corrosion failure of this type could be a limiting factor in fuel element life. It is not

TABLE 20-3. UO₂ BONDING MATERIALS (WAPD)

Material	Temp Drop in a 0.001-in. Bonding Gap at 750°F (°F)
He	288
Xe + Kr	5400
Steam	1490
50% He + 50% (Xe + Kr)	900
Hydrogen	278
Lead	2.1

apparent whether the bonding problems outlined above have actually been a limitation on fuel element operation to date. Relatively few bonding failures have been reported and it is always difficult to know if the defects existed prior to irradiation.

In terms of the very high burn-up requirements for economical power, however, bonding damage can certainly become a limitation of considerable consequence and should, therefore, be considered. Bonding in ceramic core fuel elements would be affected in a somewhat different fashion. Helium gas is the usual type of bond in UO₂ elements and would not be expected to be affected by radiation directly. The helium acts as a heat-transfer medium and its ability to transfer heat has a substantial effect on the center temperature of the oxide.

Table 20-3, based on WAPD* data, lists the effects of different materials on the temperature drop in a 0.001 in. bonding gap at 750°F.[19] It should be noted particularly that contamination of helium with the fission product gases xenon and krypton has quite a substantial effect on the temperature drop across the gap. This leads to the conclusion that fission gas release from the oxide has an effect above and beyond the internal pressure that it may exert at elevated temperature. An increase in ΔT across the gap will affect the central temperature to some extent, possibly causing melting and further fission gas release for the same surface heat flux. The advantage of using a lead bond as compared to helium can also be seen, the temperature drop across a lead layer being only 2°F. The interaction of lead with various cladding materials may, however, limit its use. Steam contamination which might arise from cladding defects in water-cooled reactors would also be expected to have an adverse effect on the temperature drop.

Effects of Irradiation on Complete Fuel Element

It now remains but to assemble the fueled core, the cladding and the bond into a fuel element and to review some examples of what happens to it under irradiation. Many capsule and loop tests have been conducted on

* Westinghouse Atomic Power Division.

(Courtesy of Argonne National Laboratory)

Figure 20-10. Views of Borax-IV fuel element: top, subassembly; bottom, assembly.

samples of clad fuel elements in order to evaluate the combination of materials before a loading is actually manufactured and run in a reactor. The information to follow is based on both sample tests and reactor loads of clad and bonded fuel elements, but in all cases it represents a version of a complete fuel element and not merely a component of one.

The interest in plutonium-bearing fuels and in those containing thorium is considerable at this time for the reasons mentioned earlier. Recent information[27] on the test of an MTR loading of aluminum-clad, aluminum-plutonium-alloy core fuel elements is encouraging from the standpoint of radiation damage. The elements contained 145 g of plutonium per element (core alloy about 14 w/o Pu) of which about 19 g were burned out. This corresponds to a plutonium depletion of about 13 per cent. Under these conditions, no radiation damage was observed upon visual examination and nothing unusual happened during the course of the cycle. These elements were removed because of decreased reactivity, and some of them will soon be replaced in the reactor and burned up further to evaluate them at higher plutonium depletions. It is planned to take the elements to about 60 per cent burn-up although it is thought that even higher burn-up than that could be tolerated without distortion. The fuel elements are of the box-type MTR design, the plutonium fuel being incorporated within aluminum cladding plates.

One fuel assembly has recently been removed from the Borax-IV experimental reactor at Argonne National Laboratory.[28] Figure 20-10 is an illustration of the Borax-IV fuel element.[3] The core material is 6.35 w/o UO_2-ThO_2, the UO_2 being 90 per cent enriched. The cladding is M-388 aluminum alloy and a lead bond is used. The ceramic pellets are 0.225 in. in diameter. The fuel element, which had been removed, showed no damage to the ceramic pellets, and the rest of the loading is continuing to operate in the reactor. The burn-up has not yet been calculated, but some very recent information[28] on MTR capsule tests of Borax-IV fuel rod samples showed no dimensional changes when tested under the conditions shown in Table 20-4. While these data are preliminary, they do indicate the long burn-up stability in this type of ceramic fuel element. The results to date are certainly most encouraging.

TABLE 20-4. RECENT DATA ON BORAX-IV FUEL ROD CAPSULE TEST

U^{235} atoms fissioned	47%
Total atom burn-up	0.92 a/o
Equivalent to:	20,614 Mwd/ton
Results	No dimensional changes observed
Material	6.36 w/o UO_2-ThO_2 pellets, lead-bonded; UO_2 enrichment—90%

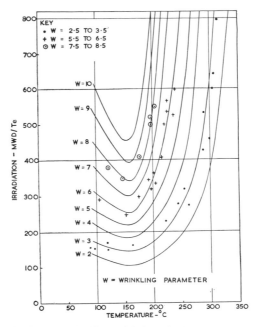

Figure 20-11. Variation of wrinkling with irradiation and temperature.[29]

A considerable amount of experience has been obtained in the operation of natural uranium, air- or gas-cooled reactors at Windscale and Calder Hall, and data on fuel element behavior have recently been made available.[29] The early Windscale fuel elements, which were machined from cast material and canned in aluminum, exhibited a surface roughening called "wrinkling," which was associated with the large grain size of the cast uranium. The dependence of wrinkling on burn-up and temperature is shown in Figure 20-11. The wrinkling parameter is measured from the radiographs of the irradiated elements and is the sum of the deviations from the mean diameter of the bar measured at 1-cm intervals along the length. The lower numbers represent slight wrinkling; the higher the number, the more severe the condition. Higher burn-up leads to more severe wrinkling and the wrinkling is most serious in the temperature range of 150 to 200°C. Elimination of wrinkling in later fuel elements, including those used in the Calder Hall reactors, was accomplished by quenching from the β-phase to give a fine grain size in the uranium.

Statistics on fuel element failures show that at Windscale less than 0.1 per cent of the total number of elements irradiated have failed. In Calder Hall, where experience is more limited, 13 out of about 30,000 elements have failed or are suspect. Several different types of failures have been observed,

Figure 20-12. Can failure due to fuel growth.[29]

including the development of large wrinkles at the ends of the slugs which pushed off the end cap; thinning of the can wall during manufacturing and subsequent fracture due to strains arising from operation; the formation of the intermetallic UAl_3 at the hottest areas of the reactor and subsequent penetration and embrittlement of the can wall; and growth of the uranium relative to the can wall causing the end of the can to be pushed off. An example of this last type of failure is shown in Figure 20-12. Very little wrinkling has occurred in these cases, but a small amount of radiation growth has taken place. Apparently, all of the dimensional change in the uranium was taken up at a local weak point in the can until rupture occurred.

Some very recent irradiation data on fueled graphite spheres have been obtained by Sanderson and Porter in connection with their gas-cooled power reactor program. The radiation testing and evaluation, which was done at Battelle Memorial Institute, took 5 months and was completed at the beginning of 1959. Table 20-5 shows some of the information covering these tests.[30] Two different methods of fabrication were used to prepare the dispersions of fuel in graphite. The admixture type, prepared at National Carbon, was made by pressing the mixture of powders, and the impregnated type, prepared at Sylvania-Corning, was made by infiltrating porous graphite with a solution of uranium nitrate and then driving off the water and calcining the nitrate to UO_2. The spheres did not crumble after irradiation and there was an increase of hardness at the surface. No

TABLE 20-5. RECENT IRRADIATION DATA ON FUELED GRAPHITE SPHERES[30]

	Impregnated (Sylcor)	Admixture (Nat'l. Carbon)
Fuel particle size, μ	~1	~100
Irradiation temp., °F	1200	1200
U^{235} burn-up, %	$1\frac{1}{2}$	$1\frac{1}{2}$
Fissions/cc of matrix	5.8×10^{18}	5.8×10^{18}
Volume shrinkage, %	1	$\frac{1}{4}$
Surface hardness	increased	increased
Compressive strength	increased	increased
Impact strength	not impaired	not impaired

NOTE: After tumbling abrasion tests, both types showed no spalling, cracking or peeling of the surface.

spalling, cracking or peeling of the surface was observed. The impact strength was not impaired and the compressive strength increased slightly. The burn-up of $1\frac{1}{2}$ per cent of the U^{235} is low, but the calculated number of fissions per cc of matrix is high for uranium-graphite fuel materials. All in all, the data are very encouraging, although more information on fission gas release, longer burn-ups and the like still remain to be determined.

There is much more to be said about the behavior of fuel elements under irradiation. This subject, by itself, has been the sole topic of discussion in week-long conferences in the past and there will undoubtedly be other such meetings in the future. Although a complete review is beyond the scope of the present chapter, certain conclusions can be drawn from the information presented which can be summarized as follows:

1. A factor of considerable importance in the economical production of power in a reactor is the degree to which fuel elements can be burned up before they have to be removed because of radiation-induced damage.

2. As would be expected, the major radiation damage problems in achieving long burn-up are associated for the most part with the fueled-core portion of the element, rather than with the cladding or the bond. The difficulties have to do primarily with the ability of the core to retain fission gases and to resist distortion, especially at high operating temperatures.

3. Uranium metal and alloys have desirable features for use in fuel elements, but they also have certain limitations. There are two different methods by which uranium and its alloys distort under irradiation: at lower temperatures by a growth mechanism associated with preferred orientation of the crystal structure; and at higher temperatures by a volume increase caused by the pressure of precipitated fission gas within the structure.

4. Uranium oxide has excellent dimensional stability, but its poor thermal conductivity and low uranium-atom density impose certain limitations on its use.

5. Radiation information on the use of plutonium as a fuel and on combinations of uranium and thorium alloys and ceramics is encouraging insofar as radiation damage behavior is concerned. This is of utmost importance because it establishes the applicability of materials made in, or to be used as, fuel elements in a breeder reactor. It thus becomes possible to realize a huge source of power above and beyond that available from natural uranium, at least from the standpoint of the satisfactory use of these materials in a reactor.

6. New materials for new reactor concepts are encouraging from the radiation damage standpoint. While it is true that the data are preliminary, the use of materials such as uranium carbide gives promise of fuel elements which will exceed in performance those presently being used.

7. While, at the present time, radiation damage effects usually limit the life of the fueled core of the element, longer burn-up core materials may impose limitation of the life of the cladding or the bond. This may be true not only from the standpoint of radiation damage, but from the corrosion and strength standpoint, as well.

8. Finally, the experience to date on radiation damage failure during reactor operation has been good. This is, without doubt, due to the careful testing that is carried out before a new type of fuel element is actually used. With the requirements for increased temperature and burn-up that are in store, this type of evaluation will have to be carried out for many years to come, despite the high costs involved. There is still no substitute for a use test.

References

1. ASTM Special Technical Publication No. 208, Second Pacific Area Meeting Papers, Symposium on Radiation Effects on Materials, Vol. 1.
2. U.S. Atomic Energy Comm. papers prepared for Radiation Effects Review Meeting, Chicago, July 31–Aug. 1, 1956. Report TID-7515, "Radiation Effects on Materials."
3. U.S. Atomic Energy Comm. Fuel Elements Conference, Paris, Nov. 18–23, 1957, AEC Report TID-7546.
4. Kittel, J. H., and Paine, S. H., "Effect of Irradiation on Fuel Materials," Second United Nations International Conference on The Peaceful Uses of The Atomic Energy, Geneva (1958) P/1890.
5. "Reactor Core Materials," **1** (2) (May 1958), prepared by Battelle Memorial Inst. for U.S. Atomic Energy Comm.
6. "Power Reactor Technology," **1** (2) (February 1958), prepared by General Nuclear Eng. Corp. for U.S. Atomic Energy Comm.
7. Zaimovskii, A. S., *et al.*, "Influence of Uranium Structure and Properties upon its Behavior Under Irradiation," Second United Nations International Conference on The Peaceful Uses of Atomic Energy, Geneva (1958) P/2191.
8. Hasiguti, R. R., "Fundamental Researches in Physical Metallurgy of Nuclear Fuels in Japan," Second United Nations International Conference on The Peaceful Uses of Atomic Energy, Geneva (1958) P/1324.

9. Seeger, A. K., "On the Theory of Radiation Damage and Radiation Hardening," Second United Nations International Conference on The Peaceful Uses of Atomic Energy, Geneva (1958) P/998.

10. Hayward, B. R., and Bentle, G. G., "Effect of Burnup on Metallic Fuel Elements Operating at Elevated Temperature," Second United Nations International Conference on The Peaceful Uses of Atomic Energy, Geneva (1958) P/617.

11. Leeser, D. O., *et al.*, "Radiation Stability of Fuel Elements for the Enrico Fermi Power Reactor," Second United Nations International Conference on The Peaceful Uses of Atomic Energy, Geneva (1958) P/622.

12. Dienes, G. J., and Damask, A. C., "Radiation Enhanced Diffusion in Solids," Second United Nations International Conference on The Peaceful Uses of Atomic Energy, Geneva (1958) P/612.

13. Barnes, R. S., and Greenwood, G. W., "The Effect of Gases Produced in Reactor Materials by Irradiation," Second United Nations International Conference on The Peaceful Uses of Atomic Energy, Geneva (1958) P/29.

14. Willis, A. H., "Sources of Fuel Element Instability," Second United Nations International Conference on The Peaceful Uses of Atomic Energy, Geneva (1958) P/616.

15. "Power Reactor Technology," **1** (1) (Dec. 1957), prepared by General Nuclear Eng. Corp. for U. S. Atomic Energy Comm.

16. "Reactor Core Materials," **1** (1) (March 1958), prepared by Battelle Memorial Inst. for U. S. Atomic Energy Comm.

17. *Ibid.*, **1** (3) (Aug. 1958).

18. *Ibid.*, **1** (4) (Nov. 1958).

19. "Power Reactor Technology," **1** (3) (June 1958) (see Ref. 15).

20. *Ibid.*, **1** (4) (Sept. 1958).

21. Chalder, G. H. *et al.*, "The Fabrication and Properties of Uranium Dioxide Fuel," Second United Nations International Conference on The Peaceful Uses of Atomic Energy, Geneva (1958) P/192.

22. "Experience at Chalk River of Irradiated Uranium Oxide," Report ⚡UK/C 6/114, Atomic Energy of Canada, Ltd., Sixth UK/Canada Tech. Conf., Oct. 1957.

23. Westinghouse Elec. Bettis Plant, "Resume of Uranium Oxide Data. VII," U. S. Atomic Energy Comm. Report WAPD-PWR-PMM-491 (Sept. 1956).

24. *Ibid.*, IX., Report WAPD-TM-44 (Mar. 1957).

25. Private communication from B. Dunnington of Battelle Memorial Inst.

26. Makin, M. J. *et al.*, "The Mechanical Properties, Embrittlement and Metallurgical Stability of Irradiated Metals and Alloys," Second United Nations International Conference on The Peaceful Uses of Atomic Energy, Geneva (1958) P/80.

27. Private communication from MTR operating personnel.

28. Private communication from J. Schumar and others at ANL.

29. Eldred, V. W. *et al.*, "Fuel Element Behavior under Irradiation," Second United Nations International Conference on The Peaceful Uses of Atomic Energy, Geneva (1958) P/50.

30. Private communication from L. Stoughton of Sanderson and Porter.

31. Barney, W. K., "Irradiation Effects in UO_2," Second United Nations International Conference on The Peaceful Uses of Atomic Energy, Geneva (1958) P/615.

32. Robertson, R. F. S. *et al.*, "Behavior of Uranium Oxide as a Reactor Fuel," Second United Nations International Conference on The Peaceful Uses of Atomic Energy, Geneva (1958) P/192.

SPECIFICATIONS FOR ARMY PACKAGE POWER REACTOR (APPR-1) FUEL AND CONTROL ROD COMPONENTS*

R. J. Beaver, R. C. Waugh and C. F. Leitten

Oak Ridge National Laboratory, Oak Ridge, Tennessee

I. Summary

Final specifications are presented on the stainless steel fuel and control rod components developed for service in the 10-Mw Army Package Power Reactor, a heterogeneous, pressurized-water unit designed for producing power in remote locations. The specifications cover design and material requirements as well as the fabrication procedures developed and adopted for manufacturing the extended-life fuel element and the enriched boron[10] absorber section of the control rod. Included in the procedural specifications are methods for preparing uranium dioxide-boron carbide-stainless steel cermet cores; techniques for roll bonding this material into composite stainless steel plates; procedures for brazing these plates into flat-plate fuel units and the finishing operations required to prepare the assembly for loading into the reactor core. Procedures are also described for manufacturing the absorber sections of the control rod. The procedural specifications are specific for manufacturing these components at ORNL, and merely represent a detailed guide in the event other fuel element fabricators are requested to furnish additional fuel elements and absorber sections.

II. Introduction

In 1953, the Metallurgy Division at ORNL initiated a program to develop reliable fuel elements and control rod absorber sections for the heterogeneous pressurized-water 10-Mw Army Package Power Reactor. This reactor was designed to produce economical power in remote locations. The minimum core life of one year was proposed, which necessitated a high uranium investment, a burnable poison, and corrosion resistant protective cladding for the fuel and absorber sections. The materials were to be relatively economical and simple to fabricate. After a careful survey of possible materials for fuel elements, it was decided to utilize thin composite flat plates consisting of a fuel section containing uranium dioxide and boron carbide, in a low-carbon type 302B stainless steel matrix, and a protective cladding of type 304L stainless steel. Each plate was joined to side plates and separated to permit necessary cooling during reactor operation.

Because of the hafnium shortage, it was necessary to select another high neutron absorbing material for the absorber section of the APPR control rod. It was decided for this application to utilize enriched boron contained in an iron matrix of composite stainless steel clad plates. These plates were joined together to form a rectangular parallelpiped.

---

* These specifications were originally published as AEC report No. ORNL 2225 (Aug. 7, 1957).

As a result of the development work, specifications were prepared for manufacturing APPR-1 fuel elements and absorber sections. The stationary fuel unit consists of 18 flat composite plates separated a nominal distance of 0.134-in. by brazing into grooved stainless steel side plates. End adapters are welded to both ends of the unit for positioning in the reactor. Each fuel plate consists of a 0.020-in. thick fuel core containing 28.62 g U^{235}, in the form of uranium dioxide; 0.0268 g B^{10}, in the form of natural boron carbide; and 99.80 g of low-carbon type 302B stainless steel. The core is prepared by powder metallurgy processing and is clad by roll-bonding with type 304L stainless steel. The final cladding-core-cladding thicknesses are 0.005-0.020-0.005-in., respectively. The fuel element of the control rod is similar in design except that the fuel unit is limited to 16 plates; has 9 cobalt-bearing flux suppressor combs at one end; and a handle instead of end adapters. Each fuel bearing section in the composite plate of this unit contains 26.11 g U^{235} in the form of uranium dioxide; 0.0245 g B^{10} in the form of natural boron carbide; and 91.56 g of low-carbon type 302B stainless steel.

The absorber section of the control rods consists of four 0.155-in. thick composite plates, clad with type 304L stainless steel. These plates are welded together to form the sides of a rectangular parallelpiped. Each plate contains a 0.090-in. thick core of elemental boron in an iron matrix, prepared by powder metallurgy processing. The boron is enriched in B^{10} at the 93 per cent level. The core in each plate contains 14.7 g of B^{10}.

The specifications include the required quantities of the critical material and procedures for manufacturing the fuel and absorber sections for the reactor. The procedural specifications are based not only on past development work but also on experience in manufacturing 100 enriched APPR-1 fuel elements and 15 absorber sections.

III. Stationary Fuel Element

A. *Number of active plates per fuel element*

1. Short plates	16	
2. Long plates	2	

B. *Fuel content*

1. U^{235}, g	515.16		
2. Tolerances			
a. Weighing	±0.03%		
b. Enrichment assay	±0.10		
c. Ratio of U_T/UO_2	±0.25		
d. Handling	−0.19		
Totals		+0.38%	−0.57%
3. Enrichment	Highly enriched		
4. UO_2, approx. g	631.66		

C. *Boron¹⁰ content, g*   0.447

1. Tolerance			
a. Natural boron in boron carbide (75.9%)	±1.00%		
b. Weighing	±0.30%		
c. Possible losses during sintering	−3.50		
d. Handling	−0.20		
Totals		+1.30%	−5.00%

IV. Control Rod Fuel Element

A. *Number of active plates per fuel element*
    1. Short plates   14
    2. Long plates   2
B. *Fuel content*
    1. U^{235}, g   417.76
    2. Tolerances
        a. Weighing $\pm 0.03\%$
        b. Enrichment assay ± 0.10
        c. Ratio of U_T/UO_2 ± 0.25
        d. Handling -0.19

            Totals $+0.38\%$ -0.57%
    3. Enrichment   Highly
                            enriched
    4. UO_2 , approx. g   512.23
C. *$Boron^{10}$ content, g*   0.363
    1. Tolerances
        a. Natural boron in boron carbide $\pm 1.00\%$
           (75.9%)
        b. Weighing $\pm 0.30\%$
        c. Possible losses during sintering -3.50
        d. Handling -0.20

            Totals $+1.30\%$ -5.00%

V. Control Rod Absorber Sections

A. Number of plates per section—4
B. Total $boron^{10}$ content, g   56.4
    Tolerances $\pm 1.0\%$

VI. Material and General Design Specifications

A. *Composite fuel plates for stationary fuel element.*
    1. Uranium Dioxide Power—shall contain approximately 88 per cent uranium in which the U^{235} isotope has been upgraded to 93 per cent. Powder of a selected size (44 to 88 μ) shall be prepared as follows:
        a. UO_3 hydrate crystals shall be grown hydrothermally in an autoclave at 250°C for 10 hr from a UO_4 hydrate–10% uranyl nitrate aqueous solution.
        b. The UO_3 hydrate crystals shall be rinsed thoroughly to remove all traces of nitrate.
        c. The rinsed UO_3 hydrate crystals shall be fired at 1750°C under a hydrogen atmosphere during which the hydrated water is removed and the material is reduced to UO_2 .
        d. The material shall be screened and the 44 to 88 μ size range removed.
        e. Only material free of agglomerates, platelets, rods, and clinging surface fines shall be acceptable.
    2. Prealloyed Stainless Steel Powder—AISI low-carbon stainless steel type 302B such as supplied by Vandadium Alloys Steel Co., Latrobe,

Pa. in a size less than 149 μ and irregular particle shape. A typical chemical analysis for the powder used in APPR-1 shall be as follows:

C—0.07 w/o	Cr—18.22 w/o
Mn—1.00	Ni—8.52
S—0.012	Si—2.39
P—0.010	Fe—Balance

3. Boron Carbide Powder—supplied by Norton Chemical Company, screened to less than 44 μ size containing 75.9 per cent natural boron. Tolerances ±1.00%
4. Frame and Cladding Material—wrought stainless steel AISI type 304L.
5. *Material balance of fuel-bearing core section:*

Material	Weight (g)	Weight (%)	Uncertainty (%)
U^{235}	28.62		+0.38 −0.57
UO_2*	35.09	25.98	
B_4C†	0.1880	0.14	
B^{10}	0.02482		±1.30
SS	99.80	73.88	+0.01 −0.20
Totals	135.08	100.00	

* Based on 87.63% U in UO_2 ; 93.07% enrichment.
† Based on 75.9% natural boron in B_4C and 17.39 w/o B^{10} in natural boron.

6. *Heat transfer surface, cm^2:*
   a. Minimum   338.6
   b. Maximum   362.8
7. *U^{235} Distribution per plate, g/cm^2:*
   a. Minimum   0.079
   b. Maximum   0.085
8. *Homogeneity:*
   a. Uranium   ±2%
   b. Natural boron   ±20%
   c. The above values shall be based on the analytical results of six evenly spaced samples along the active core length of a prototype depleted APPR fuel plate prepared from materials which were blended and fabricated in accordance with APPR specifications.
   d. As a qualitative evaluation of homogeneity every 25th plate is to be radiographed and filed as a permanent record.
B. *Composite fuel plates for control rod fuel elements.*
   1. Uranium Dioxide Powder—shall contain approximately 88 per cent uranium in which the U^{235} isotope has been upgraded to 93 per cent. Powder of a selected size (44 to 88 μ) shall be prepared as follows:
      a. UO_3 hydrate crystals shall be grown hydrothermally in an autoclave at 250°C for 10 hr from a UO_4 hydrate-10% uranyl nitrate aqueous solution.
      b. The UO_3 hydrate crystals shall be rinsed thoroughly to remove all traces of nitrate.
      c. The rinsed UO_3 hydrate crystals shall be fired at 1750°C under a hydrogen atmosphere during which time the hydrated water is removed and the material is reduced to UO_2 .
      d. The material shall be screened and the 44 to 88 μ size range removed.
      e. Only material free of agglomerates, platelets, rods, and clinging surface fines shall be acceptable.

2. Prealloyed Stainless Steel Powder—AISI low-carbon stainless steel type 302B such as supplied by Vanadium Alloys Steel Co., Latrobe, Pa. in a size less than 149 μ and irregular particle shape. A typical chemical analysis for the powder used in APPR-1 shall be as follows:

C—0.07 w/o	Cr—18.22 w/o
Mn—1.00	Ni— 8.52
S—0.012	Si— 2.39
P—0.010	Fe—Balance

3. Boron Carbide Powder—supplied by Norton Chemical Company, screened to less than 44 μ size containing 75.9 per cent natural boron.
   Tolerances ±1.00
4. Frame and Cladding Material—wrought stainless steel AISI type 304L.
5. *Material balance of fuel bearing core section:*

Material	Weight (g)	Weight (%)	Uncertainty (%)	
U^{235}	26.11		+0.38	−0.57
UO_2*	32.01	25.87		
B_4C†	0.1717	0.14		
B^{10}	0.0245	73.99	+1.30	−5.00
SS	91.56		+0.01	−0.20
Totals	123.74	100.0		

* Based on 87.67% U_T in UO_2 ; and 93.07% enrichment.
† Based on 75.9% natural boron in B_4C, and 17.39 w/o B^{10} in natural boron

6. *Heat transfer surface, cm^2:*
   a. Minimum   316.3
   b. Maximum   331.0
7. U^{235} *distribution per plate, g/cm^2:*
   a. Minimum   0.078
   b. Maximum   0.082
8. *Homogeneity:*
   a. Uranium   ±2%
   b. Natural boron   ±20%
   c. The above values shall be based on the analytical results of six evenly spaced samples along the active core length of a prototype depleted APPR fuel plate prepared from materials which were blended and fabricated in accordance with APPR specifications.
   d. As a qualitative evaluation of homogeneity every 25th plate is to be radiographed and filed as a permanent record.
C. *Composite plates for control rod absorber section.*
   1. B^{10} Powder—supplied by Hooker Electrochemical Co., Niagara Falls, N. Y.
   2. Iron Powder—such as supplied by Plastic Metals Division of the National Radiator Co., Johnstown, Pa.: screened to −100 mesh particle size. A typical chemical analsyis for the iron powder used in APPR-1 is as follows:

C—0.03 w/o	P—0.005 w/o
O_2—0.26	Cr—0.008
Mn—0.002	Ni—0.020
S—0.015	Fe—Balance

3. Frame and Cladding Material—wrought stainless steel AISI type 304L.
4. *Material balance of core in absorber plate:*

Material	Weight (g)	Weight (%)	Uncertainty (%)
Enriched boron*	15.90	3.23	±1.0
Iron	476.99	96.77	

* Based on 95.56% total boron in material and 92.82% B^{10} in the total boron. Specifications require 14.1 g of B^{10} per plate.

5. Homogeneity of B^{10}. The above value shall be based on the analytical results of five evenly spaced samples along the length of an actual APPR-1 absorber plate prepared from materials which were blended and fabricated in accordance with APPR specifications.

D. *Side plates and combs.*
 1. Side plates—wrought Stainless AISI type 304L—supplied in U. S. standard gage 18 (nominally 0.050-in. thick).
 2. Combs—Haynes 25 Combs, (0.15% C–20% Cr–10% Ni–15% W–1% Si–1.5% Mn–2% Fe–balance Co). Thickness is nominally 0.050-in.

E. *End adapters.*
 Precision cast AISI type 304 stainless steel to 125 rms finish.

F. *Brazing alloy.*
 Coast Metals NP Powder Alloy, −150 mesh, such as furnished by Coast Metals, Inc., Little Ferry, N. J.
 The chemical analyses for the powder based on ORNL results were:

Ni—49.46 ± 0.90 w/o
Fe—26.58 ± 0.90
Si—11.30 ± 0.15

Mo—7.55 ± 0.50 w/o
P—3.98 ± 0.70
Mn—0.72 ± 0.10
Cr—0.41 ± 0.25

VII. Procedures for Manufacturing Fuel Elements

A. *Fuel core manufacturing.*
 1. *Calculation of material required in the fuel cores.*
  a. The U^{235} and the total uranium in the uranium dioxide varies from batch to batch. The U^{235}/UO_2 ratio shall be accurately determined for each batch of oxide prior to calculating the weight of UO_2 required to obtain the weight of U^{235} specified per plate.
  b. The natural boron in the boron carbide varies depending on the grade. The boron-bearing material shall be chemically analyzed and the percentage of natural boron determined for each batch of boron carbide received prior to calculating the weight of boron carbide required to obtain the weight of B^{10} specified per plate.
 2. *Weighing and blending.*
  a. The stainless steel, uranium dioxide, and boron carbide for each core compact shall be individually weighed in a 4-oz capacity jar which serves as the blending container. The weighing of the uranium dioxide shall be conducted inside an especially designed dry box.
  b. The jars shall be loaded into an oblique blender and blended dry for 2 hr. At this time approximately 0.1 g of dodecyl alcohol shall be added to each core mixture by means of an atomizer. The material shall then be reblended for an additional hour.

3. *Cold pressing.*

Pressing operations shall be conducted inside a dry box. The contents of each bottle shall be carefully transferred to the die cavity with the aid of a camel hair brush. A 50 per cent by volume carbon tetrachloride-stearic acid mixture shall be used as a die lubricant. The core shall be formed by hydraulically pressing at 33 tsi to a nominal size of 1.80 x 2.40 x 0.310-in., and 1.80 x 2.18 x 0.310-in. for the stationary and control rod cores, respectively.

4. *Sintering.*

A stainless steel sintering boat containing ten compacts shall be placed in a high temperature furnace and fired for $1\frac{1}{4}$ hr at 1177°C (2150°F) in a dry hydrogen atmosphere. The minimum dewpoint maintained shall be at least −60°F as measured by an Alnor Dewpointer.

5. *Coining.*

Each core shall be coined at 33 tsi with two load applications in the cold pressing die.

6. *Quality control and inspection.*

The materials weight loss which occurs during core manufacturing shall be determined by weighing each batch of ten cores. Loss in excess of that corresponding to 1 g of U^{235} per 18-plate assembly shall be cause for rejection. All cores shall be visually inspected for flaws.

7. *Storage.*

Acceptable cores shall be stored in a desiccator for subsequent use in the preparation of composite fuel plates.

8. *Billet assembly.*

  a. Material—AISI type 304L

  b. Dimensions:

   (1) *Frame for stationary fuel plate:*
   Outside sheared dimensions: $4\frac{7}{16}$ x $4\frac{1}{2}$ x 0.280 in.
   Inside punched dimensions: 1.856 x 2.430 x 0.280 in.
   Width of shoulders: $1\frac{1}{32}$-in.

   (2) *Cover plates for stationary fuel plate:*
   $4\frac{7}{16}$ x $4\frac{1}{2}$ x 0.065 in. as sheared

   (3) *Frame for control rod fuel plate:*
   Outside sheared dimensions: $4\frac{7}{16}$ x 4 x 0.280 in.
   Inside punched dimensions: 1.869 x 2.205 x 0.280 in.
   Width of shoulders: $2\frac{9}{32}$-in.

   (4) *Cover plates for control rod fuel plate:*
   $4\frac{7}{16}$ x 4 x 0.070 in. as-sheared

  c. The frame and cover pieces shall be degreased and brushed with a stainless steel wire wheel prior to billet assembly. The cover pieces shall be preplaced and attached by spot resistance welding prior to heliarc welding of the billet edges. The corners of the billet shall be left unwelded for a nominal length of $\frac{1}{4}$ inch.

9. *Hot rolling.*

The billets shall be preheated for a minimum of 20 min. in an open muffle purged with hydrogen. Furnance temperature shall be 1150°C (2102°F). The billets shall be rolled to plates, preferably on a heavy-duty mill such as 20-in. diameter x 30-in. face hot breakdown mill. The billets shall be reheated for a minimum of 2 min. between each pass.

After the final pass the plates shall be reheated for 2 min. and air-quenched. They shall be reduced from an initial billet thickness of 0.410 in. for the stationary fuel plate and 0.420 in. for the control rod fuel plate to 0.040 in., nominal which represents 90.3 and 90.5 per cent hot reduction, respectively. The reductions per pass, based on mil settings during the hot-rolling sequences, shall be 2 at 10 per cent, 1 at 20, 4 at 40, 2 at 30, and 1 at 20 per cent. The plate shall be rotated 180° about its longitudinal and transverse axes after each mill pass.

10. *Fluoroscoping of hot-rolled plate.*

The core of the hot-rolled plate shall be located by fluoroscopy and the plate marked for shearing of the excess peripheral stainless steel.

11. *Shearing of hot-rolled plate.*

The hot-rolled plate shall be sheared on a Power Squaring Shear to $3\frac{1}{2}$ in. wide and 22 in. long. The hot-rolled plate may be pickled in a 15% HNO$_3$–5% HF aqueous solution to remove oxide scale.

12. *Cold rolling.*

The plates shall be cold-reduced preferably on a 4-high mill similar to the type provided with a 5-in. diameter work roll and a 14-in. face. The plates shall be reduced to a finished thickness of 0.030 in. $\pm$ 0.001 inch. The reduction per pass shall be less than 5 per cent. The rolls shall be lubricated with SAE-90 weight oil. The lubricant shall be removed from the finished plate by degreasing.

13. *Marking and shearing.*

After cold rolling, the composite plates shall be fluoroscoped to locate the fuel core section. A template, designed to locate the dimensions shown in the fuel plate drawings, shall be used to center the fuel core within the plate. Markings shall be made on the inactive portions of the fuel plate to locate the edges to be sheared. The plates shall be sheared on a power driven shear, equipped with stops to shear to a $2^{15}\!/_{16}$-in. width. The plate shall be sheared $\frac{1}{16}$ in. over finished size along all ends. The mechanics of shearing shall be to shear along the one marked edge, sighting by eye, place this edge against the stop, and shear the opposite edge. The ends shall be sheared along the marks located during the previous fluoroscopic examination.

14. *Machining fuel plates.*

Twenty-five sheared fuel plates shall be stacked between $\frac{1}{8}$-in. thick aluminum plates in a jig and straddle-machined to the final dimensions specified. After straddle-machining to proper width, the plate shall be machined to the final length specified.

15. *Degreasing fuel plates.*

Each fuel plate shall be separately degreased. The degreasing shall be thorough and random plates from each batch of degreased plates are to be tested with absorbent paper such as Kleenex to insure that the plates are clean.

16. *Deburring fuel plates.*

The plates shall be placed on a flat surface, and the burr removed by filing.

17. *Inspection of machined plates.*

Each machined fuel plate shall be separately fluoroscoped and the dimensions inspected with template designed to locate maximum and minimum fuel core boundaries specified. Those plates in which an inactive edge width of less than 0.100 in. is indicated shall be radiographed and the inactive edge accurately measured. Those plates with inactive edge widths of less than 0.100 in. shall be referred to the authorities responsible for operation of the reactor for approval to be used in fuel elements. Those plates which do not lie within the length boundaries specified but are not more than ½ in. out of tolerance shall be radiographed and the dimensions accurately determined. These plates shall be referred to proper authorities for utilization as special cases. Acceptable plates shall be stored in a safe while awaiting further handling.

18. *Assembling of fuel plates for flatten-annealing.*
    The completely fabricated and machined plates shall be flattened-annealed. A mixture of 1 part by volume of Fisher Polishing, Grade No. 1, 5F Precisionite Levigated Alumina and 10 parts water shall be brushed on one side of each plate. The plates shall be allowed to dry in air for 15 min. and then shall be stacked together with the coated side of each plate adjacent to the uncoated side of its neighbor. The maximum number of plates per stack shall be 25. A batch shall be placed between two ⅜-in. thick stainless steel platens, containing bolt holes 5 in. apart along each longitudinal side. The fuel plates shall be centered with relation to the bolt holes and firmly pressed together by bolt pressure. The batch shall be placed in a drying oven at 150C° and allowed to dry at least 16 hr.

19. *Annealing of fuel plates.*
    The stacked batch of plates shall be placed in a controlled atmosphere furnace at a temperature not exceeding 300°C. The furnace shall be purged with helium of at least a −40°F dewpoint as measured with an Alnor Dewpoint Recorder. The flow conditions shall be sufficient to purge air from the furnace. The temperature of the furnace shall be increased at a rate not to exceed 200°C/hr until the temperature reaches 650°C. The furnace shall then be purged with purified hydrogen, with a minimum dewpoint of −80°F as measured with an Alnor Dewpointer. The flow conditions shall be sufficient to bright-anneal stainless steel. The furnace temperature shall then be increased, at a rate not to exceed 200°C/hr until a temperature of 1125°C has been attained. The batch shall be held at this temperature for 3 hr/in. of stacked plates, and furnace cooled to 300°C or less. Helium shall be purged through the furnace until all hydrogen has been exhausted from the furnace. The batch shall be removed from the furnace and permitted to cool in air, to room temperature.

20. *Cleaning of fuel plates after annealing.*
    The plates shall not be cleaned in a halogen containing acid. After removing the plates from between the platens, the alumina shall be removed by scrubbing in hot water. Care shall be exerted to insure that the plates do not become damaged. The plates shall be spaced in a holder to permit separation and dried thoroughly, either in air or in a drying oven.

21. *Storage of plates.*
    The plates shall be stored in a safe prior to assembling into fuel elements.

B. *Assembling of component parts into stationary fuel units.*

The parts shall be assembled in a 300 series stainless steel fixture which confines the parts during assembling and brazing. The fixture shall consist of a 1-in. thick base plate with skids attached to the bottom of the plate to allow ease of insertion and removal of the fixture in the furnace. "U" shaped supports, ⅞-in. thick and spaced 5½ in. apart, are rigidly fastened to the base plate. A comb holder is attached to one end during assembling, but removed prior to brazing. After assembling, a baffle such as a 3-plate shield, consisting of 0.030-in. thick plates spaced ⅛-in. apart, shall be placed on top of the supports to minimize temperature gradients.

The procedure for assembling the fuel unit in the fixture is given below:

1. Since flexibility is desired, the inside dimensions of the jig are designed oversize and shim plates are therefore required. Prior to assembling, the inside dimensions of the fixture shall be measured with a micrometer. The thickness of the shim plate shall be determined by subtracting from the inside dimensions of the fixture: (1) the width dimensions of the fuel plate; (2) 0.010 in. of clearance for braze metal in the assembly joints; and (3) 0.005 in. clearance in the fixture. These measurements shall be made prior to assembling each unit to insure that no appreciable dimensional changes in the jig occur after brazing cycles.

2. Two shim plates shall be positioned against each row of supports.

3. Two side plates shall be positioned against the shim plates with the grooved sides facing each other.

4. A comb shall be placed in the comb holder, which shall be attached to the rear of the fixture.

5. The bottom fuel plates shall be inserted in the bottom grooves of the side plates and through the teeth of the rear comb. The fixture shall be rotated clockwise 45° from the horizontal and the dry braze metal powder applied through a 0.035-in. diameter hole drilled into a stainless steel cone-shaped applicator and spread along the entire length of the side-plate fuel-plate joint.

6. The dry braze powder shall be cemented in position by applying "Colmonoy" Nicrobraze Cement through a 19-gage hypodermic needle attached to a 5cc syringe, and allowed to dry for at least 30 seconds.

7. A ¼-in. wide stripe of "Colmonoy" Green Stopoff shall be applied adjacent to the cemented braze powder along the entire length of the plate.

8. The fixture shall be rotated counter-clockwise back to the horizontal and through the opposite 45°. Operations described in item 6 shall be repeated for the opposite side plate-fuel plate joint.

9. The balance of the short plates shall be individually assembled in the manner described in items 5, 6, 7, and 8. Assembly shall proceed from bottom to top.

10. Prior to inserting the top plate, the front comb shall be attached to the unit. Care shall be exercised so that all 16 short plates are fully inserted to the root of the slot. The dry braze powder shall be applied at the 16 short plate-comb joints, and the bottom plate-comb joint. The powder shall be cemented in place with Nicrobraze Cement.

11. After assembling the top plate and applying the braze powder and cement to the top plate-side plate joints, the comb holder shall be removed.

12. The fixture shall be rotated 90° horizontally and braze powder applied at the top plate-rear comb and top plate-front comb joints and cemented into place with Nicrobraze Cement.

13. A ½-in. wide stripe of "Colmonoy" Green Stopoff shall be applied across the width of the grooved surface of each side plate, 1 in. inside the front and rear of the fuel unit.

C. *Assembling of component parts into control rod fuel units.*

These units shall be assembled in the same manner as described in "B", with the fllowing exceptions:

1. Nine Haynes 25 combs are placed at the rear of the fuel element. These combs are nominally 50 mils thick. The distance between the handles and the first comb is nominally 0.062 inch. The distance between the other combs are nominally 0.133 inch.

2. After assembling each plate, Coast Metals NP Braze Metal is applied on both sides of the top fuel plate—Haynes 25 comb joints.

3. After complete assembly the front comb is inserted through slots in the two inner long plates as the last operation and Coast Metals NP Braze Metal is applied on one side of all fuel plate-comb joints.

D. *Attachment of handles to side plates of the control rod fuel assembly.*

1. Prior to assembling, the handles shall be positioned on the grooved side of the control rod side plate and fastened by heliarc welding. The positioning shall be fixed so that the inside edges of the handles act as stops for the fuel plates during assembly.

E. *Brazing fuel assemblies.*

The procedure to be followed for brazing fuel assemblies is as follows:

1. Two calibrated chromel-alumel thermocouples shall be mechanically attached to front and rear of the fuel unit at the mid-plate location. Careful observations should be made during repeated cycles to ascertain necessity for new thermocouples.

2. The baffle shall be placed on top of the brazing fixture prior to insertion of the fixture into the furnace.

3. The fixture, containing the fuel unit with attached thermocouples, shall be inserted into the furnace at a location in which the thermal gradient from rear to front of the fuel unit does not exceed 10°C.

4. The temperature of the furnace upon insertion of the fuel unit shall not exceed 300°C.

5. The furnace shall be maintained under a helium purge during insertion of the fuel unit.

6. After insertion, the furnace door shall be closed and the temperature of the furnace increased at the rate not to exceed 200°C per hour. The helium purge shall continue until the furnace temperature has exceeded 650°C. The dewpoint of the entering helium is to be recorded on the Alnor Dewpointer and shall be at least −40°F.

7. After the furnace temperature reaches 650°C, hydrogen shall be purged through the furnace. The entering hydrogen should have a dewpoint of at least −80°F as recorded by the Alnor Dewpointer. The flow conditions of the hydrogen shall be sufficient to permit bright-annealing of stainless steel.

8. Temperature shall be recorded every 15 min. from the thermocouples on the fuel unit, as the unit is slowly heated. The thermal gradient

along the length of the fuel unit at 700°C shall not exceed 25°C. Dew-point measurements are to be recorded every 30 minutes.

9. When the fuel unit reaches a temperature of 1000°C, the thermal gradient shall not exceed 10°C. The dewpoint of the exit hydrogen at this temperature shall be at least −50°F as recorded by the Alnor Dew-pointer.

10. When the fuel unit reaches a temperature of 1100°C, the temperature shall be recorded every 60 seconds. The braze metal flows at 1130°C. When the fuel unit reaches this temperature care shall be exerted to insure that the time above 1130°C does not exceed 8 minutes.

11. After brazing, the fuel unit and fixture shall be furnace cooled to at least 300°C, prior to removal from the furnace.

12. If during the heating cycle one of the thermocouples loses calibration, the unit shall be permitted to heat to brazing temperature, and temperature measurements recorded with the remaining thermocouple.

13. Prior to removal of the fixture from the furnace, the furnace is to be purged with helium at a sufficient rate and length of time to insure that the furnace atmosphere will not contain a combustible mixture.

F. *Machining and attachment of end adapters to fuel unit.*

The following procedures may be used to machine stationary fuel elements and weld end adapters to dimensions shown in the assembly drawing.

1. *Premachining of the end boxes.*

The end boxes are purchased in the as-cast condition and are premachined as listed below:

    a. A special split mandrel mounted vertical on a milling machine shall be used to support the bored boxes while the extreme outside flat surfaces are straddle milled to 2.860 in. square.

    b. The above mill fixture shall be used to position the end boxes for machining the male end connection to the brazed fuel section. These shall be matched to the individual unit in order to insure a 0.002 to 0.003-in. clearance in the fuel unit.

    c. The inside of the boxes shall be given a hand polish to insure a 125 micro-in. surface finish.

2. *Premachining of the fuel unit.*

    a. The as-brazed fuel unit shall be mounted in parallel vises on a mill table to allow access to both ends. Both ends shall be squared without removing the unit. The cut shall be made with the side of a long end mill.

    b. The excess braze metal shall be removed from the inside of the ends by hand, thus removing interference of the braze metal to the insertion of the end box.

3. *Assembly of parts.*

    a. The end boxes shall be inserted in the fuel unit with $\frac{1}{32}$-in. welding clearance left between the end of the fuel unit and the shoulder of the end box.

    b. Alignment shall be checked with an indicator on the squared section of the end box and the center and edges of the side plates.

    c. Combination quench bars and clamp pads shall be placed approximately $\frac{1}{8}$ in. from the end of the fuel unit. A $\frac{1}{16}$ x 1 x 3-in. stainless strip shall be used under a "C" clamp over the side plates and a $\frac{1}{8}$ x

2 x 2½-in. aluminum strip shall be placed under the "C" clamp holding the ends of the fuel plates.

   d. Alignment of the end box with the fuel unit shall be rechecked after drawing the above clamps snug.

   e. The assembled unit shall be placed in a welding jig which clamps both the end box and the fuel unit to further insure the maintaining of alignment of the end boxes during welding.

4. *Welding.*

All welding shall be done by the heliarc method. No filler material shall ordinarily be used. In case of excess gap, a low-carbon type 308 stainless steel filler metal may be added. Attachment of end adapters shall be as follows:

   a. A tack weld shall be made at the center of one of the side plates.

   b. The opposite side plate shall be welded in its entirety.

   c. The tacked side plate shall be welded over its full width.

   d. The fuel plates shall be welded to the end adapter.

   e. The opposite end of the fuel unit shall be welded as described above.

   f. The welded assembly shall be measured for alignment as specified in stationary fuel element drawing.

5. *Final Machining.*

   a. The end boxes shall be turned between centers in an engine lathe.

   b. Small 4-jaw chucks shall be mounted on either end of the lathe to allow freedom in shifting for truing of the center line.

   c. The centering points "D" and "E", shown in ALCO Fuel Element Drawing, shall be established on the fuel unit.

   d. The unit shall be placed in the lathe between the two 4-jaw chucks with the inlet end box at the tailstock and shifted to bring the imaginary center at points "D" and "E" in true center.

   e. Beginning with the inlet box, the round sections of the end boxes shall be turned to 5 mils above finished dimensions.

   f. The alignment shall be rechecked prior to taking the finish cut to produce the 125 micro-in. finish desired.

   g. The fuel assembly shall be removed from the lathe.

   h. The fuel assembly shall be placed in parallel vises on the milling machine. The ends of the end boxes shall be milled to proper length and the length of the fuel element finished to specifications.

   i. The retaining hole for spring shall be located, milled and countersunk.

   j. The unit shall be removed from the milling machine and a hole drilled for positioning the pin. A drill jig shall be used to insure duplication of this pin from unit to unit.

   k. Excess weldment, burrs, etc., shall be removed.

   l. The alignment pin and spring shall be installed after final inspection of the fuel assembly.

G. *Final inspection of fuel elements.*

   1. *Stationary fuel element.*

      a. Subsequent to brazing and prior to attachment of end adapters, the fuel unit shall be inspected as follows:

         (1)*Plate spacings.*

            Each plate spacing shall be measured with an elliptical probe at four locations along the length: 2½, 10, 17, and 24½ inches. This inspection shall result in 64 measurements. The average deviation from the nominal 0.133-in. spacing between plates shall not exceed ±10 per cent. Measurements exceeding these tolerances shall be referred to responsible authorities.

(2) *Distance from top and bottom plates to the edges of the side plates.*

The distance from the top surface of the top plate and the bottom surface of the bottom plate to the edges of the side plate shall be measured with a depth micrometer. This inspection is to be repeated after the end adapters have been attached and final machining and cleaning operations have been completed. The nominal dimension shall be 0.033-in. with a deviation of ± 0.013 in.

(3) *Assembly width.*

The width of the fuel unit shall be measured at six locations along the length of the unit; namely, 1, 6, 11, 16, 22 and 26 inches, as well as two locations across the height of the unit. The inspection shall result in 12 measurements. The nominal measurement shall be 2.833 in. with a deviation of ±0.011 inch.

(4) *Cross-sectional perpendicularity and length camber.*

The fuel unit shall pass through a box 34-in. in length, with inner cross-sectional dimensions of 2.896 x 2.896 in.

b. The 2.250-in. diameter of the outlet end adapter and the 2.495-in. diameter of the inlet end adapter shall be inspected to facilitate subsequent concentricity inspection.

c. Rings shall be placed around the end adapters and the assembly placed in matched "V" blocks. Concentricity measurements shall be made with an indicator at points "D" and "E," shown in the fuel element assembly drawing, by rotating the assembly through 180°.

d. The element, with the attached end rings, shall be placed on "V" blocks which rest on a surface plate and the perpendicularity of surface Z to axis Y shown in the fuel element drawing, shall be measured with a square.

e. The nominal 29¼-in. length between shoulders of the end adapters, specified in the fuel element drawing, shall be measured with a 36-in. vernier caliper.

f. The nominal 33⅝-in. total length of the assembly, as specified in the fuel element drawing, shall be measured with a 36-in. vernier caliper.

g. The fuel assembly shall pass through a box 34-in. in length, with inner cross-sectional dimensions of 2.896 x 2.896 in., without interference.

2. *Control rod fuel unit.*

a. Subsequent to brazing, the fuel unit shall be inspected as fllows:

(1) *Plate spacings.*

Each plate spacing shall be measured with an elliptical probe at four locations along the lenth: 2½, 10, 17, and 24½-in. This inspection shall result in 64 measurements. The average deviation from the nominal 0.133-in. spacing between plates shall not exceed ±10 per cent. Measurements exceeding these tolerances shall be referred to responsible authorities.

(2) *Distance from top and bottom plates to the edges of the side plates.*
The distance from the top surface of the top plate and the bottom surface of the bottom plate to the edges of the side plate shall be measured with a depth micrometer. The nominal dimension shall be 0.072-in. with a deviation of ±0.013 inch.

(3) *Assembly width.*
The width of the fuel unit shall be measured at 5 locations along the length of the unit; namely, 1, 6, 11, 16, and 22 in., as well as two locations across the height of the unit. The nominal measurement shall be 2.612 in. with a deviation of ±0.011 inch.

(4) *Cross-section perpendicularity and length camber.*
The fuel unit shall pass through a box, 26 1/16 in. in length with inside cross-sectional dimensions of 2.650 x 2.650 in., without interference.

II. *Identification system.*

1. Since the uranium dioxide is received in batches in which the U/UO_2 ratio varies, each batch of cores manufactured shall be designated with individual "AP" numbers.

2. Each billet shall be marked with its identifying "AP" number.

3. After hot rolling, each plate shall be marked with its specific "AP" number, which it will retain until the mill scale is removed.

4. After the mill scale is removed from the plates and the plates sheared to size for cold rolling, they shall be numbered serially by stamping the number at one end only. The numbers for the control rod plates shall contain the prefix "C."

5. After fluoroscopic examination but prior to shearing, the cold-rolled plates shall be numbered serially by scribing identifying numbers with an electric vibrator, 1/8 in. inside the marks at each end of the plate which locate the sheared length. The number for the control rod plate shall be prefixed with the letter "C" and shall be scribed at the plate end which is opposite the end which butts the absorber section.

6. After the fuel elements have been brazed, numbers shall be scribed with an electric vibrator on each side plate. The numbers for the stationary fuel elements shall proceed serially from "S-1" to successively higher numbers. The numbers for the control rod fuel elements shall proceed serially from "C-1" to successively higher numbers.

7. After the end adapters have been attached and the fuel elements machined to final size, the number identified on the side plates shall be stamped in digits 1/2 in. high, on the top and bottom sides of the outlet end adapter, 1/4 in. from the fuel plate-end adapter joint.

I. *Cleaning.*

1. After inspecting the machined fuel element, the element shall be degreased. The fuel element shall be vibrated while clean dry air is blown through to remove possible machine shavings, dirt, etc. The element shall be again degreased.

2. After cleaning, the openings in the end adapters shall be sealed with masking tape to prevent any contamination of the inner parts of the element during storage and shipment.

VIII. Manufacturing Procedures for Absorber Sections.

A. *Core manufacturing.*

1. *Calculations.*

Enriched B^{10} and iron are specified as the powder materials for the absorber core. The required weight of enriched boron shall be calculated after each batch of boron received is analyzed for concentration of total boron in the material, and concentration of B^{10} in the boron. Each billet contains three stacked cores. Under this procedure, the materials required for each core shall be calculated on the basis of 4.7 g of B^{10} per individual core.

2. *Weighing and blending.*

The iron and boron powders for each individual core shall be weighed and placed in a 4-oz capacity jar, which serves as the blending container.

Weighing tolerances of the iron are ±0.010 g. Weighing tolerances of the boron are +0.003, −0.000 g. The materials shall be blended dry for 2 hr in an oblique blender.

3. *Cold pressing.*

The contents of each blended jar shall be placed in the cavity of a 2.08 x 2.27-in. die, leveled, and cold-pressed under 33 tsi. After pressing a quantity of cores, they shall be divided into groups of three and each group weighed. This weighing provides a base for ascertaining the average handling loss of each core prior to sintering.

4. *Sintering.*

Three groups of cores (9 cores each) shall be placed on a stainless steel boat and sintered under hydrogen for 1 hr at 1121°C (2050°F). The minimum dewpoint for the hydrogen shall be −60°F as measured with an Alnor Dewpointer. Upon completion of the sintering operation, each group of cores shall be weighed and the average sintering loss per core recorded.

5. *Coining.*

The cores shall be coined under 33 tsi with the core centered in the die cavity.

6. *Quality control and inspection.*

The materials weight loss which occurs as a result of handling during core manufacturing is recorded. If the loss per batch of 3 cores exceeds 2.0 g, the batch shall be rejected. All cores shall be examined for flaws and dimensions measured.

7. *Storage of cores.*

Cores not being processed into billets shall be stored in a desiccator.

B. *Plate manufacturing.*

1. *Frame material and dimensions.*

a. Material—AISI type 304L (0.03 max. C) stainless steel.

b. Dimensions:

(1) Outside length—4.297 ± $\frac{1}{32}$ in.

(2) Outside width—3.875 ± $\frac{1}{32}$ in.

(3) Inside length—2.297 ± 0.005 in.

(4) Inside width—2.108 + 0.005 − 0.000 in.

(5) Thickness—1.000 ± 0.002 in.

(6) Finish—125 rms

(7) An entrance hole, 0.225 in. in diameter, shall be drilled in the center of the 3.875 dimension listed in (2) above, $\frac{3}{8}$ in. through the edge. A corresponding 0.225-in. diameter hole shall be drilled perpendicular to and meeting the first hole to form a "T" and permit evacuation of the inner parts of the billet.

(8) Tolerances listed shall be held to prevent out-of-squareness of the inner and outer frame dimensions.

2. *Cover plate material and dimensions.*

   a. Material—AISI type 304L stainless steel.

   b. Dimensions:

   (1) Length—$4^{11}\!\!/_{16} \pm \frac{1}{32}$ in.

   (2) Width—$4\frac{1}{4} \pm \frac{1}{32}$ in.

   (3) Thickness—0.320 ± 0.005 in.

3. *Evacuation stem material and dimensions.*

   a. Material—AISI type 316 stainless steel tubing.

   b. Dimensions—0.225 in. OD x 0.175 in. ID x 10.0 in. long.

4. *Billet preparation.*

   a. All parts shall be thoroughly degreased and wire-brushed prior to assembling.

   b. The evacuating stem shall be inserted $\frac{1}{8}$ in. into the hole provided in the frame and welded with a type 18-8 stainless steel filler rod to the frame. The tube shall be purged with helium during welding.

   c. Three cores shall be stacked into the hole in the frame and the cover plates clamped to each side of the frame. The cover plates shall overhang the frame $\frac{3}{16}$ in. on all sides to facilitate welding.

   d. The cover plates shall be heliarc welded to the frame using two welding passes employing a type 18-8 stainless steel filler wire.

   e. The billet shall be leak-detected under water and 20 lb helium pressure for defective welds.

   f. The billet shall be evacuated to a final vacuum of less than 10 μ as indicated on a thermocouple vacuum gage. During this period, the billet shall be periodically heated to approximately 500°C to drive off any entrapped gases. The intermittent heating shall be continued until there is no further indication of loss in vacuum upon reheating.

5. *Hot rolling.*

   The billets shall be preheated in hydrogen for 90 min. at 1100°C in an open muffle. The billet shall be rolled on a heavy-duty mill, such as a 20 x 30-in. mill, at a 10 per cent reduction per pass as recorded by mill settings. Reheat times while the billet is more than 0.500-in. thick shall be 5 min., with subsequent 3-min. reheating times until the billet is reduced to 0.154 to 0.156 in. actual thickness. A single rolling direction shall be maintained, although the plate shall be rotated 180° about its longitudinal axis after every pass. As the thickness of the plate approaches 0.170 in., the core length shall be measured. Between passes, during reduction from 0.170 in. to finished thickness, the core length shall be measured with a tape to insure that the plates are not rolled oversize in length. After the billet is rolled through the last mill pass, it shall be annealed for 5 min. in the hydrogen-purged open muffle. After this annealing period, the plates shall be air-quenched to room temperature.

6. *Shearing of plates after hot rolling.*

Because of the "end effects" at the core ends, the end of the plate which was the leading end during rolling shall be carefully identified. The plates shall be sheared on a power-driven shear to 34-in. long, and within $1\frac{1}{2}$-in. of the trailing end of the core.

7. *Pickling of plates.*

The hot-rolled oxide shall be removed from the plates by cleaning in a 15% HNO_3–5% HF aqueous solution.

8. *Flattening of plates.*

Six plates shall be painted with a thin film of levigated alumina-water mixture, stacked between two $\frac{3}{8}$-in. thick stainless steel platens, tightly bolted together, and dried at 150°C for 2 hr. The pack shall be inserted in a protective atmosphere furnace, designed to bright-anneal stainless steel, held for 1 hr at 900°C, slowly furnace-cooled to 300°C removed from the furnace, and air-cooled to room temperature.

9. *Radiographing and marking of plates.*

Prior to radiographing, a stack of six plates shall be skim-cut along one edge to obtain a true plate edge reference. Two radiographs of the plates shall be taken; the first to obtain over-all dimensions, and the second to obtain a clear radiograph of the trailing end of the core. From these radiographs, measurements shall be taken and transposed to the plate to delineate the core on the surface of the plate in the following manner:

a. Measurements obtained from the radiographs shall be transposed to the plate and the core area delineated. Markings shall be scribed on the plate to locate sheared and finished plate boundaries.

b. The location of the trailing end of the core is critical since the engineering drawing specifies a minimum of $\frac{1}{4}$ in. of inactive stainless steel at this end. The end shall be located from the radiograph, and a mark scribed $\frac{1}{4}$ in. from the core end. From this scribed mark, a distance of $26\frac{1}{16}$ in. shall be measured to the opposite end of the plate, and a mark scribed. These marks shall represent the final machined plate length. Additional lines, $\frac{1}{8}$ in. outside of the machining marks shall be scribed at the ends and along the edges. These lines shall represent the sheared length and width dimensions. An identifying number shall be scribed at the leading end of the plate which contains the nominal 5-in. length of inactive stainless steel.

10. *Shearing of plates prior to machining.*

In shearing to width dimensions, the plate shall be clamped to the shear table with three vises spaced at equal intervals along the plate length. The plates shall be sheared in a power-driven shear suitable for shearing $\frac{3}{16}$-in. thick stainless steel. It shall not be required to clamp the plate ends prior to shearing.

11. *Machining to final size.*

Each plate shall first be machined to final width dimensions. One side of the plate shall be clamped on the mill table and securely locked into position. The opposite side shall be machined to the machining marks. The clamps shall be removed without disturbing the plate, and the opposite side of the plate clamped and securely locked into position. The remaining sheared side shall be machined to the machining marks in the manner as described.

The end of the plate at which the minimum ¼-in. active stainless end is specified is individually machined to the scribed machining mark. In machining to final specified length, six plates shall be stacked and the opposite end machined.

12. *Degreasing and deburring.*

The plates shall be degreased and deburred by placing the plate on a flat plate and mechanically filing at a 45° angle along all edges.

13. *Final inspection of plate.*

All finished machined plates shall be radiographed to delineate the inactive stainless steel in which the core is encased. Measurements shall be made from the radiographs to determine acceptance or rejection. Plates with less than 0.080-in. inactive stainless at any point along the edges shall be rejected. Plates with less than ³⁄₁₆ in. at the end specifying a nominal ¼-in. inactive stainless shall be rejected.

C. *Manufacturing of the absorber section.*

1. All plates shall be degreased prior to assembling.

2. A graphite block, 2.307 in. square and 26¹⁄₁₆ in. long shall be used to position the plates to meet specified inner dimensions for the absorber section. A ½-in., 45° cut shall be machined from all corners of the block to prevent contact of graphite and stainless steel during subsequent welding.

3. Assembling and welding procedures.

   a. Plate No. 1 shall serve as the base plate and lie on a flat surface plate.

   b. The graphite block shall lay on plate No. 1. The right side of the block shall lie approximately 0.155 in. inside the base plate.

   c. Plate No. 2 shall be placed perpendicular to the surface plate, with the edge butting the surface plate and its inner surface butting the edge of plate No. 1.

   d. Plate No. 3 shall be placed perpendicular to plate No. 1 with its edge butting the inside of plate No. 1.

   e. Plate No. 4 shall be placed on top of the graphite block, with its right edge butting the inner surface of plate No. 3 and its inner surface butting the edge of plate No. 2.

   f. The plates shall be assembled with all identifying plate numbers at the same end of the absorber section.

   g. The assembly shall be rigidly held together with 5 in. "C" clamps. After clamping, the end of the section with the ¼-in. nominal inactive stainless shall be squared. The width and height of the box shall be measured with a micrometer. If dimensions are less than 2.600 in., a shim shall be placed at the proper joints to increase the dimensions to 2.619 ± 0.010 inches.

   h. At this time, only the joints between plates No. 1 and 2 and No. 1 and 3 shall be heliarc welded. These joints shall be first tack welded at the corners. Three-inch long welds shall be initiated from the corners inward along the length, and staggered from opposite corners until a continuous weld has been produced along the entire joint. No filler rod shall be used.

   i. After cooling to room temperature, the "C" clamps shall be removed from the assembly, and the top plate and graphite jig removed.

   j. A second graphite jig shall replace the previous jig. The two wedge-shaped parts fit together to form a rectangular block with over-all dimensions of 1.80 x 2.307 x 30 inches. The split block wedge design is to permit ease of removal after welding. Since the width of the block is $\frac{1}{2}$ in. narrower than the first block, it shall be centered in the partially welded absorber box with a $\frac{1}{4}$-in. clearance between the sides of the graphite and the sides of the absorber plates.

    k. The top plate shall be placed on top of the graphite block with its right edge butting the inner surface of plate No. 2 and its inner surface butting the edge of plate No. 3. It shall be secured with 5-in. "C" clamps.

    l. The plate shall be heliarc welded to the two side plates in the manner described in item (h) above.

    m. While the absorber box is still warm, the clamps shall be removed and split graphite block removed by tapping the wedge.

4. *Final machining.*

    a. In accordance with the absorber assembly drawing, $\frac{3}{8}$-in. diameter holes shall be drilled through the solid stainless steel sides of the absorber box, the holder pin driven through, and heliarc welded to the sides of the box.

    b. The edges of the box shall be rounded to a radius of approximately $\frac{1}{32}$ in. by filing.

    c. A chamfer shall be machined along the inside edges of the un-numbered end of the absorber section. This chamfer shall be approximately 45° and to a depth of 0.050 in.

    d. The entire outer surface of the box shall be sanded with fine emery paper to remove any excess weld material.

    e. The entire inner surface of the box shall be scratch-brushed with a stainless steel brush to remove any surface contamination.

    f. The final machined section shall be degreased.

5. *Final inspection.*

The absorber section shall fit through a test box 26 $\frac{1}{16}$ in. in length with inside cross-sectional dimensions of 2.650 x 2.650 in. without interference.

D. *Identification system.*

1. After the plates have been marked for shearing and final machining, a number shall be stamped on both surfaces of the plate inside the final machining mark at the end of the plate which has the nominal 5-in. length of inactive stainless steel. Each plate shall be numbered serially to successively higher numbers.

2. After the final inspection of the absorber section, a number, $\frac{1}{2}$ in. in height, shall be stamped on each plate 1 in. inside the end of the absorbing section which has the nominal 5-in. length of inactive stainless steel. Each section shall be numbered serially to successively higher numbers.

IX. Drawings Required in Manufacturing Fuel Assemblies and Control Rods.

The engineering detailed drawings were prepared by ALCO Products, Inc., Schenectady, N. Y., and may later be subjected to revision. Care shall be exerted when manufacturing the fuel elements and control rods to ascertain that the drawings contain the latest revision and that these drawings are in the hands of the responsible parties. The items required are shown in detail in the engineering drawings listed below:

1. ALCO Dwg D 9-13-2007 Rev. 12/28/55
2. ALCO Dwg D 9-13-2006 Rev. 12/28/55
3. ALCO Dwg D 9-13-2014 Rev. 4/17/56
4. ALCO Dwg D 9-13-2011 Rev. 12/28/55
5. ALCO Dwg R 9-13-1003 Rev. 5/2/56
6. ALCO Dwg D 9-13-1004 Rev. 3/30/56
7. ALCO Dwg C 9-13-2023 Rev. 3/30/56
8. ALCO Dwg C 9-13-2022 Rev. 3/30/56
9. ALCO Dwg C 9-13-2070   12/13/56
10. ALCO Dwg A 9-13-2078   12/13/56
11. ALCO Dwg A 9-13-2077   12/13/56
12. ALCO Dwg A 9-13-2024 Rev. 12/28/55
13. ALCO Dwg B 9-13-2008 Rev. 12/28/55
14. ALCO Dwg D 9-13-2017 Rev. 4/24/56
15. ALCO Dwg D 9-13-1002 Rev. 3/30/56
16. ALCO Dwg A 9-13-2019 Rev. 12/28/55

ACKNOWLEDGMENT

These specifications were prepared with the able assistance of J. H. Erwin of ORNL, and in cooperation with J. F. Haines, R. D. Robertson, J. Tully, E. C. Edgar, J. L. Meem, and J. G. Gallagher of ALCO Products, Incorporated.

BIBLIOGRAPHY ON SOLID FUEL ELEMENTS

HELEN C. FRIEDEMANN

1. Anon., "APPR Fuel Elements. Fabrication Technique," *Nuclear Power*, **3**, 110–11 (1958).
2. Anon., "Design Parameters in the ORNL Gas-Cooled Reactor Study," *Nuclear Eng.*, **3**, 282–5 (1958).
3. Anon., "Fabrication of Fuel Elements for Nuclear Reactors," *Engineer*, **202**, (5262) 788–91 (1956).
4. Anon, "Fuel Elements Conference Held in Paris. Books 1 and 2. Nov. 1957," AEC Report TID-7546 (March 1958).
5. Anon., "Powder Metallurgy Makes Better Reactor Fuels and Components," *Nucleonics*, **13** (12) 24–6 (1955).
6. Anon., "Power Reactors in Canada. NPD and CANDU Studies," *Nuclear Eng.*, **3**, 334–8 (1958).
7. Anon., "PWR Fuel Element Specifications," AEC Report TID-5302 (Rev.) (n.d.).
8. Anon., "The DFR Fuel Element," *Nuclear Power*, **2**, 329–30 (1957).
9. Anon., "The ORNL Design Study," *Nuclear Eng.*, **3**, 277–81 (1958).
10. Adams, O, E., Jr., "Comparison of Elastic Stresses in Solid and I and E Fuel Elements," AEC Report HW-56893 (1958).
11. Albrecht, W. L., "Effect on Power Cost of Substituting Aluminum for Zirconium Fuel Cladding in a Boiling Water Reactor," AEC Report CF-58-7-86 (1958).
12. Alexander, L. G,. "Transient Conduction in Nuclear Reactor Fuel Elements," *Nuclear Sci. and Eng.*, **2**, 73–86 (1957); see also AEC Report CF-56-8-124 (1956).
13. Alexander, L. G., "Effect of Nonuniform Neutron Flux Distribution on the Temperature Distribution in Thick Fuel Elements," AEC Report CF-55-10-118 (1955).
14. Allis-Chalmers Mfg. Co., "Fuel Element Subassembly Nozzle Test in Hot Sodium for Atomic Power Development Assoc.," AEC Report AECU-3658 (1957).
15. Allred, W. B., and Savage, H. C., "Bending of a Fuel Assembly," AEC Report ORNL-551 (1957).
16. Alter, H. W., *et al.*, "A Device to Remove Aluminum Jackets Mechanically from Bonded Uranium Slugs," AEC Report KAPL-1139 (Del.) (1957).
17. Ambartsumyan, R. S. *et al.*, "Fuel Elements for Pressurized Water Reactors of Atomic Power Plants," 2nd Intntl. Conf. on Peaceful Uses of Atomic Energy, Geneva (1958) P/2196.
18. Ambrose, T. W. and Waters, E. D., "Hydraulic Characteristics of the Mark I Fuel Element," AEC Report HW-57344 (1958).
19. American Machine and Foundry Co., "Four Months Status Summary Report on

Industrial Participation Program. Appendix D. Fuel Element Fabrication Program for Nuclear Power Group," AEC Report AMF-GR-3-54 (1957).

20. Ames Laboratory, "Metallurgy Information Meeting, May 2–4, 1956," AEC Report TID-7526 (Pt. 1) (1956).

21. Anderson, J. B., "Fuel Elements for Nuclear Reactors," Preprint #78, ASME, Nuclear Eng. and Sci. Congr., Cleveland (1955); see also *Trans. ASME,* **79,** 29–33 (1957).

22. Anselone, P. M. *et al.,* "Steady State Temperature Distributions in Hollow Slugs," AEC Report HW-30266 (1957).

23. Argonne National Laboratory, "The Experimental Boiling Water Reactor (EBWR)," AEC Report ANL-5607 (1957).

24. Armenoff, C. T., "Fuel Elements for the Organic Moderated Reactor Experiment," AEC Report NAA-SR-1934 (1957).

25. Arnold, W. H., Jr., "Analysis of Experimental Data Reactivity of Plutonium-Bearing Fuel Rods," AEC Report YAEC-57 (1958).

26. Aronin, L. R. and Pickett, J. J., "Core-to-Clad Interdiffusion Studies on Zirconium-Clad U-10 w/o Mo Alloy Fuel Pins," AEC Report NMI-4403 (1958).

27. Atherton, J. E. and Gurinsky, D. H., "Testing of BNL Fuel Cartridges," in "Proc. Met. and Materials Inf. Meeting, Apr. 1951, Oak Ridge," AEC Report TID-5061 (Del.) Vol. 1, p. 42–56.

28. Ayres, J. A. *et al.,* "The Use of Aluminum as Fuel Cladding in High Temperature Water-Cooled Reactors," 2nd Intntl. Conf. on Peaceful Uses of Atomic Energy, Geneva (1958) P/1430.

29. Bailey, R. E., "Irradiation Effects on Zirconium-Clad U-Zr Fuel Plates," AEC Report ANL-5825 (1958).

30. Bailey, W. J., "Fabrication of Al-Pu Fuel Elements for Lattice Tests in Support of Plutonium Recycle Test Reactor," AEC Report HW-51855 (1958).

31. Balent, R., "Basis for Criticality Calculations for Slightly Enriched Uranium, Plate-Type Plutonium Converter Reactor," AEC Report NAA-SR-Memo-507 (1957).

32. Barney, W. K., "Metallography of Irradiated UO_2-Containing Fuel Elements," AEC Report KAPL-1836 (1958).

33. Barney, W. K. *et al.,* "Development of Ferritic Stainless Steel-UO_2 Dispersion Fuel Elements," AEC Report KAPL-1908 (1958).

34. Barr, H, *et al.,* "Development of a Low Enrichment UO_2 Fuel Element," presented at Am. Nuclear Soc., Pittsburgh, June 1957.

35. Baumeister, E. B., "Preliminary Heat Transfer Studies of OMR Fuel Elements," AEC Report NAA-SR-1998 (1957).

36. Bean, C. H., "Roll Cladding U-Zr and U-Zr-Nb Alloys with Zircaloy-2 for Plate-Type Fuel Elements," AEC Report ANL-5628 (1958).

37. Beard, A. P. and Honeyman, R. N., "Preparation of Zirconium-Base Dispersion Fuels," in "Nuclear Metallurgy. V," p. 41–8, AIME IMD Spec. Report No. 7 (1958).

38. Beaver, R. J., "Specifications for Stainless Steel MTR Irradiation Test Element. Irradiation Request ORNL-17," AEC Report CF-55-6-31 (1957).

39. Beaver, R. J., "Minutes of Meeting to Clarify Status of APPR-1 Fuel Elements," AEC Report CF-56-7-149 (1957).

40. Beaver, R. J., "Irradiation Experiment on Uranium Dioxide-Aluminum Powder Fuel Plates. Irradiation Request ORNL-22," AEC Report CF-55-6-13 (1956).

41. Beaver, R. J., "Irradiation Experiment on Aluminum Fuel Element Containing U_3O_8 Dispersion," AEC Report CF-56-12-116 (Rev.) (1957).
42. Beaver, R. J., "Irradiation Experiment on Aluminum Fuel Element Containing Uranium Dicarbide Dispersion," AEC Report CF-56-12-117 (1956).
43. Beaver, R. J., "Irradiation Experiment on ETR Boron-Containing Fuel Elements," AEC Report CF-55-9-12 (1957).
44. Beaver, R. J., "Pertinent Specifications for Fabrication of Plutonium Fuel Elements," AEC Report CF-55-7-76 (1957).
45. Beaver, R. J., "Irradiation Experiment on Aluminum Fuel Plates Containing a 48 w/o Uranium-52 w/o Aluminum Alloy with a 20% Enrichment in the U-235 Isotope," AEC Report CF-56-6-148 (1956).
46. Beaver, R. J. and Feldman, M. J., "MTR Test No. 3 of APPR Fuel Element," AEC Report CF-55-4-163 (1957).
47. Beaver, R. J. *et al.*, "Specifications for Army Package Power Reactor (APPR-1) Fuel and Control Rod Components," AEC Report ORNL-2225 (1957).
48. Beck, W. N., "Development of Ultrasonic Techniques for Inspecting EBWR Cast Uranium Alloy Cores and Fuel Plates," AEC Report ANL-5653 (1957).
49. Beeley, R. J., "A Pebble-Bed Reactor for Stationary Power Plants," AEC Report NAA-SR-895 (1957).
50. Behmer, R. E. and Hoffman, B. L., "Heat Transfer and Economic Considerations for Selecting Core Sizes and Configurations," *Nuclear Sci. and Eng.*, **2**, 14–23 (1957).
51. Bellarts, H. J. *et al.*, "Examining Irradiated Fuels under Water," *Nucleonics*, **14**, (1) 30–3 (1956).
52. Bennett, C. A. and Lane, J. J., "Diameter Measurements of Slugs Before and After Prolonged Heat Treatment," AEC Report HW-8879 (1957).
53. Bentley, R. R., "Effect of Thermal Cycling on the Thermal Transfer from a Sand-Blasted Slug to an Unbonded Jacket," AEC Report CP-2882 (1957).
54. Best, C. D. and Martinelli, R. C., "Second Report on Convection Currents in the Fuel Slug. Appendix A. Model Laws for Fuel Migration Experiment," AEC Report KAPL-M-CDB-3 (1956).
55. Bettis, E. S., "Hydraulic Test of Oak Ridge Research Reactor Dummy Fuel Element," AEC Report CF-56-4-27 (1956).
56. Bettman, M. *et al.*, "On the Dimensional Instability of Uranium and of Clad Plates Subjected to Thermal Cycling," AEC Report MTA-36 (1955).
57. Blade, E. and Cutler, J. A., "Temperature Distribution Analysis for a Mechanically Bonded Fuel Element," AEC Report TID-5263 (Del.) (1957).
58. Blanco, R. E., "Processing of Power Reactor Fuels," *Nuclear Sci. and Eng.*, **1** (5) 409–19 (1956).
59. Bodmer, E. *et al.*, "Manufacture of Internally Cooled Pressurized Tube Elements of Metallic Uranium by a Zone Melting Process," 2nd Intntl. Conf. on Peaceful Uses of Atomic Energy, Geneva (1958) P/240.
60. Bodzin, J. J., "Examination and Heat Treatment of Three Zr-Clad U-10 w/o Mo Fuel Pins for APDA, Inc.," AEC Report AECU-3802 (1958).
61. Bodzin, J. J., "Metallurgical Examination of Three Uranium-10 w/o Mo Fuel Rods to Determine Conformance to APDA Specification," AEC Report AECU-3651 (1957).
62. Bodzin, J. J. and Alessi, T. A., "Thermal Cycle Test in Sodium of an APDA Fuel Pin," AEC Report AECU-3650 (1957).
63. Bodzin, J. J. and Alessi, T. A., "Thermal Cycle Test in Sodium of Nine APDA Fuel Pins," AEC Report AECU-3803 (1958).

64. Bodzin, J. J. *et al.*, "Thermal Cycle Test of an APDA Fuel Pin," AEC Report AECU-3648 (1957).

65. Boeglin, A. F. *et al.*, "Continuous Dissolution of Uranium-Aluminum Reactor Fuels," *AIChE J.*, **2**, 190–4 (1956).

66. Boettcher, A. *et al.*, "Structure of Fuel Elements in the Karlsruhe Research Reactor, FR-2" 2nd Intntl. Conf. on Peaceful Uses of Atomic Energy, Geneva (1958) P/1004.

67. Boettcher, A. *et al.*, "Fuel Elements for a High Temperature Reactor," 2nd Intntl. Conf. on Peaceful Uses of Atomic Energy, Geneva (1958) P/1005.

68. Booth, A. H., "A Method of Calculating Fission Gas Diffusion from UO_2 Fuel and Its Application to the X-2-f Loop Test," Canad. Report CRDC-721 (1957).

69. Booth, A. B., "A Suggested Method for Calculating the Diffusion of Radioactive Rare Gas Fission Products from UO_2 Fuel Elements and a Discussion of Proposed In-Reactor Experiments that May Be Used to Test Its Validity," Canad. Report DCI-27 (1957).

70. Bowers, D. J. *et al.*, "Effect of Ceramic or Metal Additives in High UO_2 Bodies," AEC Report BMI-1177 (1957).

71. Bowman, F. E., "An Evaluation of Dispersion-Type Fuel Materials," presented at 2nd Winter Meeting, Am. Nuclear Soc., New York, Oct. 1957.

72. Briggs, A. B., "Endurance Tests on SAR Zircaloy-3 Fuel Element Welds; Test Number 507," AEC Report KAPL-M-S3G-RE-507 (1956).

73. Briola, J., "Automatic Welding of Fuel Elements," 2nd Intntl. Conf. on Peaceful Uses of Atomic Energy, Geneva (1958) P/1161.

74. Brooks, H., "Some Principles of Pin Fuel Design," AEC Report KAPL-M-HB 27 (1957).

75. Brown, A. J., "Fabrication of the First of Two Y-Shaped Rod Extrusion Billets," AEC Report KAPL-M-AJB-2 (1956).

76. Brown, H. F. and Traxler, R. C., "Report on the Fabrication of the Fuel Cartridge," AEC Report KAPL-M-HFB-1 (1957).

77. Brown, J. R., "Critical Experiments on Water-Moderated Lattices of Slightly Enriched UO_2 Fuel Rods," AEC Report WAPD-BT-8, p. 73-0 (1958).

78. Brown, J. R., "Kinetic and Buckling Measurements on Lattices of Slightly Enriched Uranium or UO_2 Rods in Light Water," AEC Report WAPD-176 (1958).

79. Brown, J. R. *et al.*, "Reactor Properties of Water-Moderated Slightly Enriched Uranium Lattices," AEC Report WAPD-117 (1957).

80. Brownell, L. E. *et al.*, "Design of MTR Fuel Element Source Shipping Cask for Railway Mobile Irradiation Facility," AEC Report AECU-3624 (1957).

81. Bruce, F. R., "Chemical Processing of Aqueous Blanket and Fuel From Thermal Breeder Reactors," *Chem. Eng. Progr.*, **52**, 347–52 (1956).

82. Bruch, C. A. *et al.*, "Fuel Elements for Heterogeneous Reactors," AEC Report KAPL-M-CAB-1 (Del.) (1957).

83. Brunstetter, D. G., "Inspection and Fabrication of YAEC Critical Experiment Fuel Rods," AEC Report YAEC-64 (1958).

84. Buntz, B. J., "Uranium Ingot Production at Atomic Energy Comm. Feed Material Production Centers," in "Nuclear Metallurgy. IV," p. 17–21, AIME IMD Spec. Report No. 4 (1957).

85. Burke, T. J. *et al.*, "Fabrication of High Density UO_2 Fuel Components for the First Presurized Water Reactor Core," in "Nuclear Metallurgy. IV," p. 135–43, AIME IMD Spec. Report No. 4 (1957).

86. Butler, F. *et al.*, "Development of Manufacturing Techniques for the Calder

Hall Fuel Element," 2nd Intntl. Conf. on Peaceful Uses of Atomic Energy, Geneva (1958) P/317.

87. Cadwell, J. J. and Merckx, K. R., "Elastic Solution for the Thermal Stresses in a Finite Solid Cylinder Fuel Element," AEC Report HW-45965 (1956).

88. Cagle, C. D. and Emlet, L. B., "Slug Ruptures in the Oak Ridge National Laboratory Pile," AEC Report ORNL-170 (1957).

89. Calkins, G. D. *et al.*, "Radiation Specimens of a Fuel Element. Experiments PW-1-9, 1-10 and 1-11," AEC Report BMI-X-116 (Del.) (1957).

90. Carlvik, I. and Pershagen, B., "Fast Fission Effect in a Cylindrical Fuel Element," AEC Translation 3315 (Trans. from Atomenergi A-B [Sweden] report AEF-70 [1956]).

91. Carlvik, I. and Pershagen, B., "Calculation of the Ratio Between the Flux at the Surface and the Average Flux (Disadvantage Factor) for a Cylindrical Fuel Element," AEC Translation 3313 (Trans. from Atomenergi A-B [Sweden] Report AEF-68 [1956]).

92. Carroll, H. W. and Michel, C. J., "Standard Operating Procedure for Fabricating NAA Enriched Slugs," AEC Report FMPC-489 (1957).

93. Cashin, W. M. *et al.*, "Observations on an Irradiated Ribbonlike Fuel Element," AEC Report KAPL-M-WMC-4 (1957).

94. Center, C. E., "Fabrication of Extruded Uranium-Aluminum Rods for CP-3 Reactor," AEC Report CF-50-5-102 (1957).

95. Chalder, G. H. *et al.*, "The Fabrication and Properties of Uranium Dioxide Fuel," 2nd Intntl. Conf. on Peaceful Uses of Atomic Energy, Geneva (1958) P/192.

96. Cherel, G. and Block, J., "Examination of Uranium Slugs from the EL-2," French Report CEA-688 (1957).

97. Chernick, J. and Kaplan, I., "The Escape of Fission Products from an Uranium Rod. Application to the BNL Reactor," AEC Report BNL-20 (1955).

98. Christ, J. G. and Lorenz, F. R., "Preliminary Reference Manufacturing Process for PWR Fuel Elements (U-Mo Fuel). Rev. No. 2," AEC Report WAPD-FE-753 (1957).

99. Christenko, P. I. *et al.*, "Rod Fuel Elements for Gas-Cooled Heavy Water Power Reactors," 2nd Intntl. Conf. on Peaceful Uses of Atomic Energy, Geneva (1958) P/2053.

100. Clark, A. C. and Newmarch, D. A., "Diffusion Theory of Fine Structure in Thermal Neutron Reactor Assemblies Consisting of Cylindrical Fuel Elements set in a Square Lattice Array," Brit. Report AERE RP-R 1657 (1955).

101. Clark, M., Jr., "Temperature of, and Stresses in, Cylindrical Fuel Elements During Pile Flashes. Application to Brookhaven Reactor," AEC Report BNL-86 (1955).

102. Cobb, R. F. and Wigton, D. A. (Comps. and Eds.), "Shippingport PWR Core I Fuel Component Fabrication Process and Equipment Manual," AEC Report WAPD-NCE-5215 (1957).

103. Cockrell, W. L., "Fabrication of Fuel and Food Elements for a Converter Reactor," AEC Report NAA-SR-Memo-344 (1957).

104. Cohen, P., "Reliability of PWR Fuel Element Thermocouples at High pH with LiOH," AEC Report WAPD-CDA-126 (1957).

105. Cohen, W. C. and Davidson, J. K., "Relaxation Times and Magnitudes in the Thermal Bowing of the Fuel Element Jackets," AEC Report KAPL-1690 (1957).

106. Cole, R. K., "Resonance Capture by a Standard Hanford Natural Uranium Slug," AEC Report HW-33108 (1956).
107. Combustion Engineering, Inc., "Summary of Progress in Unclassified Areas of Reactor Technology," AEC Report CEND-0005-RS-25 (1958).
108. Cooley, W. C., "Buckling of Flat Fuel Plates Caused by Thermal Expansion, with Application to the Converter Reactor," AEC Report NAA-SR-Memo-225 (1957).
109. Correy, T. B., "Fusion Welding of Al-Si Bonded Fuel Elements," AEC Report HW-48978 (1957).
110. Corsetti, C., "Fabrication Technology of Ceramic Fuel Elements," *Energia Nucleare (Milan)*, **5**, 509–21, 579–90 (1958) (in Italian).
111. Crocker, L. P. and Creek, C. E., "Fission Product Diffusion Through Clad Cermet Fuel Elements," AEC Report CF-57-12-69 (1957).
112. Crooks, D. C., "Nickel Plating Porous UO_2 Stainless Steel Dispersion-Type Fuel Cores," AEC Report KAPL-M-DDC-1 (1957).
113. Cunningham, J. E., "MTR Fuel and Control Rod Element Meeting," AEC Report CF-53-1-150 (1957).
114. Cunningham, J. E., "Information Paper on MTR Fuel Elements," AEC Report CF-53-12-119 (1957).
115. Cunningham, J. E., "Specifications on Stainless Steel STR Irradiation Test Element," AEC Report CF-55-1-113 (1957).
116. Cunningham, J. E., "Development of Braze-Clad Material for Construction of MTR Fuel Elements," AEC Report CF-53-12-96 (1957).
117. Cunningham, J. E. and Adams, R. E., "Techniques for Canning and Bonding Metallic Uranium with Aluminum," in "Fuel Elements Conference Held in Paris. Nov. 1957," AEC Report TID-7546, p. 102–19 (1958).
118. Cunningham, J. E. and Beaver, R. J., "Stainless Steel-UO_2 Fuel Components for APPR," in "Nuclear Metallurgy. V," p. 29–40, AIME IMD Spec. Report No. 7 (1958).
119. Cunningham, J. E. and Beaver, R. J., "Specifications and Fabrication Procedures for APPR-1 Core II Stationary Fuel Elements," AEC Report CF-58-7-72 (1958).
120. Cunningham, J. E. *et al.*, "Stainless Steel Fuel Elements for Compact Power Reactors," 2nd Intntl. Conf. on Peaceful Uses of Atomic Energy, Geneva (1958) P/1925.
121. Cunningham, J. E. *et al.*, "Fuel Dispersions in Aluminum-Base Elements for Research Reactors," in "Fuel Elements Conference Held at Paris. Nov. 1957," p. 269–97, AEC Report TID-7546 (1958).
122. Cunningham, J. E. *et al.*, "Fuel Dispersion in Stainless Steel Components for Power Reactors," in "Fuel Elements Conference Held at Paris. Nov. 1957," p. 243–68, AEC Report TID-7546 (1958).
123. Cuthbert, F. L. *et al.*, "Production of Low Enrichment Uranium Fuel Element Cores," 2nd Intntl. Conf. on Peaceful Uses of Atomic Energy, Geneva (1958) P/1889.
124. Dahlberg, R. C. and Evans, T. C., "Spiral Fuel Element for Gas-Cooled Reactor," *Nucleonics*, **16** (4) 106–8 (1958).
125. Dalrymple, R. S., "Autoclaving of Anodized Slug Jackets," AEC Report HW-25649 (1956).
126. Dayton, R. W., "The Metallurgy and Fabrication of Uranium Alloy Fuel Ele-

ments," in "Fuel Elements Conference Held at Paris. Nov. 1957," p. 302–65, AEC Report TID-7546 (1958).

127. Deily, G. J., "Plaster of Paris Replicas of Reactor Fuel Slugs," AEC Report ANL-5055 (1957).

128. Dempsey, R. H. *et al.*, "ETR: Core and Facilities," *Nucleonics*, **15** (3) 44–7 (1957).

129. Dopchie, H., "Study of an Enriched Uranium-Graphite System Cooled by Air," Belgian Report (AEC No.) NP-6278 (1956).

130. Douglas, D. L., "Application of Carbonyl Plating to the Coating of Hanford Fuel Elements," AEC Report KAPL-M-DLD-1 (1957).

131. Dryden, C. E., "Economics of Shipping Spent Nuclear Fuel Elements," *Nucleonics*, **14** (7) 76 (1956).

132. Dryden, C. E. and Frame, J. M., "Batch vs. Continuous Processing," *Chem. Eng. Progr.*, **52,** 371–4 (1956).

133. Dunning, J. R. and Prentice, B. R. (Eds.), "Advances in Nuclear Engineering, I and II," New York, Pergamon Press, 1957.

134. Eck, J. E. *et al.*, "Feasilibity of Uranium Oxide as a PWR Fuel Material. II. Irradiation Effects in UO_2 ," Presented at Metallurgy Inf. Meeting, Iowa, May 2–4, 1956.

135. Edgar, E. C., "Inspection of Dummy Fuel Loading Used During the Non Critical Test Run," AEC Report APAE-Memo-99 (1957).

136. Eichenberg, J. D., "Effects of Irradiation Cycling on Pressurized Water Reactor Blanket Fuel Elements," AEC Report WAPD-167 (1957).

137. Eldred, V. W. *et al.*, "Fuel Element Behavior Under Irradiation," 2nd Intntl. Conf. on Peaceful Uses of Atomic Energy, Geneva (1958) P/50.

138. Engel, H., "Calculation of the Multiplication Factors of Double Grid Fuel Elements," *Atomkern Energie*, **2,** 168–76 (1957) (in German).

139. Epel, L. G., "Temperature Structure in Gas-Cooled Reactor Fuel Elements and Coolant Channel," AEC Report CF-58-5-97 (1958).

140. Erhard, A. E. *et al.*, "Processing of the Core Fuel Used Initially in the Experimental Breeder Reactor," AEC Report IDO-14331 (1957).

141. Erkman, J. O., "Criticality Conditions for 1.75 Percent Enriched Uranium Slugs," AEC Report HW-25614 (1957).

142. Erwin, J. H. and R. J. Beaver, "Effect of Pressure Differentials on Deflection of the Outer Fuel Plates of Brazed APPR Fuel Elements," AEC Report CF-57-2-34 (1957).

143. Evans, E. A., "Fabrication and Enclosure of Uranium Dioxide," AEC Report HW-52729 (1957).

148. Evans, R. *et al.*, "Atomic Power Development Associates Progress Report," AEC Report NMI-1148 (1955).

145. Everson, I., "Determination of Optimum Gap Between Fuel Plates," AEC Report E-443/N-3 (1953).

146. Fairchild, H. B., " 'Cane' and 'Bamboo' Fuel Rods," AEC Report N-2322 (1957).

147. Faull, N. A., "Burst Slug Detection," Brit. Report AERE-RS/L-4 (1954).

148. Figg, W. S., "Sizing of a Three-Piece Cylindrical Fuel Element for the Plutonium Recycle Program Reactor," AEC Report HW-46781 (1957).

149. Fillmore, F. L., "Buckling of Graphite Moderated Lattices Containing Seven-Rod Fuel Clusters," AEC Report NAA-SR-1535 (1956).

150. Fischer, R. L., "Specifications for Cleaning Zircaloy Fuel Rod Components," AEC Report AECD-4164 (n.d.).

151. Forbes, S. G., "A Nondestructive Method for Fuel Assaying," AEC Report IDO-16114 (1955).
152. Francis, W. E. and Marsden, L. L., "Experimental and Theoretical Values of the Gamma Decay Dose Rate and Heating from Spent MTR Fuel Elements," AEC Report IDO-16247 (1956).
153. Francis, W. E. and Marsden, L. L., "Gamma Ray Dose and Heating from Spent MTR Fuel Elements," *Nucleonics,* **15** (4) 80–3 (1957).
154. Franco, G. and Pedretti, A., "Temperature Measurements in an Aluminum Clad Uranium Slug," *Energia nucleare (Milan),* **3,** 39–45 (1956) (in Italian). Translated in Brit. Report IGRL/T-W-34 (1957).
155. Frank, P. W., "Evaluation of the Reference PWR Fuel Element Failure Detection System," AEC Report WAPD-PWR-CP-2027 (Rev.) (1956).
156. Frank, P. W. and Vogel, K. H., "The PWR Failed Element Detection and Location System," AEC Report WAPD-T-559 (1957).
157. Frankhouser, W. L., "Selection of PWR Fuel Rod Bundle Design and Proposed Tests for Evaluation of PWR Fuel Rod Bundles and Natural Fuel Assemblies," AEC Reports WAPD-FE-950 (1955) and WAPD-FE-979 (1957).
158. Frankhouser, W. L. and Kasberg, A. H., "Preliminary Evaluation of PWR Fuel Rod Assembly Methods," AEC Report WAPD-MDM-28 (1957).
159. Fraser, J. P., "Velocity Depression Due to the Wall Bounding a Matrix of Reactor Fuel Elements," AEC Report KAPL-M-PF-5 (1958).
160. Freede, W. J., "Photography and Study of Flow Patterns Concerning the SRE Fuel Element Assembly," AEC Report NAA-SR-Memo-1117 (1956).
161. Freede, W. J. and Shimazaki, T. T., "Determining Coolant Flow in SRE Fuel Elements," *Nucleonics,* **15** (2) 64–7 (1957).
162. Freshley, M. D., "Plutonium-Aluminum Fuel Element Development," AEC Report HW-52457 (1957).
163. Freshley, M. D. *et al.,* "Plutonium Fuels Development," 2nd Intntl. Conf. on Peaceful Uses of Atomic Energy, Geneva (1958) P/1776.
164. Freund, G. A. and London, A. L., "A General Method for Comparing Thermal Performance of Fuel Element Geometries and Coolants for Non Boiling Reactors," AEC Report ANL-5589 (1957).
165. Friel, D. D., "Underwater Microscope for Examination of Savannah Fuel Slugs," AEC Report AECD-3974 (1955).
166. Frisch, E., "Parallel-Flow, Rod-Type Fuel Element Design Study," AEC Report WAPD-AD(M)-14 (1957).
167. Fritz, R. J., "Hold-up Times for Safe Fuel Rod Removal from the Schenectady Reactor," AEC Report KAPL-M-RJF-1 (1957).
168. Fromm, L. W., "Pressure Drops and Lifting Effects of Stacked Fuel Rods in a Simulated Pile Fuel Channel," AEC Report M-3956 (1957).
169. Garvey, J. E., "Dependence of Thermal Utilization and Resonance Escape Probability upon Fuel Element Density in D_2O Cooled and Moderated Systems," AEC Report AECD-4021 (1956).
170. Gaus, H., "Temperature Distribution in the Interior of Uranium Rods in Stationary Operation," German Report (AEC No.) NP-6270 (1954?).
171. Gauthron, M., "Thermopneumatic Cladding," in "Fuel Elements Conference Held at Paris, Nov. 1957," AEC Report TID-7546, p. 18–26 (1958).
172. Gauthron, M., "Fuel Elements of Heterogeneous Piles with Thermal Neutrons," *Energie nucleaire,* **2,** 120–4 (1958) (in French).
173. Giedt, W. H., "Design and Development of a Fuel Plate Surface Thermocouple for Special Power Excursion Reactor Tests," AEC Report IDO-16388 (1957).

174. Glatter, J., "Fabrication of Bulk Form Uranium Dioxide for Use as Nuclear Reactor Fuel," in "Nuclear Metallurgy. IV," p. 131–34, AIME IMD Spec. Report Series No. 4 (1957).

175. Glatter, J. *et al.*, "Manufacture of PWR Blanket Fuel Elements Containing High Density Uranium Dioxide," 2nd Intntl. Conf. on Peaceful Uses of Atomic Energy, Geneva (1958) P/2380.

176. Goslee, D. E. and Frank, L., "Unbonded Fuel Elements," Presented at 2nd Winter Meeting, Am. Nuclear Soc., New York, Oct. 1957.

177. Green, R. E., "Lattice Experiments with 19-Element UO_2 Rods in ZEEP," Brit. Report UK/C/6/109 (1957).

178. Green, S. J. and Williams, J. S., Jr., "Fuel Element Temperature Response in the 'Beyond Burnout' Heat Transfer Region," AEC Report WAPD-TH-414 (1958).

179. Grimble, R. E. *et al.*, "Heat Transfer and Friction Flow Characteristics of Cylindrical Parallel Rods with Transverse Cylindrical Spacers," AEC Report AECD-3975 (1955).

180. Guay, W. J., "Corrosion of Aluminum-Uranium Fuel Assemblies in SF Storage Basin Water," AEC Report IDO-14213 (Del.) (1957).

181. Gurinsky, D. H., "The Fabrication of the Fuel Elements of the BNL Reactor," in *Proc. 1st Intntl. Conf. on Peaceful Uses of Atomic Energy,* **IX**, p. 221–230, United Nations, New York (1956); see also "Metallurgy and Fuels," p. 511–22, New York, McGraw-Hill Book Co., Inc., 1956.

182. Gurinsky, D. H. and Dienes, G. J., "Nuclear Fuels," Princeton, D. Van Nostrand Co., Inc., 1956.

183. Haefele, W., "On the Effectiveness of Disconnected Rods of Thermal Reactors in View of Their Diameter, Number and Arrangement," German Report (AEC No.) NP-6275 (1956).

184. Haefele, W. *et al.*, "p- and f-Factors in Aluminum-Clad, Heavy Water-cooled Fuel Element in a Heavy Water Reactor," German Report (AEC No.) NP-6272 (1956).

185. Hage, W., "Temperature and Pressure Distribution in a Cylindrical Unclad Sufficiently Long Core," *Atomkern Energie,* **3,** 49–53 (1958).

186. Halpine, P. A., "PWR Core (Fuel Rod Size)," AEC Report WAPD-RD-58 (1957).

187. Hammers, R. C., "Model 17A Fuel Rod," AEC Report KAPL-M-RCD-34 (1956).

188. Handwerk, J. H., "Ceramic Fuel Elements in the ThO_2-UO_2 and UO_2-PuO_2 Systems," in "Fuel Elements Conference Held at Paris. Nov. 1957," p. 526–548, AEC Report TID-7546 (1958).

189. Handwerk, J. H., and Noland, R. A., "Oxide Fuel Elements for High Temperatures," *Chem. Eng. Progr.,* **53,** 60F-2F (1957).

190. Handwerk, J. H. *et al.*, "Uranium Oxide-Containing Fuel Element Composition and Method of Making Same," U. S. Pat. 2,805,473 (1957).

191. Handwerk, J. H. *et al.*, "Manufacture of the ThO_2-UO_2 Ceramic Fuel Pellets for BORAX-IV," AEC Report ANL-5678 (1957).

192. Hanks, G. S. *et al.*, "Rolling of Uranium," in "Nuclear Metallurgy. IV," p. 73–86, AIME IMD Spec. Report No. 4 (1957).

193. Hanson, G. H. and McMurry, H. L., "Nuclear Aspects of Proposed 19-Plate Fuel Assemblies," AEC Report IDO-16046 (1957).

194. Hanson, G. H. *et al.*, "MTR Two-Week Operating Cycles Fuel Requirements and Loading Arrangement for Initial Operations," AEC Report IDO-16112 (1956).

195. Hardy, H. K., "Metallurgical Research and Development for Nuclear Power," *J. Inst. Metals*, **84**, 229–39 (1956).

196. Hardy, H. K., "Fabrication of Fuel Elements," *Atomwirtschaft*, **3**, 99–102 (1958) (in German).

197. Hardy, H. K. and Lawton, H., "Assessment and Testing of Fuel Elements," 2nd Intntl. Conf. on Peaceful Uses of Atomic Energy, Geneva (1958) P/306.

198. Harris, D. R., "A Lattice of Slightly Enriched UO_2 Fuel Rods Partly Immersed in Light Water," AEC Report WAPD-TM-114 (1957).

199. Harteck, P. and Dondes, S., "Glass Fibers. A New Form for Reactor Fuels," *Nucleonics*, **15** (8) 94–8 (1957).

200. Hausner, H. H., "Powder Metallurgy in Nuclear Engineering," in "Proc. of Symposium on Rare Metals. Bombay, India," UNESCO/NS/RM Paper V.2/23, (Dec. 1957).

201. Hausner, H. H., Ed., "Powder Metallurgy in Nuclear Engineering," American Soc. for Metals, Cleveland (1958).

202. Hausner, H. H., "Economics of Fuel Element Production," Presented at Symposium on "Future Market for Uranium," Uranium Inst. of America, Denver (Dec. 1957).

203. Hausner, H. H. and Mills, R. G., "Uranium Dioxide for Fuel Elements," *Nucleonics*, **15** (7) 94–103 (1957).

204. Hausner, H. H. and Roboff, S. B., "Materials for Nuclear Power Reactors," New York, Reinhold Publishing Corp., 1955.

205. Haynes, W. B. and Proudfoot, E. A., "The Ultrasonic Inspection of Cast and Wrought Uranium-12 w/o Molybdenum Alloy," AEC Report WAPD-129 (1955).

206. Hayward, B. R., "Effects of Burnup on Metallic Fuel Elements Operating at Elevated Temperature," 2nd Intntl. Conf. on Peaceful Uses of Atomic Energy, Geneva (1958) P/617.

207. Hayward, B. R. and Corzine, P., "Thorium-Uranium Fuel Elements for SRE," 2nd Intntl. Conf. on Peaceful Uses of Atomic Energy, Geneva (1958) P/785.

208. Hayward, B. R. and Woolsey, C. C., "Fuel Element Economics in Sodium Graphite Power Reactors," AEC Report AECU-3499 (1955).

209. Heisler, M. and Shimazaki, T., "Cooling of Tubular Fuel Elements," AEC Report NAA-SR-Memo-468 (1957).

210. Helstrom, C. W., "Emission Rate of Fission Products from a Hole in the Cladding of a Reactor Fuel Element," AEC Report AECU-3220 (1956).

211. Henderson, C. M. *et al.*, "Various Methods of Preparing Uranium Dioxide for Fuel Element Use," in "Nuclear Metallurgy. IV.," p. 123–30, AIME IMD Spec. Report No. 4 (1957).

212. Henry, K. M. and Anno, J. N., "Element after Heating," AEC Report CF-55-11-94 (1955).

213. Hermans, M. E. A., "The Preparation of Uranium Dioxide Fuel for a Suspension Reactor," 2nd Intntl. Conf. on Peaceful Uses of Atomic Energy, Geneva (1958) P/552.

214. Hill, J. F., "The Use of Enriched Uranium in a Power Reactor," AEC Report NURG-M-6 (1956).

215. Hirsch, H. H., "A Powder Metallurgy Technique for Combining Insoluble Materials as Applied to $Al\text{-}UO_2$ Fuel Elements," AEC Report TID-5061 (Del.) p. 527–37 (1957).

216. Hochschild, R., "Nondestructive Testing of Uranium Slugs," AEC Reports NYO-3575 and NYO-3578 (1957).

217. Hoge, H. R., "Experiment 10-m-2 'Evaluation of the Bond Between the U-Mo Fuel and Cladding Material'," AEC Report WAPD-FE-489 (1957).

218. Holm, M. W., "The Determination of U-235 Burn-out in Fuel Rods," AEC Report IDO-16036 (1955).

219. Holm, M. W. *et al.*, "Nuclear Constants for the MTR with 168-g Fuel Elements and 131-g Fuel Bearing Shim Rods," AEC Report IDO-16082 (1957).

220. Holzer, F. S., "Nuclear Fuel Cost for the AMF Closed Cycle Boiling Water Reactor," AEC Report AMF-GR-4-55 (1957).

221. Holzer, F. S. and MacPhee, J., "Study of Fuel Cost, Core and Control Problems in the AMF Closed Cycle Boiling Water Reactor," AEC Report AMF-GR-10-55 (Del.) (1957).

222. Holzworth, M. L., "Mechanical Properties of Striated Uranium Slugs," AEC Report DP-139 (1955).

223. Homeister, O. E. *et al.*, "Model Studies of the Flow Characteristics of the Fuel Elements for the Enrico Fermi Reactor," Presented at Nuclear Eng. and Sci. Conf., Chicago, March 1958.

224. Horsman, J. E., "Atomic Power Reactors and Their Fuels," Canad. Report AECL-179; see also *Chem. in Can.*, **7**, 48–52 (1955).

225. Howe, J. P., "The Metallurgy of Reactor Fuels," in "Proc. 1st Intntl. Conf. on Peaceful Uses of Atomic Energy. IX," p. 179–95, United Nations, (1956); see also in "Metallurgy and Fuels," p. 481–510, New York, McGraw-Hill Book Co., Inc., 1956.

226. Howieson, J., "Report on the First NPD-1 Single Element Irradiation and Failure," Canad. Report CRNE-744 (1957).

227. Hurst, L. K., "Some Problems Associated with the Transportation of Spent Fuel Elements," Paper #58 in "The 1957 Nuclear Industry."

228. Hurwitz, H., Jr., "Memo on Heat Conductivity in Laminated Fuel Structures," AEC Report A-4254 (1955).

229. Hutchison, C. A., Jr., "Temperatures and Thermal Stresses in Pile Fuel Rods," AEC Reports CP-3493 (1957) and MUC-CAH-7 (1958).

230. Isserow, S., "Corrosion Behavior of Defected Fuel Elements with U-2 w/o Zr Core Clad with Zircaloy-2," AEC Reports NMI-4364 and NMI-4365 (1958).

231. Jacket, H. S., "Pitting Anodic Corrosion Studies," AEC Report WAPD-ReM-16 (1956).

232. Jackey, G. F., "Extrusion Cladding Uranium with Aluminum Using the 'Schloemann' Cable-Cladding Press. Mechanical Aspects," AEC Report HW-56801 (1958).

233. Johnson, J. R., "Ceramic Fuel Materials for Nuclear Reactors," Paper No. 110, Nuclear Eng. and Sci. Congress, Cleveland, Ohio, Dec. 1955; see also "Problems in Nuclear Engineering," p. 71–78, New York, Pergamon Press, 1957.

234. Johnston, F. J. *et al.*, "Dissolution of Uranium Oxide Arising from Slug Failure," AEC Report ANL-5084 (1955).

235. Jones, A. R., "An Eddy Current Device for Measuring Aluminum Cladding on Uranium Fuel Elements," Canad. Report CRRD-750 (1958).

236. Jones, R. M., "Specifications for Fuel Assemblies for Materials Testing Reactor," AEC Report IDO-16281 (1955).

237. Jones, S. S., "Visit to Puget Sound Naval Shipyard for Drilling Uranium Slugs," AEC Report HW-24455 (1956).

238. Joseph, J. W., Jr. and Walker, J. W., "Residual Stresses in Thorium Slugs," AEC Report DP-169 (1956).

239. Judd, W. C. and Leboeuf, M. B., "Nondestructive Determination of U-235 Con-

tent of Rod-Shaped Fuel Elements by Gamma Pulse Spectrometry," AEC Report KAPL-1925 (1958).

240. Karush, W. *et al.*, "Further End Cap Temperature Calculations," AEC Report CP-2071 (1955).

241. Kasberg, A. H. and Christ, J. G., "Development of Fuel Rod End Closures and Nondestructive Testing of End Closures and Tubing," AEC Reports WAPD-FE-838 and WAPD-FE-839 (1958).

242. Kasschau, K., "Fuel Charging Machine," U. S. Pat. 2,756,858 (1956).

243. Kattwinkel, W., "Thermal Stress in a Bare Cylindrical Fuel Element of a Large Size During Heating," *Atomkern Energie*, **3**, 394–6 (1958) (in German).

244. Kattwinkel, W., "Question of Temperature Distribution in a Bare Cylindrical Fuel Element of Great Length in the Nonsteady State (Heating up)," *Atomkern Energie*, **3**, 342–5 (1958) (in German).

245. Kaufmann, A. R. *et al.*, "Zirconium Cladding of Uranium and Uranium Alloys by Co-extrusion," in "Fuel Elements Conference Held at Paris. Nov. 1957," p. 157–81, AEC Report TID-7546 (1958).

246. Kaufman, D. F. and Jenkins, R. G., "Evaluation of Zircaloy-clad U-2 w/o Zr Alloy Tube. Extrusion Nos. 26, 29, 30 and 34," AEC Reports Nos. NMI-4372 (1959), NMI-4370 (Rev.), NMI-4371 (Rev.) and NMI-4380, resp.

247. Kaulitz, D. C. and Evans, T. W., "A Rechargeable Pressurized Fuel Element Irradiation Facility," AEC Report HW-40778 (1957).

248. Kerr, W. B., "Materials Costs for Nickel Plating," AEC Report HW-39605 (1956).

249. Kesselring, K. A., "Preliminary Design Study of Magnesium-Uranium Alloy Slug," AEC Report KAPL-M-KAK-5 (1957).

250. Khristenko, P. I. *et al.*, "Pin Fuel Element for Gas-Cooled Heavy Water Power Reactor," 2nd Intntl. Conf. on Peaceful Uses of Atomic Energy, Geneva (1958) P/2053.

251. Kidson, G. V., "The Development of Bonded Fuel Elements by the Process of Extrusion Cladding," Canad. Report CRMet-703 (1957).

252. Kiehm, R. M. *et al.*, "A Molten Plutonium Fueled Reactor Concept—LAMPRE," AEC Report LA-2112 (1957).

253. King, B. W. *et al.*, "The Application of Ceramics to Hanford Fuel Elements," AEC Report BMI-860 (1958).

254. Kirchenmayer, A., "Transient Behavior of Heat Transfer from Fuel Elements to a Coolant of Constant (boiling) Temperature in a One-Dimensional Heat Flux," *Atomkern Energie*, **3**, 337–41 (1958) (in German).

255. Kisiel, T. J., "Fabrication of PWR Bundle In-Pile Tests," AEC Report WAPD-FE-919 (1957).

256. Kisiel, T. J. *et al.*, "Thermal Performance of UO_2 Fuel Rods," 2nd Intntl. Conf. on Peaceful Uses of Atomic Energy, Geneva (1958) P/1012.

257. Kitchen, S. W., "Measurement of Fuel Self-Shielding in Closely Packed Slab Lattices," AEC Report KAPL-M-SWK-7 (1957).

258. Kittel, J. *et al.*, "The Manufacture of Fuel Elements of the Argonaut Type," 2nd Intntl. Conf. on Peaceful Uses of Atomic Energy, Geneva (1958) P/1585.

259. Klein, J. L., "Evaluation of Three Zircaloy-Clad U-2% Zr Fuel Tubes," AEC Report NMI-4360 (1958).

260. Kopelman, B., "Recent Developments in Dispersion-Type Fuel Elements," in "Fuel Elements Conference, Held at Paris, Nov. 1957," AEC Report TID-7546 (1958) p. 231–42.

261. Kouts, H., "Critical Assemblies of Light Water-Moderated Slightly Enriched

Uranium Rod Lattices at Brookhaven," AEC Report BNL-3145 (Suppl.) (1956).

262. Ladd, C. M. *et al.*, "Report on Core and Blanket Design and Technology," AEC Report AECU-3678 (1958).

263. Larsen, R. P., "Dissolution of Thorium Oxide-Uranium Oxide Fuel Elements," AEC Report ANL-RCV-SL-1090 (1957).

264. Larson, W. L. and Klein, J. L., "Use of a Chip Method to Produce Homogeneous Al-U Alloy Foils," AEC Report NMI-1168 (1956).

265. Laubenstein, R. A., "Exponential Experiments on Graphite Lattices which Contain Multi-Rod Fuel Elements," 2nd Intntl. Conf. on Peaceful Uses of Atomic Energy, Geneva (1958) P/594.

266. Lawroski, S., "Recent Developments in the Pyrometallurgical Treatment of Irradiated Fuel Elements and Breeder Blanket in the United States," in "Proc. of Symposium on Rare Metals. Bombay, India," UNESCO/NS/RM/III.3/16 (Dec. 1957).

267. Leduc, C. and Segot, C., "Fuel Element's Partial Burning Within G1 Reactor," 2nd Intntl. Conf. on Peaceful Uses of Atomic Energy, Geneva (1958) P/1180.

268. Leek, C. B. *et al.*, "Reprocessing Uranium-Zirconium Alloy Reactor Fuel Elements," Presented at Nuclear Eng. and Sci. Conf., Chicago, 1958.

269. Leeser, D. O. *et al.*, "Radiation Stability of Fuel Elements for the Enrico Fermi Power Reactor," 2nd Intntl. Conf. on Peaceful Uses of Atomic Energy, Geneva (1958) P/622.

270. Lehmann, P. *et al.*, "Physical Characteristics of Some Composite Natural Uranium Fuel Elements in Heavy Water," 2nd Intntl. Conf. on Peaceful Uses of Atomic Energy, Geneva (1958) P/245.

271. LeTourneau, B. W. and Grimble, R. E., "Pressure Drop Through Parallel Rod Subassemblies Having a 1.12 Equilateral Triangular Pitch," AEC Report WAPD-TH-118 (1956).

272. LeTourneau, B. W. and Grimble, R. E., "The Calculation of Meat Eccentricity Hot Channel Factors for Rod-Type Fuel Elements," AEC Report WAPD-TH-53 (1957).

273. Lewis, W. B., "Cost Comparisons for Enriched vs. Natural Uranium Fuel and for Zirconium vs. Stainless Steel Fuel Sheathing in Bidirectional Slug Fuelled Reactors," Canad. Report DM-52 (1958).

274. Lewis, W. B., "Fuelling System for Natural Uranium Reactor with Long Rods for High Burnup Without Recycling," Canad. Report DM-42 (1957).

275. Lewis, W. B., "Low Cost Fuelling without Recycling," Canad. Report DR-39 (1956).

276. Lewis, W. B., "Uranium Oxide Fuel of Low Cost," Canad. Report DL-33 (1958).

277. Lewis, W. B., "The Significance of Developing a High Performance Uranium Oxide Fuel," Canad. Report DM-44 (1957).

278. Leyse, C. F., "Evaluation of Active Lattice Geometries and Cycle Times for the MTR," AEC Report IDO-16144 (1956).

279. Leyse, C. F., "Improvements in MTR Fuel Assemblies and Operating Procedures," AEC Report IDO-16150 (1957).

280. Lieberman, R. M., "Waterlogged Fuel Element Study," AEC Report WAPD-CP-1239 (1957).

281. Lieberman, R. M., "The Zircaloy-2 In-Pile Tube for the NRX Central Thimble," AEC Report WAPD-TM-51 (1957).

282. Lindley, P. A., "Fuel Element Design," *Atomic Energy Rev.*, **1**, 13–15 (1957).

283. Lingafelter, J. W., "High Amperage Slug Welding," AEC Report HW-27297 (1957).

284. Lloyd, H., "Manufacture of DIDO Fuel Elements," in "Fuel Elements Conference Held at Paris. Nov. 1957," AEC Report TID-7546 (1958) p. 298–301; see also Brit. Report AERE-M/L-2, 2nd ed.

285. Loch, L. D. *et al.*, "Survey of Refractory Uranium Compounds," AEC Report BMI-1124 (1956).

286. Loewenstein, P., "Extrusion of Uranium," in "Nuclear Metallurgy. IV," p. 87–94, AIME IMD Spec. Report No. 4 (1957).

287. Lojek, J. M. and Lindsay, W. T., Jr., "The Effect of Oxygenated Water on Clad- and Defected-UO_2 Fuel Specimens," AEC Report WAPD-PWR-CP-3166 (1957).

288. Lorenz, F. R., "Preliminary Extrusion Process and Tooling Specifications," AEC Report WAPD-FE-739 (1957).

289. Low, J. R., Jr., "Bursting of Fuel Pins in an Uncontrolled Reactor," AEC Report KAPL-M-JRL-3 (1957).

290. Lozier, P. G., "Program for Alternate Co-extrusion Process for Reference SAR Fuel Elements," AEC Report KAPL-M-PGL-1 (1956).

291. Luebke, E. A., "Plutonium Power Reactor with Oxide Fuel Elements," AEC Report TID-10078 (1957).

292. Luebke, E. A., "Fuel Assembly for Oxide-Fueled Plutonium Power Breeder," AEC Report KAPL-M-EAL-16 (1957).

293. Lyon, R. N., "Single Slug Electrically Internal-Heated Corrosion Unit," AEC Report CE-2544 (1957).

294. McCutcheon, D. M., and Oaks, A. E., "Radiographic Inspection of PWR Fuel Rod End Closures," AEC Report WAPD-PWR-FE-1228 (1956).

295. McDaniel, W. N. *et al.*, "Development of Core Elements for the Enrico Fermi Power Reactor," 2nd Intntl. Conf. on Peaceful Uses of Atomic Energy, Geneva (1958) P/792.

296. McGonnagle, W. J., "Nondestructive Testing of Reactor Fuel Elements," Preprint #130, Nuclear Eng. and Sci. Congr., Cleveland, Dec. 1955; see also *Nuclear Sci. and Eng.*, **2**, 602–16 (1957).

297. McGonnagle, W. J., and McLain, S., "Applications of Nondestructive Testing to Fuel Elements for Nuclear Reactors," *Non-Destructive Testing*, **15**, 86–90 (1957).

298. McGonnagle, W. J., and Paul, R. S., "New Developments in Nondestructive Testing of Reactor Fuel Elements," 2nd Intntl. Conf. on Peaceful Uses of Atomic Energy, Geneva (1958) P/2378.

299. McLain, S., and Foote, F. G., "Fuel Element Metallurgy; Corrosion and Coolant Problems," Preprint #215, Nuclear Sci. and Eng. Congr., Cleveland, Dec. 1955.

300. McLennan, J. A., "Reactor Cell Calculations for Some Cylindrically Symmetric Fuel Elements Surrounded by Moderator," AEC Report APEX-362 (1955).

301. McMurry, H. L., "Estimation of Fuel Requirements for Two Week Cycles on the MTR," AEC Report IDO-16140 (1955).

302. McMurry, H. L., "Calculated Reactivity Changes due to Reduction of Aluminum in the MTR Core," AEC Report IDO-16083 (1955).

303. McMurry, H. L. and Grimaud, A. V., "Temperature Distribution in a Fuel Plate With Exponentially Rising Power. II. Results Based on Asymptotic Solutions," AEC Reports IDO-16214 and IDO-16311 (1955).

304. McNown, J. S. *et al.*, "Tests on Models of Nuclear Reactor Elements. I. Head Losses in Blanket Subassembly. II. Studies of Diffusion," AEC Report AECU-3757 (Pts. I and II) (1956 and 1957).

305. Macherey, R. E., "Fabrication of Uranium-Base Fuel Plates and Assemblies for Experimental Boiling Water Reactor," 2nd Intntl. Conf. on Peaceful Uses of Atomic Energy, Geneva (1958) P/790.

306. Machery, R. E. and Zegler, S. T., "The Manufacture of Internal Blanket and Fuel Blanket Slugs for the Experimental Breeder Reactor," AEC Report ANL-5132 (Del.) (1957); see also ANL-5629 (1957).

307. Mallett, G. R., "327 Basin Aluminum Corrosion Test," AEC Report HW-41370 (1956).

308. Manly, W. D., "Extrusion of 2% U-Al Fuel Rods for the Argonne CP-3 Reactor," AEC Report ORNL-766 (1957).

309. Manocha, R., "Problems in Treatment of Irradiated Fuel Elements and Breeder Blankets," in "Proc. of Symposium on Rare Metals. Bombay, India," UNESCO/NS/RM/III.3/15 (Dec. 1957).

310. Markowitz, J. M., "Release of Fission Gases from Irradiated UO_2. I. Apparatus for the Measurement of Fission Gas Release from Fuel Materials During Pile Irradiation," AEC Report WAPD-180 (1957).

311. Martens, F. H. and Helfrich, G. F., "Critical Studies with G.E.-Type Fuel Elements," AEC Report ANL-5108 (1957).

312. Martin, A. V., "Maximum Force of a Warped Rod Against a Rigid Constraint," AEC Report CP-2273 (1956).

313. Martin, A. V. and Young, G., "On the Statistics of Rod Warping," AEC Report CP-2541 (1955).

314. Martin, F. S., "Head End Processes for Dissolving Stainless Steel-UO_2 Dispersion Type Fuel Elements. I. Carbide and Nitride Treatments. II. Anodic Dissolution," Brit. Report AERE C/R 2454 (1958).

315. Matheson, A. R., "Production of Reactor Fuel Elements," Presented at meeting of Atomic Industrial Forum, Washington, D. C., Sept. 1955.

316. Mauney, T. H. and Ross, W. L., "Calibration of TD 271 Fuel Assemblies," AEC Report CF-49-11-226 (1955).

317. Megeff, S. I. and Zambrow, J. L. "Fabrication of Aluminum Plate-Type Elements Containing UO_2 as the Fuel," in "Nuclear Metallurgy. V," p. 25–28, AIME IMD Spec. Report No. 7 (1958).

318. Merckx, K. R., "Thermal Stresses in Cylindrical Reactor Fuel Elements," AEC Reports HW-42665 (1956) and HW-50364 (1957).

319. Miller, R. I., "An Apparatus for the Determination of Total Gas in Fuel Element Samples," AEC Report HW-51452 (1957).

320. Miller, R. S., "Estimated Internal Pressures in Fast Oxide Breeder Fuel Elements Due to Fission Gas Release," AEC Report KAPL-M-RSM-3 (1957).

321. Milne, H. S., "Extrusion Cladding of NRE Fuel Element," Canad. Report CRE-701 (1957).

322. Miraldi, F. D. and Rossin, A. D., "Carrier Design of Irradiated APPR Fuel Elements," AEC Report KT-178 (1957).

323. Moak, W. D. and Pojasek, W. J., "The Determination of Uranium in UO_2-Al_2O_3 Fuel Elements by X-ray Emission Spectrography," AEC Report KAPL-1879 (1957).

324. Mongini, L. and Tamagnini, C. M., "Composition of the Fuel Element During the Operation of a Thermal Heterogeneous Natural Uranium Reactor," *Energia nucleare (Milan)*, **2,** 519–36 (1955) (in Italian).

325. Montagne, R. and Meny, L., "Co-extrusion Applied to the Fabrication of Solid or Disperse Fuel Elements," in "Fuel Elements Conference Held at Paris. Nov. 1957," p. 142–56, AEC Report TID-7546 (1958).

326. Mooradian, A. J., "Aluminum Sheathing of Flat Uranium Plates by Extrusion Cladding," Canad. Report CRL-46 (1957); see also in "Fuel Elements Conference Held at Paris. Nov. 1957," p. 120–141, AEC Report TID-7546 (1958).

327. Morrison, I. H. et al., "Some Techniques in Manufacture of Fuel Elements for Calder Hall," 2nd Intntl. Conf. on Peaceful Uses of Atomic Energy, Geneva (1958) P/317.

328. Murray, F. H. et al., "Calculation of the Temperature Distribution in a Slug With a Solid Aluminum Cap," AEC Report CP-1580 (1956).

329. Murray, F. and Young, G., "A Case of Rod Warping," AEC Report CP-1747 (1957).

330. Murray, P. et al., "Uranium Dioxide as a Reactor Fuel," in "Fuel Elements Conference Held at Paris. Nov. 1957," p. 432–441, AEC Report TID-7546 (1958).

331. Newkirk, H. W., Jr., "Fabrication of Uranium Dioxide Fuel Element Shapes by Hydrostatic Pressing," AEC Report HW-51770 (1957); see also *Am. Ceram. Soc. Bull.*, **37** (11) 471–5 (1958).

332. Newmarch, D. A., "The Effect of Removing Plate Fuel Elements upon the Thermal Neutron Fine Structure in Reactor Assemblies. I," Brit. Report AERE-R/R-1940 (1956).

333. Newmarch, D. A., "The Diffusion Theory of Thermal Neutron Fine Structure in Reactors with Nonuniform Spacing of the Fuel Elements. I," Brit. Report AERE-RP/R-1776 (1955).

334. Nichols, R. W., "Ceramic Fuels, Properties and Technology," *Nuclear Eng.*, **3**, 327–33 (1958).

335. Nicoll, P. A. and Sanford, E. R., "Irradiation of Plastic Fuel Tapes. III and IV," AEC Reports WAPD-P-659 and WAPD-P-687 (1958), resp.

336. Noland, R. A. et al., "Manufacture of EBR-1, Mark III Fuel and Blanket Rods," 2nd Intntl. Conf. on Peaceful Uses of Atomic Energy, Geneva (1958) P/791.

337. Nussbaum, A. I., "Rolling Mills for Fuel Elements," *Atomics and Nuclear Energy*, **9**, 128–30, 146 (1958).

338. Oak Ridge National Lab., "Technical Scope of Gas-Cooled Reactor Fuel Element Irradiation Program," AEC Report CF-58-8-4 (1958).

339. Olsen, A. R. et al., "Pitting Corrosion Observed on Active and Dummy Fuel Elements From the Bulk Shielding Reactor," AEC Report AECD-3717 (1955).

340. Oppold, W. A., "A Report on the Casting of (Slugs) in Graphite Molds," AEC Report NYO-5102 (1957).

341. Otterbein, G. L., "Investigation of the Causes of Weld Rejects," AEC Report HW-39445 (1956).

342. Palladino, N. J., "PWR Reference Blanket Fuel Rod," AEC Report WAPD-RDa-60 (1957).

343. Paprocki, S. J. et al., "Development of Cermet Fuel Elements," AEC Report BMI-1282 (1958).

344. Paprocki, S. J. et al., "Pressure Bonding of Zircaloy-clad Flat-plate UO_2 Fuel Elements," in "Nuclear Metallurgy. V," p. 13–24, AIME IMD Special Report No. 7 (1958).

345. Paprocki, S. J. et al., "Fabrication of Dispersed Uranium Fuel Elements Using "Powder Metallurgy Techniques," AEC Report BMI-1184 (1957).

346. Parkins, W. E., "Design and Development of Components for the SRE," in

"Problems in Nuclear Engineering," p. 255–9, New York, Pergamon Press, 1957.

347. Payne, J. H., Jr. and Hofmann, C. S., "Effect of Fuel Rod Length on Dimensions of Reactor Servicing Mechanisms," AEC Report KAPL-M-JHP-4 (1956).

348. Pement, F. W., "Revised Estimate of PWR Fission Product Activity with Defective UO_2 Fuel Rods," AEC Report WAPD-CDA (AD)-27 (1957).

349. Pemsler, J. P., and Greenspan, J., "The Effect of Hydrogen Coolant on Mg-Clad Uranium Core Fuel Elements," AEC Report NMI-4352 (1957).

350. Persson, R., "Exponential Pile Measurements on R3a Fuel Elements," AEC Translation, AEC-tr-3362 (translated from Atomenergi A–B (Sweden) Report AEF-65 (1956).

351. Pettus, W. G. and Dayton, I. E., "Mutual Shielding of Lattice Pins in the Resonance Energy Region," *Nuclear Sci. and Eng.*, **4**, 522–9 (1958).

352. Pickett, J. J. and Aronin, L. R., "Investigation of Co-extrusion as a Method of Producing Ta-clad U-10 w/o Mo Pin-type Fuel Elements," AEC Report NMI-4404 (1958).

353. Plott, R. F., "Leakage Testing Apparatus," U. S. Pat. 2,751,780 (1956).

354. Pobereskin, M. *et al.*, "Study of the Feasibility of a Tracer System for Locating a Fuel Element Failure in a PWR," Presented at Nuclear Eng. and Sci. Congr., Chicago (1958).

355. Powell, R. W. and Lee, P. H., "Leak Detection System," U. S. Pat. 2,777,812 (1957).

356. Price, B. R., "Density of UO_2 Fuel Components. A Resume of Present Knowledge and Related Experimental Programs," AEC Report WAPD-FE-1057 (1957).

357. Puphal, K. W., "Determination of Boron in Aluminum-Uranium Fuel Elements," AEC Report IDO-14418 (1957).

358. Quinlan, F. B. and Tverberg, J. C., "Centrifugal Casting for Plutonium and Plutonium-Uranium Plates," AEC Report HW-47015 (1957).

359. Reich, C. W., "Local Thermal Flux Distribution in SPERT III Fuel Elements by the Spherical Harmonics Method," AEC Report IDO-16327 (1956).

360. Reid, D. G. and K. K. Kennedy, "Direct Maintenance Fuel Processing Plant is Practical," *Chem. Eng. Progr.*, **52**, 394–5 (1956).

361. Rein, J. E. and Shank, R. C., "Analytical Program for Processing Zirconium-Uranium Reactor Fuel Elements," AEC Report IDO-14413 (1957).

362. Reynolds, A. G., "Negative Reactivity Effect of Fuel Element Expansion on Cold Startup Accident," AEC Report KAPL-M-AGR-1 (1957).

363. Richards, E. L., "Results of Survey on PWR Fuel Element End Closure Techniques," AEC Report WAPD-PWR-FEP-1146 (1957).

364. Richards, E. L., "A Review of Welding Methods and Processes to Determine Possible End Closure Methods for PWR Fuel Elements," AEC Report WAPD-FE-66 (1957).

365. Ringot, C., "Fabrication of the Fourth Set of Fuel Elements for the Experimental Pile, E12," in "Fuel Elements Conference, Held at Paris. Nov. 1957," p. 182–227, AEC Report TID-7546 (1958).

366. Ristic, M. and Z. Zaric, "Packed Bed Fuel Element for a Gas Cooled Heterogeneous Reactor," 2nd Intntl. Conf. on Peaceful Uses of Atomic Energy, Geneva (1958) P/1747.

367. Ritz, H. L., "The Polyzonal Spiral Fuel Element," 2nd Intntl. Conf. on Peaceful Uses of Atomic Energy, Geneva (1958) P/48.

368. Roake, W. E., "Core Temperatures of Swaged UO₂ Fuel Elements," AEC Report HW-49567 (1957).

369. Roake, W. E., "Irradiation Testing of Novel UO₂ Fuel Elements," 2nd Intntl. Conf. on Peaceful Uses of Atomic Energy, Geneva (1958) P/620.

370. Roake, W. E. and Milhollen, M. K., "Permissible Unsupported Area of PRTR Mark II Fuel Element Cladding," AEC Report HW-55519 (1958).

371. Roberts, L. E. J., "Plutonium Dioxide in Fuel Elements," Brit. Report AERE C/M-325 (1957).

372. Robertson, J. A. L. *et al.*, "Behavior of Uranium Oxide as a Reactor Fuel," 2nd Intntl. Conf. on Peaceful Uses of Atomic Energy, Geneva (1958) P/193.

373. Roll, I. B., "Aluminum-clad, U-Al Core Tubes for NRU Reactor," AEC Report BMI-4910 (1958).

374. Roth, H. P., comp., "Technical Papers of the Tenth Metallographic Group Meeting Held at Knolls Atomic Power Lab. Oct. 24, 1955," AEC Report TID-7523 (Pt. 1) (1955).

375. Rubin, B. F. *et al.*, "Melting and Fabrication of Fuel Elements for a Physics Critical Experiment," AEC Report WAPD-163 (1957).

376. Runnalls, O. J. C., "Uranium Dioxide—A Promising Nuclear Fuel," Canad Report CRL-51 (1958).

377. Runnalls, O. J. C., and Wauchope, K. L., "The Preparation and Sheathing of Pu-Al Fuel Alloys for the NRX Reactor," Canad. Report CRL-47 (1957); see also "Fuel Elements Conference Held at Paris. Nov. 1957," p. 778–788, AEC Report TID-7546 (1958).

378. Saitta, V. F., "Corrosion Test Procedure for the Selection of Crystal Bar Zirconium for Use in Naval Reactor Fuel Elements," AEC Report ANL-4450 (1957).

379. Saller, H. A. *et al.*, "Centrifugal Casting of Plate-Type Fuel Elements," AEC Report BMI-1053 (1957).

380. Saller, H. A. *et al.*, "Low Melting Alloys for Cast Fuel Elements," AEC Report BMI-1002 (1957).

381. Saller, H. A. *et al.*, "The Casting of Radiator-Type Fuel Elements of the Uranium-Chromium Eutectic Alloy," AEC Report BMI-959 (1957).

382. Saller, H. A. *et al.*, "The Development of Cast Fuel Elements," AEC Report BMI-983 (1957).

383. Sanders, J. P., "Deformation of MTR Fuel Element in Static Pressure Tests," AEC Report CF-55-4-24 (1956).

384. Sanderson, M. J., "Processing of Ceramic Fuel Material," Paper 57 in "1957 Nuclear Industry, etc."

385. Sanford, E. R. and DeAgazio, P. N., "Pile Irradiation of Fuel Bearing Plastic Tapes," AEC Report WAPD-BT-8, p. 104–14 (1958).

386. Sawyer, H. F. *et al.*, "Fabrication of Prototype Fuel Elements for the Experimental Boiling Water Reactor and Experimental Breeder Reactor," AEC Report ANL-5568 (1957).

387. Schlein, H., "A Radiation Gauge for Inspection of OMRE Fuel Plates," AEC Report NAA-SR-2040 (1958).

388. Schoenberg, N. *et al.*, "Production of Uranium Dioxide Bodies for Fuel Elements," 2nd Intntl. Conf. on Peaceful Uses of Atomic Energy, Geneva (1958) P/182.

389. Schultz, A. B., "Pressure Drop Tests on Twisted Ribbon Core Assemblies," AEC Report ANL-5189 (1957).

390. Segasser, C. L., "Determination of Pressure Drop Factors Through Typical Fuel Element Channels for High Temperature Gas-Cooled Thermal Piles," AEC Report ORNL-89 (1957).

391. Seymour, W. E. and Barney, W. K., "Metallography and Irradiation Behavior of Stainless Steel-UO_2 Dispersion Fuel Elements," Presented at Metallurgy Inf. Meeting, Iowa, May 1956.

392. Shackleford, M. H., "The Analysis of the Temperature and Thermal Stresses in the Beryllium of SIR Fuel Element Core Rod," AEC Report KAPL-M-MHS-22 (1957).

393. Shank, W. B. and Frankel, M., "Final Report on Swell Detection by Pusher Method," AEC Report CP-2774 (1957).

394. Shapiro, S., "A New Fabrication Technique for Production of Stainless Steel Oxide Dispersion Fuel Elements," 2nd Intntl. Conf. on Peaceful Uses of Atomic Energy, Geneva (1958) P/784.

395. Sharbaugh, J. E., "Product Specification for PWR Core-1 Blanket Fuel Rod Bundle," AEC Report AECU-3837 (1958).

396. Sheinhartz, I., "Methods for Fabrication and Properties of Porous Uranium Fuel Elements," AEC Report SCNC-259 (1958).

397. Sherman, J. and Sherba, P. S., "PWR Reference Fuel Rod Design," AEC Report WAPD-RDa-71 (1957).

398. Shevchenko, V. B. *et al.*, "Some Peculiarities in Treating Irradiated Fuel Elements at the First Atomic Power Station in the USSR," 2nd Intntl. Conf. on Peaceful Uses of Atomic Energy, Geneva (1958) P/2182.

399. Shuck, A. B., "Centrifugal Casting of U-Zr Alloy Rods," in "Nuclear Metallurgy. IV," p. 39–50, AIME IMD Special Report No. 4 (1957).

400. Shuck, A. B., "Remote Fuel Fabrication—How it was Done for EBR-II," *Nucleonics*, **15** (12) 50–3 (1957).

401. Shuck, A. B., "The Development of Equipment and Methods for Centrifugally Casting Reactor Fuel Slugs," AEC Report ANL-5123 (1957).

402. Shuck, A. B., "Development of Methods for Casting and Fabricating Enriched Uranium Fuel Slugs," AEC Report ANL-4617 (1957).

403. Shuck, A. B., "Manufacture of Enriched Uranium Fuel Slugs for Experimental Breeder Reactor," AEC Report ANL-4847 (Rev.) (1957).

404. Sibbitt, W. L. and Etherington, H., "Analysis of the Maximum Thermal Stresses Generated in the Fuel Tubes During Steady State Operation of a High Temperature Pile," AEC Report MonN-292 (1957).

405. Sisman, O., "Testing of MTR Fuel Element," in "Proc. Metallurgy and Materials Inf. Meeting, Apr. 1951, Oak Ridge," AEC Report TID-5061 (Del.) Vol. I, p. 57–8.

406. Skipper, R. G. S., "Heat Transfer within Reactor Fuel Elements," *G.E.C Atomic Energy Review*, **1**, 141–6 (1958).

407. Sloman, M. L., "PWR Failed Element Detection and Location System Multiport Sampling Valve," AEC Report WAPD-PWR-PMA-1517 (1958).

408. Smith, C. D. *et al.*, "Feasibility Report on Production of Fuel Rods for MTR Critical Experiment," AEC Report CF-49-10-209 (1957).

409. Smith, C. D. *et al.*, "Production of Fuel Assemblies for the MTR Mock-up Critical Experiments," AEC Report ORNL-951 (1957).

410. Smith, C. O., "Thermal Stresses in Externally Clad Cylindrical Fuel Elements," *Nuclear Sci. and Eng.*, **3**, 540–7 (1958).

411. Smith, K. F. *et al.*, "Mechanical Stabilization of Uranium Fuel Elements," AEC Report ANL-5377 (1957).

412. Smith, S. S. and Hawtin, L. R., "How to Can Uranium Fuel," *New Scientist*, **3** (75) 28–31 (1958).
413. Snyder, H. J., "Gaseous Contamination of Zircaloy-2 Cladding During Fuel Rod Fabrication by Extrusion and Drawing," AEC Report WAPD-FE-894 (1957).
414. Snyder, H. J., "Hot Straightening of Reference Fuel Element Rod by Vertical and Horizontal Stretching," AEC Report WAPD-FE-407 (1957).
415. Sowman, H. G. *et al.*, "Recent Developments in the Fabrication of High Density Uranium Dioxide Fuel Components and of Stainless Steel-UO_2 Dispersion Type Fuel Elements," Presented at Metallurgy Inf. Meeting, Iowa, May 1956.
416. Spiewak, I. and Hafford, J. A., "Abrasion Test of Thoria Pellets," AEC Report CF-54-3-44 (1957).
417. Stahl, C. R. and Kesselring, K. A., "Design, Evaluation and Operating Experience of Oxide Pin Type Fuel Elements and Assemblies," 2nd Intntl. Conf. on Peaceful Uses of Atomic Energy, Geneva (1958) P/786.
418. Stahl, C. F. *et al.*, "Fast Fuel Rod Design and Analysis (FFR-2)," AEC Report KAPL-423 (1957).
419. Stehn, J. R., "Gamma Ray Monitoring of Fuel Elements," AEC Report KAPL-M-JRS-6 (1952).
420. Stenquist, D. R., "Extrusion of Uranium Dioxide Fuel Cores," AEC Report HW-51747 (1957).
421. Stenquist, D. R. and R. J. Anicetti, "Fabrication of Ceramic Fuel Elements by Swaging," in "Nuclear Metallurgy. V," p. 1 12, AIME IMD Special Report No. 7 (1958).
422. Stohr, J. A. *et al.*, "The Fuel Elements in Pressurized Gas Reactors," 2nd Intntl. Conf. on Peaceful Uses of Atomic Energy, Geneva (1958) P/1157.
423. Storchheim, S., "Fabricating and Testing Tubular Fuel Elements," *Nucleonics*, **15** (1) 85–91 (1957).
424. Story, J. S., "Escape of Gamma Radiation From Uranium Rods in a Pile Heat Evolved in the Moderator," Brit. Report AERE T/R 2218 (1949).
425. Stromquist, W. K., "Pressure Differences Across Plates Adjacent to Thin Annuli in Fuel Assembly," AEC Report ORNL-548 (1956).
426. Stutz, D. E. *et al.*, "Radiographic Procedures for PWR-Type Fuel Elements," AEC Report BMI-1016 (1955).
427. Stutz, D. E. *et al.*, "Nondestructive Inspection of PWR Reference Fuel Element Closures," AEC Report BMI-966 (1957).
428. Stutz, D. E. *et al.*, "Eddy Current Inspection of a Possible PWR Fuel Element," AEC Report BMI-1031 (1957).
429. Sulzer, P. and Bodmer, E., "Manufacture of Internally Cooled Pressurized-Tube Elements of Metallic Uranium by Zone Melting Process," 2nd Intntl. Conf. on Peaceful Uses of Atomic Energy, Geneva (1958) P/240.
430. Surosky, A. E., "Fabrication and Quality Control Methods for APPR Fuel Elements," AEC Report NDA-2063-6 (1958).
431. Swanson, J. L. and Welch, F. H., "Teflon Critical Experiment Fuel Elements," *Nucleonics*, **15** (8) 90, 92–3 (1957).
432. Swanson, J. L. and Welch, F. H., "Fabrication of Teflon Critical Experiment Fuel Elements," AEC Report APEX-277 (1956).
433. Thewlis, J. and Derbyshire, R. T. P., "Nondestructive Testing of Fuel Elements for DIDO," *J. Soc. Nondestructive Testing*, **16,** 154–7 (1958).
434. Thurber, W. C. *et al.*, "The Application of a Nominal 48 w/o U-Al Alloy to

Plate-Type Aluminum Research Reactor Fuel Elements," AEC Report ORNL-2351 (1958).

435. Thys, P. C. and Koch, D. W., "Sodium Bonding of APDA Blanket Elements," AEC Report BW-7065 (1957).

436. Tingey, F. H. and Vance, F. P., "Statistical Analysis of MTR Fuel Element Nondestructive Assay Data," AEC Report IDO-16198 (1957).

437. Tippets, F. E., "Analysis of the Transient Conduction of Heat in Long Cylindrical Fuel Elements for Nuclear Reactors," AEC Report HW-41896 (1956).

438. Tippets, F. E., "Heat Transfer Analysis of Internally-Externally Cooled Cylindrical Fuel Elements for Nuclear Reactors," AEC Report HW-33434 (Rev.) (1954).

439. Todd, F. C. *et al.*, "An Evaluation of Heating Methods for Thermal-Rupture Tests of Ceramic Fuel Elements," AEC Report BMI-T-54 (1955).

440. Treco, R. M. *et al.*, "Fabrication of Zirconium 'S' Rod Thimble Tubes," AEC Report BRB-1 (1956).

441. Trilling, C. A., "Fuel Rod Cooling in Natural Uranium Reactors," AEC Report TID-10086 (1957).

442. Turnbull, H. F. *et al.*, "Manufacture of Seed Fuel Elements of First PWR Core," 2nd Intntl. Conf. on Peaceful Uses of Atomic Energy, Geneva (1958) P/787.

443. Turner, C. J. and Williams, L. R., "Manufacture of Fuel Elements for the Dounreay Fast Reactor," 2nd Intntl. Conf. on Peaceful Uses of Atomic Energy, Geneva (1958) P/44.

444. Ullmann, J. W. and Arnold, E. D., "Decay and Storage of Irradiated Fuel," AEC Report CF-56-4-51 (1956).

445. Vagi, J. J. and Martin, D. C., "Development of Methods for Sealing Ends of PWR Fuel Rod," AEC Report BMI-942 (1957).

446. Vance, F. P. and Hudson, M. N., "Report on MTR Fuel Assembly Data Correlation," AEC Report IDO-16001 (1957).

447. Vance, F. P. and Tingey, F. H., "Evaluation of Process Variables in the Recovery of Spent Reactor Fuel," *Chem. Eng. Progr.*, **52**, 375–80 (1956).

448. Van Mulders, E., "Flow Tests of BR-2 Fuel Elements," AEC Report NDA-2561-1 (1958).

449. Van Winkle, R., "Temperature Distribution in a Single Plate which has a Varying Neutron Flux from the Edge to the Center of the Plate," AEC Report CF-48-12-101 (1956).

450. Vogelsang, W. F., "Critical Experiments in a Uranium-Zirconium Water-Moderated Core with Plate Fuel Elements and Slab Geometry," AEC Report WAPD-TM-100 (1957).

451. Volpe, J. J. and Smith, G. G., "Two Region Studies in Slightly Enriched Water Moderated Uranium and Uranium Dioxide Lattices," AEC Report WAPD-TM-119 (1958).

452. Waldman, L. A. and Cohen, P., "Fretting Wear of Zircaloy-2 Pellets and Consequences Thereof," AEC Reports WAPD-CPM-2 and WAPD-T-313 (1956).

453. Walker, D. E., "The Fabrication of Fuel Subassemblies for the BORAX-II Reactor," AEC Report ANL-5559 (1958).

454. Walker, D. E., "BORAX-II Reactor: Manufacture of Fuel and Blanket Elements," AEC Report ANL-5721 (1958).

455. Warner, W. T., Ed., "Final Report on Reactor Fuel Element Research, Development, and Production," AEC Report BNL-54 (1956).

456. Waugh, R. C. and Beaver, R. J., "Recent Developments in the Powder Metal-

lurgy Application of Uranium Oxides to Aluminum Research Reactor Fuel Elements," AEC Report CF-57-9-60 (1957).

457. Waugh, R. C. and Cunningham, J. E., "The Application of Low Enrichment Uranium Dioxide to Aluminum Plate-Type Fuel Elements," Presented at Metallurgy Inf. Meeting, Iowa, May 1956.

458. Weber, C. E., "Radiation Effects in Nonmetallic Fuel Elements," 2nd Intntl. Conf. on Peaceful Uses of Atomic Energy, Geneva (1958) P/1802.

459. Weber, C. E., "Fuel Element Design," *J. Metals*, **8** (4) 651–9 (1956).

460. Weber, C. E. and Hirsch, H. H., "Dispersion-Type Fuel Elements," in "Proc. 1st Intntl. Conf. on Peaceful Uses of Atomic Energy. IX," p. 196–202, United Nations, New York (1956); see also "Metallurgy and Fuels," p. 523–34, New York, McGraw-Hill Book Co., Inc., 1956; see also "Powder Metallurgy in Nuclear Engineering," p. 224–241, Cleveland, American Soc. for Metals, 1958.

461. Webster, J. W. and McMurry, H. L., "Effect of Flux of a Fuel Plate in Reflector," AEC Report IDO-16084 (1955).

462. Weinberger, W., "Development of Fabrication Techniques and Manufacturing Specifications for APPR Fuel Plates," AEC Report SCNC-262 (1958).

463. Weinberger, W. and Kalish, H. S., "Terminal Report on Processing Techniques for Experimental ALPR Plates," AEC Report IR-104 (1957).

464. Weinberger, W. and Kalish, H. S., "The Fabrication of Stainless Steel-UO_2 Fuel Plates," Presented at Nuclear Eng. and Sci. Congr., Chicago, Mar. 1958.

465. Westinghouse Elec. Corp., "Failed Element Detection and Location System. Shippingport Atomic Power Station Manual. II," AEC Report TID-7020 (1958).

466. Westinghouse Elec. Corp., "Proposed 80,000 kw PWR Plant. Core Design and Power Cost Estimate," AEC Report WIAP-8 (1958).

467. Westinghouse Elec. Corp., "Fission Gas Pressures Within PWR Core-1 Fuel Rods and Proposed PWR Core-2 Fuel Elements," AEC Report WAPD PWR-PMM-1034 (1957).

468. Westinghouse Elec. Corp., "Metal Fuel Element Development Program," AEC Report WAPD-FE-928 (1957).

469. Westphal, R. C., "Thermal Conductivity of Reactor Fuel Element Materials," AEC Report AECD-3864 (1955).

470. White, A. M. and Greenspan, J., "Power Reactor Program. Progress Reports," NMI-4350, 4351, 4353, 4354, 4355, 4357, 4361, 4362, 4363, 4366—May 30, 1957 through July 6, 1958.

471. White, D. W. *et al.*, "Irradiation Behavior of Dispersion Fuels," in "Fuel Elements Conference Held at Paris. Nov. 1957," p. 717–747, AEC Report TID-7546 (1958).

472. Wick, O. J. *et al.*, "Plutonium Fuels Development," 2nd Intntl. Conf. on Peaceful Uses of Atomic Energy, Geneva (1958) P/1776; see also AEC Report HW-52035 (1957).

473. Wilkins, J. E., Jr., "The Distribution of Thermal Neutrons in a Slug with Thick End Caps," AEC Report CP-1989 (1955).

474. Williams, J., "Dispersion-Type Fuel Elements based on Fissile Ceramics," in "Fuel Elements Conference Held at Paris. Nov. 1957," p. 554–62, AEC Report TID-7546 (1958).

475. Williams, R. O., "ORNL Slug Problem—Causes and Prevention (Thesis)," AEC Report CF-50-7-160 (1957).

476. Willis, A. H., "Sources of Fuel Element Instability," 2nd Intntl. Conf. on Peaceful Uses of Atomic Energy, Geneva (1958) P/616.
477. Wilson, C. D., "Irradiated Process Slug Film Sampling Apparatus," AEC Report HW-25928 (1957).
478. Wilson, J. E., "Diffusion of Fission Products from Beryllia Fuel Rod Material," AEC Report CT-3765 (1956).
479. Wilson, T. R. Jr. and Elgert, O. J., Eds., "Hydraulic Tests in the MTR Lattice," AEC Reports IDO-16308 and IDO-16267 (Supplement) (1956).
480. Witt, Frank J., "Fission Product Release from KAPL-30 Fuel Element Failure," AEC Report KAPL-M-SMS-72 (1957).
481. Woodfine, B. C., "Selection of Fuel Canning Materials for Carbon Dioxide-Cooled Nuclear Reactors," *Atomic Energy Rev.*, **1,** 91–6 (1957).
482. Woodrow, J., "Heat Transfer Problems in Uranium Rods," Brit. Report AERE-9ER/3 (1947).
483. Wright, W. J., "Preliminary Fabrication Studies on U-Th-Be Fuel Elements," Brit. Report AERE-M/M-179 (1957).
484. Wyatt, L. M., "British Practice in Uranium Metal Fuel Element Manufacture," in "Proc. of Symposium on Rare Metals. Bombay, India," UNESCO/NS/RM/IV.1/18 (Dec. 1957).
485. Wyatt, L. M., "The Production of Reactor Fuel Elements. II and III," *Nuclear Power,* **1,** 82–8, 125–9 (1956).
486. Wyatt, L. M., "The Production of Reactor Fuel Elements. I. From Ore to Uranium Metal," *Nuclear Power,* **1,** 23–8 (1956).
487. Yaggee, F. L., "The Manufacture of Enriched ZPR-III Fuel Plates," AEC Report ANL-5599 (1957).
488. Yaggee, F. L. *et al.*, "Injection Casting of Uranium-Fissium Alloy Pins," in "Nuclear Metallurgy. IV," p. 51–62, AIME IMD Special Report No. 4 (1957).
489. Young, G., "Flexibility of Cartridges with Jacket Sliding on One Side Only," AEC Report N-1145 nd (1957).
490. Zambrow, J. L., "Progress Report on the Fabrication of Wire Fuel Elements," AEC Report SEP-49 (1957).
491. Zapp, F. C., "Sample Holder for Irradiation Test on Th-U Alloy Fuel Plate," AEC Report CF-52-11-240 (1956).
492. Zerbe, J. E., and Jacket, H. S., "Pressure Drop for Short Flat Plate Fuel Elements," AEC Report WAPD-ReC(A)-35 (1957).
493. Zimin, M. A., "Evaluation of Heat Releasing Elements of Various Forms," in "Fizika i Teplotekhnika Reaktorov," p. 149–63, Moscow, Publishing House on Atomic Power, 1958.
494. Zinn, W. H., "A Letter on EBR-1 Fuel Meltdown," *Nucleonics,* **14,** (6) 35, 103–4, 119 (1956).

INDEX

Figures in boldface type indicate sections or chapters dealing with the topics.